SCIENTISTS AT WAR

SCIENTISTS
AT
WAR

By

WILFRID EGGLESTON

OXFORD UNIVERSITY PRESS
London   Toronto   New York
1950

Oxford University Press, Amen House, Toronto
LONDON   GLASGOW   NEW YORK   MELBOURNE
WELLINGTON   BOMBAY   CALCUTTA   MADRAS   CAPE TOWN
Geoffrey Cumberlege, Publisher to the University

Printed in Canada
by
THE HUNTER ROSE COMPANY LIMITED

ACKNOWLEDGEMENTS

I RECEIVED courtesies from so many people during the writing of this book that I cannot list them all. But I am especially conscious of the kindness of Dr. C. J. Mackenzie, President of the National Research Council, and of the following members of his staff: Dr. W. H. Cook, Dr. F. H. Sanders, Dr. J. L. Gray, Dr. J. T. Henderson, Dr. D. C. Rose, Dr. L. E. Howlett, Mr. S. J. Cook, Mr. J. L. Orr, and Dr. H. H. Saunderson. Dr. Arnold Pitt gave me invaluable aid in writing the proximity fuse chapter; and Dr. H. M. Barrett extended warm hospitality on the occasion of my visit to the Experimental Station at Suffield, Alberta. Among those who read sections of the manuscript and offered valuable suggestions were Mr. B. G. Ballard, Dr. G. S. Field, Dr. G. C. Laurence, Dr. Otto Maass, Dr. B. W. Sargent, Brigadier G. P. Morrison, Dr. G. H. Ettinger, Dr. C. H. Best, and Dr. Duncan Graham. I was privileged to read and draw from an account of the wartime activities of the Applied Biology Division written by F. T. Rosser and M. W. Thistle, for which I am grateful. The historical sections of the Department of National Defence extended useful courtesies. Miss M. S. Gill, of the Library of the National Research Council, and Mr. F. A. Hardy, Parliamentary Librarian, were, as always, obliging and resourceful. Arthur G. Roberts, a recent graduate of the Department of Journalism, Carleton College, gathered most of the photographs used in this volume. The Misses Wheaton and Ellis, of the President's Office, National Research Council, supervised the transcription of the early drafts of the book. My wife, Magdalena, not only helped me with typing, but contributed much to the arrangements which made it possible to maintain progress in spite of the distractions of a busy life.

CONTENTS

LIST OF ILLUSTRATIONS

*Illustrations whose source is not acknowledged were supplied
by the National Research Council*

CHAPTER I

THE HISTORICAL BACKGROUND

THE prominent role played by science in World War II needs no laboured exposition. Both sides drew prodigiously from the insight and cunning of scientists past and present. It would be impossible to prove that the United Nations won simply because their scientists were better. The ingredients of success were complex and manifold, and no scientist would seek to claim any of the glory due to the front-line forces. Yet one can hardly explore the scientific aspects of World War II without seeing how much the victorious side owed to the corps of devoted scientists, men and women, who matched wits with the enemy in the creation and design of new weapons of war, and in inventions that made new techniques of war possible. Each new scientific thrust of the enemy had to be met, countered, and bettered. Fortunately for the United Nations, their scientists proved capable of measuring up in wits and imagination to the most ingenious brains in the pay of the Axis powers, and, after a long, fateful sequence of reverses and triumphs, of coming out on top in the end.

While nothing could hide from the public the broad course of military and geopolitical fortunes as they unfolded between 1939 and 1945, this fearfully momentous, though subtle, contest between the scientists backstage (a duel which had begun, of course, much earlier—long before the outbreak of military hostilities) was guarded with the utmost secrecy. Its more dramatic consequences only broke through to the knowledge of the general public in the see-saw of battle and in the frequently puzzling succession of set-backs and victories which seemed to be inadequately explained by the known military factors. As we now know, these set-backs and victories were often due to the introduction of some radically new weapon or counter-measure of war by one side or the other. Thus, behind the grossly audible military theme of the global campaigns, a more sensitive ear might have heard this vast secret and subtle counterpoint. When hostilities ended, sensational disclosures about the scientific "war behind the war" were possible. In several countries fascinating accounts of hitherto secret war science have appeared. This book is an attempt to tell something about the Canadian contribution.

It is not, of course, an official scientific history of Canada's role in World War II. An attempt has been made here to report to the Canadian people, in layman's language, some of the highlights of our achievement. It is illustrative and impressionistic, but neither exhaustive nor definitive. In these pages it will be shown how, largely through the agency of the National Research Council, the wartime scientific research of this country was mobilized and directed, and the book goes into some detail on specific achievements. The author gratefully acknowledges the invaluable help he has received from many sources, enumerated in some detail elsewhere. Such errors, omissions, or misplaced emphasis as may appear are the sole responsibility of the author. The manuscript was read before publication by the Defence Research Board, with an eye to fulfilling security regulations.

It came to me very early in my preliminary studies for this volume that it would be impossible to tell the story of *Canada's* wartime scientific achievement without relating it fairly intimately to the much broader scientific struggle of the whole war. Indeed, it seemed to me at times that my task was a bit like that of describing the most exciting World Series baseball game in history, in terms, say, of the prowess of the third baseman on the winning side—a player who repeatedly contributes to smart fielding manoeuvres throughout the game, including participation in a couple of vital triple plays, one who gets up to bat at a critical moment and drives in a run, a player who cannot be described, of course, as the outstanding star of the game, since that honour belongs to the star pitcher, or to the "Babe" Ruth of the outfield, but one whose assistance stands out as an essential ingredient of victory. In order to do justice to Canada's scientific contributions, I have sought, therefore, to picture many of them against the broad background of Allied achievements, especially those of Britain and the United States, with which the Canadian scientific effort was closely and constantly coordinated.

In an address to the Royal Canadian Institute on January 19, 1946, Dr. C. J. Mackenzie, President of the National Research Council, explained the impact and bearing which Canada's military position in World War II had upon our scientific research. In the early stages, he said, Canada was not very close to military operations, and the scientists in Canada were therefore not in a position to draft their wartime programme against a comprehensive background of needs and possibilities. It was always necessary to remember, too, that Canada was not a major military power, and that its armed forces could not go to war as separately trained and equipped units, but must fight with and use equipment adopted by Canada's major allies. To contribute effectively on the scientific and technical front, Canada had to work in cooperation, not alone. "It was early apparent," Dr. Mackenzie explained, "that if we did develop a new arm, a new device, a new plane, it would never be used unless adopted by the United Kingdom forces; and we took a firm stand then that if we were to work efficiently, we must start on every problem with the full knowledge available to our Allies; and further, that we must work cooperatively on common problems."

This policy was, of course, consistently carried out, and it prevented endless waste on duplicate effort, and the development and production of useless (because unrelated and unrequisitioned) new equipment.

In an analogy also drawn from the world of sport, Dr. Mackenzie, in the same address, vividly pictured the broad course of the scientific struggle as it was fought between 1939 and 1945:

"In many ways," he said, "war is like a gigantic football game, played on a field of unlimited size where quarters are measured in years not minutes, and where new plays are worked out during the encounter. One side tries a new play that may succeed for a while until it is diagnosed and a defence is worked out. When a football team is down on the scoreboard and time is running out, its tactics are not those of its opponents, and the plays most effective for a light, fast team are not necessarily best for a heavy, powerful one. If the teams were of unequal numerical strength and if the number of present and potential substitutes differed, the tactics would differ still more. So it is

in war. The guided missiles, the V-1 and V-2, did not come
as a surprise to the Allies; they came out of a tactical need that
was the enemy's, not ours. It was not that we were incapable
of developing these weapons, but rather that such plays did
not seem the best for us at that time. I saw a crude form of
flying and guided bomb in trials in 1940, and in particular our
American allies put many types through the development stage,
but we did not go into large production because it was not
considered the best weapon for us at that time. The Germans
turned to V-1 when their bombers were denied the air, and
not until then. At the beginning of the war, England put a
high priority on fighter planes and anti-aircraft defence, but
had also equipped all her population with gas-masks. Germany at that time was stressing the dive-bomber, but although
equipped offensively for gas warfare, did not dare to use it,
as her civilians were not protected; later we had air supremacy
and it was not tactically desirable for her to use gas. Each
side stressed scientifically those things that seemed of most importance to its own side. The Germans developed the V-1 and
V-2 and, undoubtedly, if the war had continued, would have
produced other more terrible members of that family, but we
produced the proximity fuse (in my mind one of the cleverest
and most intriguing ideas of the war), which defeated the V-1.
The atomic bomb more than balanced the V-2 on the scientific
chess board.

"The battle of the Atlantic against the U-boat is an excellent
example of what I have said. Our interests were diametrically
opposed. The Germans were hunting merchant ships; we were
hunting submarines and mines. From 1939 to V-E Day, it was
a series of new plays and counter-measures.

"The Captain of the *Graf Spee,* when captured, said that
Germany regarded the magnetic mine as a secret weapon that
could not be countered, and believed that it would prove to be
a deciding factor in the war, but British scientists solved that
problem promptly, and, in Halifax and Ottawa, Canadian
scientists in 1939-40, with only the sketchiest information, also
worked out and put into operation a scheme for protecting all
the many ships leaving Halifax Harbour, and they also built
specially designed sweeps to clear the approaches to that port.

"Then came the German acoustic torpedo, a clever device that was troublesome for a while, until our scientists produced a counter-measure.

"Radar changed submarine strategy, as aeroplanes fitted with hunting devices could seek out and destroy such craft by day or at night when they were surfaced for breathing. Taking the offensive, the Air Force carried the fight right into the Bay of Biscay as soon as the scientists had provided the needed special aids, special radar gear, searchlights, and armament for the final kill.

"This in turn brought large and faster submarines that were so armed that they could fight it out on the surface with aircraft. Then there was the Schnörkel or breathing nose, which permitted a submarine to run submerged, not at slow speed on batteries, but at high speed on its engines, with little danger of being picked up by radar at a distance. And so it went, the advantage swinging to one side, then to the other. I believe the Navy will be the last to underestimate the initiative, daring and competence of the German submarine service, but I think we can say that our scientific developments, coupled with the courage, skill, and competence of our naval officers and men, enabled us to keep on the winning side of a battle that was not over until V-E Day.

"Radar has become an old story to most of you and perhaps one should not mention it, but for me it has not lost any of its glamour, and I cannot help repeating that without it England would have been defeated in 1940 and an invasion of this continent certainly would have been attempted in 1941 or 1942. No one who knows can deny that without radar, the strategic bombing of Germany, which softened her for the invasion, would have been impossible; neither can anyone say definitely that the Germans would not have been successful in their submarine campaigns had it not been for radar. When D-Day came, newer aids again played a vital part, and even on V-J Day still newer and more effective sets were being developed. It can be said, then, that from the day war was declared until the Japanese accepted unconditional surrender, radar occupied a prominent place in the front lines of battle.

"One can't help thinking how close was that game of war, and I am profoundly impressed by the alarming part that timing played. Ask yourself what would have happened if the United Kingdom scientists had waited until 1938 (instead of 1935) to start radar developments. Or what would have happened if the V-1 and V-2 had come into production in 1941, not 1945?[1] Or if the Germans, not the Americans, had made the first atomic bomb?"

Military leaders and the chief scientific advisers could follow this "football match" much more intelligently than the general public, because they had some access to secret military information which censorship was withholding from all others, including the enemy. It is curious to go back now and trace behind the newspaper headlines of the decade 1935-45 some of the once unseen—but now visible—milestones and landmarks of the scientific backstage war. In January 1935, for example, the whole world was talking about the Saar plebiscite, but only a few scientists and Air Force executives in Britain knew of the formation that month of the vastly important Tizard Committee of Research on Air Defence. Still fewer knew of the first radar tests in history, being held near Daventry, on February 26 of that year. Hitler, with great fanfare, reoccupied the Rhineland on March 7, 1936; six days later, using new towers at Bawdsey, British scientists working in great secrecy located, by use of radar, an aircraft flying at 1500 feet and at a distance of 75 miles. In 1938, there was world-wide publicity over the Nazi persecution of the Jews, but few marked the fateful migration of outstanding Jewish nuclear physicists and chemists to the New World, and to the sanctuary of Britain: Fermi, Meitner, Frisch, Halban, and others. Like another and greater Jewish emigrant, Albert Einstein, they threw in their lot with the Allies, who benefited greatly from their wizardry. The world watched breathlessly, in the summer of 1940, the critical fortunes of the Battle of Britain, but did not know that without the magic of radar, even the peerless few of the R.A.F. could not have possibly

[1] "It seemed likely that, if the German had succeeded in perfecting and using these new weapons six months earlier than he did, our invasion of Europe would have proved exceedingly difficult, perhaps impossible." Dwight D. Eisenhower, *Crusade in Europe* (Doubleday & Co., New York, 1948), p. 260.

HEADQUARTERS OF THE NATIONAL RESEARCH COUNCIL, OTTAWA

Opened in 1932

FOUNDER AND PRESIDENTS OF THE NATIONAL RESEARCH COUNCIL

(centre) Dr. Henry Marshall Tory, Founder and President, 1928-35; (left) General A. G. L. McNaughton, President, 1935-39; (right) Dr. C. J. Mackenzie, President since 1939

stemmed Goering's massive air invasion. Even so, the margin was of the closest. Backstage, during those eventful months of 1940, other developments of the greatest consequence for the future were unfolding, but they could not even be whispered of at the time. At Birmingham, the cavity magnetron, which made microwave radar possible (and thus eventually the defeat of the U-boat, and the Allied air mastery of Europe), was invented early in 1940, and was first made in an industrial model in July of that year; while a month later the Tizard Scientific Mission secretly set sail for the shores of North America and prepared that three-way scientific pooling of scientific knowledge and manufacturing capacity which did so much to turn the tide of battle—only just in time, in 1943-44. The defence of Malta appeared heroic enough in bare news dispatches, but few were aware that only radar had made it possible. Nor did we know at the time that only radar had saved Ceylon. The battle of Matapan was hailed as a brilliant victory for British sea power, which it was: again, it was the new electro-magnetic searchlight and range-finder embodied in radar that had made it possible. The escape of the *Scharnhorst* and the *Gneisenau* was in turn a Nazi scientific triumph, though the public could not be told so: the British radar watching their movements had for the moment been effectively jammed.

Much mysterious ebb and flow of the aerial warfare over Europe puzzled uninformed observers, as when our air losses over Germany would rise staggeringly for a while, seeming to doom mass raiding to permanent abandonment, only to be followed a few weeks later by a resumption of our raids using still larger aerial squadrons, which surprisingly got right through and came back practically unscathed. The public did not know that this was another phase of the "football match", the earlier Nazi success having been due to the introduction of new German radar equipment, and the successful resumption of Allied air raids to the rapid introduction of improved "jamming" devices which blinded the Nazi radar "eyes". The Nazis scored again with rocket-firing planes at Schweinfurt and introduced jet-propelled fighters with considerable effect, but to every new challenge the Allied military and scientific teams eventually found an answer.

Much was told of the events of D-Day, but it did not come out until long afterwards how the Germans had then employed for the first time on the coasts of Normandy a deadly new type of mine on a novel principle, against which the existing Allied sweepers were of little or no use. Or how the complete failure of the Nazis to offer adequate air opposition on the coasts of Normandy on D-Day—a fatal omission—was largely due to the elaborate feints and fakes and deceptions used to deceive the Nazi radar "eyes" located along the European coast, thus bewildering and scattering the Nazi counter-offensive—"the greatest hoax in history", as a London publication later headlined it.

Nor was it possible to explain at the time that the proximity fuse, a radically new invention kept under the tightest of secret covers, was mainly responsible for the speed and thoroughness with which the V-1 was beaten. Or that Hitler's last great counter-offensive, the thrust toward Antwerp which developed into the Battle of the Bulge, was blunted by this spectacular device on which a crew of Canadian and American scientists had begun to work in earnest as early as September 1940.

Dunkirk and Canada

Canada began active mobilization for war, of course, early in September 1939, and this general activity included some mobilization of scientific resources as well as of manpower and industrial might. But the decision of Hitler not to turn westward immediately after the rapid subjugation of Poland led, in Canada as well as in Britain and in France, to an uncertain and demoralizing period of anxiety during which many Canadians believed that this was destined to be a slow war of economic attrition, and that the Axis could be beaten fairly bloodlessly by a policy of economic blockade and limited military participation. For seven months the progress of mobilization everywhere was sluggish. Then, on April 9, 1940, the " 'Twilight War' broke into the glare of the most fearful military explosion so far known to man," as Winston Churchill so aptly expressed it.* The

* The Gathering Storm (Houghton Mifflin Co., Boston, 1948), p. 650. The phrase "twilight war" was first used in this connection by Neville Chamberlain in a private letter published by his biographer; see Feiling, The Life of Neville Chamberlain (Macmillan and Co. Ltd., London, 1946), p. 424.

military position of the Allies deteriorated with appalling rapidity in the seventy days from the occupation of Oslo to the surrender of France, and, as it did so, the fundamental response to the war underwent a profound revolution in Canada as elsewhere. This was rapidly reflected in the Canadian scientific world, as well as in military and industrial circles. "It was," writes Dr. Mackenzie, "in those darkest of all days when the Germans were overrunning the Low Countries and France that the real foundations of our scientific war activities were laid." Two of the most important consequences which followed almost at once from the new spirit in Britain and Canada were the dispatch to North America of the British Scientific Mission headed by Sir Henry Tizard, and the gifts of money for war research from a few patriotic and wealthy Canadians, a fund which reached $1,300,000 and which was administered by the War Technical and Scientific Development Committee. Both of these events were of the greatest importance in the mobilization of Canadian war science, and are described in some detail in subsequent pages.

The Background of Mobilization

What was there in the Canadian scientific community in 1939 to mobilize? Before attempting an answer, it is necessary to refer back briefly to the steps which had led to the creation of the National Research Council, and to the erection of the national laboratories on Sussex Street at Ottawa.

The National Research Council had its origins in World War I. J. D. Bernal, the British historian of scientific policy, has pointed out[2] how much advantage the Germans possessed in 1914 owing to the superiority of their research, both in numbers and in the intimacy of the relationship of their science with German industry. It was imperative, as the First World War developed, for the Allies to improvise quickly an expansion of scientific and industrial services. Accordingly, in 1915, Britain created a committee to foster scientific and industrial research. Early in 1916, the Secretary of State for the Colonies recommended a similar plan to the governments of the Dominions. On June 1, 1916, a cabinet Committee of six ministers was set

[2] In *The Social Function of Science* (Macmillan and Co. Ltd., London, 1942), p. 30.

up at Ottawa to introduce similar principles in Canada, and in November of that year, on their recommendation, an Honorary Advisory Committee for Scientific and Industrial Research was created. This was the parent of the present National Research Council. The new body was composed of eleven (later fifteen) representatives of scientific, technical, and industrial interests in Canada. Unfortunately there was not yet much in Canada to coordinate or mobilize; the Committee had no laboratories nor other facilities; and so the war of 1914-18 ended with little of a tangible nature to show as a consequence of the new machinery. But if it bore no immediate fruit, it was, nevertheless, one of the most profitable long-term investments of that day. Of the subsequent institution of the Laboratories of the National Research Council, Dr. A. Norman Shaw of McGill wrote in 1938: "It is probable that this step will live in history as an outstanding example of governmental foresight in our time—any recent example of foresight of comparable importance is indeed difficult to find." Had he been writing this in 1945, Dr. Shaw would have possessed even stronger evidence for his conviction.

The first thing done by the new Committee in 1917 was a survey of research facilities. "The principal result was the disclosure of the fact that these were pitifully inadequate. There was, indeed, some research under way in Dominion Government departments and in the universities, and also in the laboratories of a few of the large industrial concerns, but funds available for such purposes were limited, the physical equipment was insufficient even for the small amount of work under way, and the number of men trained in the methods of research was but a fraction of that required. At that time there was an almost complete lack of public appreciation of the practical value of research."[3]

Despite this disclosure of the acute need of national laboratories for research, and a recommendation of the Honorary Advisory Council that such be built, the Dominion Government did not reach a decision to provide such facilities until 1928.

[3] *The Organization of Research in Canada,* a submission by the National Research Council to the Royal Commission on Dominion-Provincial Relations, March 19, 1938, p. 6.

Temporary accommodation was obtained in 1929 in some old mill buildings at the mouth of the Rideau River, and plans were begun for a massive new structure on Sussex Street, above the Ottawa River. These magnificent quarters were opened and partly equipped in 1932. The older buildings were retained and served for a time for the Division of Mechanical Engineering, and for the instrument and model shops of the Council. These, and a still-unequipped radar field station a few miles from Ottawa, constituted the entire laboratory plant of the National Research Council at the outbreak of war in 1939.

Prior to the opening of the first laboratories in 1929, the functions of the Council had been essentially confined to granting financial aid to research students and workers in various universities, and to organizing and supporting cooperative research programmes of a national character, carried out in available laboratories across Canada. The first of these projects had had the important effect of greatly increasing the number of trained scientists in Canada: it built a foundation for the extensive Canadian research of World War II, which owed so much to the key men and women trained through Council assistance between the two wars. Research centres were fostered, and nearly a thousand of Canada's most brilliant scientific students were aided in the first twenty years of activity. The second of these achievements led to a number of major research programmes, using the device of "Associate Committees" which originated in Canada. These tackled such national problems as black stem rust of wheat, tuberculosis, the control of internal animal parasites, the utilization of waste natural gas, and aeronautical research.

Founders of the Council

A word must be said here of two outstanding personalities behind the early growth of the National Research Council. The name of Dr. Henry Marshall Tory is inseparably connected with the first days. He came back to Canada in 1919 after serving as President of Khaki College, and at Edmonton he launched "a tireless nationwide campaign to awaken the leaders of education and industry to the value of scientific discovery. He founded and was first Chairman of the Alberta Council of Scientific and Industrial Research. In 1923 he became Chairman of the National Research Council, and for the next five years Dr. Tory divided his enormous energies between the organization of the multitudinous research projects of the National Research Council and the administration of his growing university. When the National Research Laboratories were established at Ottawa in 1928, Dr. Tory became President of the Council and Chief Executive Officer. Thus, at 64 years of age he began a new career. Immediately, under his direction, began the planning of the great laboratories now known all over the world."[4]

At the time of Dr. Tory's death in February 1947, Prime Minister Mackenzie King testified that through his work on scientific committees and the large part he played in planning the National Research Laboratories at Ottawa, Dr. Tory had "rendered services of incalculable value to government, to science and to industry throughout our country." Not the least of Dr. Tory's gifts was his capacity to quicken the spark of talent in young men and women and to inspire in them a deep devotion to service. By the time he had reached retirement age he had drawn to the Council staff at Ottawa many of the most brilliant scientists of Canada, names which stand out vividly in the story of the wartime research achievements of 1939-45.

The second President of the National Research Council was Major-General A. G. L. McNaughton (now General the Honourable), who was appointed in October 1935 after a brilliant military, scientific, and academic career. As soldier-scientist he had acquired a wide reputation in World War I for his ingenious counter-battery work in sound-ranging, and in 1926 he had invented, with Colonel W. A. Steel of Ottawa, the Cathode Ray Direction Finder. General McNaughton was recalled to duty with the Army on the outbreak of war in 1939 and was appointed to take the First Canadian Division overseas. During his four years of office as President of the Council, years which coincided with steadily mounting world-wide tension arising out of Axis aggression in Europe and Asia, General

[4] Dr. E. A. Corbett, "Dr Henry Marshall Tory," *Food for Thought* (March, 1948).

McNaughton had anticipated several vital lines of war research, and had initiated a series of scientific inquiries in radio, ballistics, and chemical warfare, which rapidly bore fruit when hostilities began. On October 17, 1939, General McNaughton assumed his new duties as Officer Commanding the First Canadian Division, and on the following day Dean C. J. Mackenzie came to Ottawa from the University of Saskatchewan as Acting President of the National Research Council.

Since 1935 Dr. Mackenzie had been a member of its Advisory Council. He was a graduate in engineering of Dalhousie and Harvard, and as a young man had practised his profession in the Maritimes and on the prairies, had served overseas in the First World War (54th Battalion C.E.F.), and had been awarded the Military Cross. He reopened the Engineering Faculty of the University of Saskatchewan after the First World War, and had served as Dean of the Engineering College at Saskatchewan since 1921.

It was Dr. Mackenzie's heavy responsibility to guide the Council through nearly six years of war, and the accomplishments described in these pages bear constant witness to his energy and vision. He took over, in his own words, "a virile, enterprising, rapidly growing institution with a young but highly qualified and experienced staff particularly suited for adaptation to the urgent scientific needs of war." The exactions and stresses of war posed a supreme challenge to this youthful institution, and the reader may judge for himself from the evidence exhibited in these pages to what extent the challenge was successfully met.

When war broke out the Council possessed a single laboratory, a total staff of about 300 employees, and was operating on an annual budget of $900,000. Within a few months the staff had expanded to nearly 2,000, and it was spending nearly $7,000,000 annually. During the war it established twenty-one additional laboratories, some small and temporary, others large and of a permanent nature. These were located from Halifax to Vancouver, and included such unexpected developments as temporary laboratories for research in ice structures at Lake Louise, Jasper, Edmonton, Saskatoon, and Winnipeg. Before hostilities were over the Council had become associated with nearly every scientific aspect of the war. It had built an explosives experimental station at Valcartier, large laboratories for nuclear research at Montreal, and the Atomic Energy Plant at Chalk River. The Council had established large radar research laboratories and a field station near Ottawa, naval research stations on both coasts, and, on a site near Ottawa, a permanent group of nine buildings and wind tunnels for aeronautical and engineering research.

When war broke out, practically every laboratory in Canada offered its facilities to the government. Laboratories and staffs in industry and college research were in due course welded into an informal and flexible but highly effective cooperation. During the war, twenty major associate research committees with nearly a hundred sub-committees were operated under the aegis of the Council. On these committees sat hundreds of Canada's most eminent professional men and scientists from universities and from industry. In addition to the work carried out in the Council's own laboratories, there were at times as many as 280 active projects in thirty other laboratories across Canada. Research was done where it could best be done, and by the best people available. Cooperation was exceptionally effective.

Scientific cooperation extended beyond national boundaries. The National Research Council set up liaison offices in London, Washington, and Ottawa. Through these channels intelligence and reports on secret projects being worked out in the three countries flowed freely. Senior members of the Council staff served on defence committees: they attended innumerable conferences and meetings so as to integrate the Council's scientific work with the requirements of the armed services. Before hostilities ended, Canada had set up high standards of organization, mobilization, and liaison—as effective, indeed, as in any country in the world.

Period of the "Twilight War"

Some useful developments were launched between the sinking of the *Athenia* in 1939 and the Nazi invasion of Norway, as for example in the fields of radar, ships' de-gaussing against the magnetic mine, and explosives; but by and large it was a frustrating and difficult period. The National Research Council eagerly awaited the assignment of specific tasks by the armed services, but these were slow in forthcoming, and many imaginative scientists grew restless at the thought of what German ingenuity might meanwhile be concocting. The United States was not at war, and so her own war research was jealously sealed off from the rest of the world, including, of course, ourselves. The United Kingdom and France showed little inclination to share their scientific super-secrets with Canada. Also, so long as there was any possibility that the war might still be won on a "business as usual" footing, there persisted commercial interests in Britain which frowned on any suggestion that secret blueprints, industrial "know-how", and exclusive patents, should be allowed to be transmitted into North American hands, where they might prove to be industrially embarrassing to Britain in post-war competition. The belittling idea was even advanced that Canada could most usefully serve the common cause by sending a few of her top-ranking engineers and scientists to lend the British a hand in the laboratories of the United Kingdom. To be fair, it should be added that there were sound security arguments against any wider dispersal of ultra-secret research than was necessary; and for Britain to share fully with Canada, located where she was, meant risking leaks through the United States back to Germany.

It was difficult for Canadian scientists to know what, under the circumstances, was most badly needed, and where their energies could best be applied. And even in fields which were obviously destined to be of the greatest importance in the war, it was not easy in the early months to cope with official and governmental inertia and tradition, especially as the requirements of utmost secrecy made a wide or general appeal for action—even at times a frank approach to the Dominion Cabinet—impossible. The philosophy of limited participation continued to thrive in some quarters even after the swift annihilation of Poland had demonstrated the fearful might of Hitler's war machine. An example will best illustrate the public temper of the time. As early as April 1939, General McNaughton had agreed to a proposal of the chief of the Radio Section that funds for development work should be immediately sought, and that twenty extra men be added to the staff of the Radio Section (for work on radar). Earliest estimates had proposed the expenditure of $140,000, or $38,000 for an alternative smaller scheme. In June, the Canadian Chiefs of Staff, impressed by growing threats of war, stepped this up sharply, and submitted a plan to the government involving the expenditure of $750,000 for the purchase of British radar equipment. None of these proposals materialized. The $750,000 plan was not sanctioned, nor was the tiny staff of radar workers immediately augmented. A month later, in July 1939, the sum of $105,000 was requested in order to initiate radar experimental work in Canada, and to pay for an additional staff of twenty-three men. No action was taken. Shortly afterwards, General McNaughton left for Britain and while there discussed with the United Kingdom authorities in August the desirability of manufacturing radar equipment in Canada, but his recommendation was not accepted. When hostilities broke out things moved a bit faster, but still on a modest scale, so that on September 5, 1939, General McNaughton decided to cancel a proposed experiment on the ionosphere at Churchill and transfer the $3,000 vote thus released over to radar research. The Department of National Defence at the same time made available equipment and supplies valued at about $12,000, and the Canadian Army, in October 1939, assigned four men to work with the Radio Section. Dr. R. W. Boyle, Director of the Division of Physics, returned in November 1939 from an investigation of certain features of research work in Britain, and on the basis of his findings a request was made for an appropriation of $57,000 to cover radar research for the remainder of the fiscal year (till March 31, 1940), and to allow fifteen more employees to be engaged. This was not approved, and no additional funds were granted until the beginning of the new fiscal year, April 1, 1940, when $60,000 was appropriated for the purpose. A layman can only guess how serious was the loss of time. This experience is mentioned to show what are, perhaps, the normal and even inevitable obstacles to be met and overcome in the mobilization of an habitually peaceful nation when suddenly faced by a well-camouflaged national peril.

After Dunkirk, the idea of limited participation rapidly vanished, even in North America, and no requests for financial assistance for Canadian war research were subsequently rejected or even questioned. "This nation," as Dr. Mackenzie phrased it in his address to the Royal Canadian Institute, then "embarked upon an all-out programme of military preparation, industrial production, and financial commitments that staggered the imagination."

The Tizard Mission

The British Scientific Mission which came to Canada and the United States in August and September of 1940, headed by Sir Henry Tizard, Rector of Imperial College and Chairman of the Aeronautical Research Committee, resulted in one of the most decisive developments of the war. Among other things, it paved the way for the fullest, freest cooperation between the scientists and engineers of the United Kingdom, the United States, and Canada. The United States, still a neutral, gained enormously by immediate access to all of Britain's spectacular war secrets, among other advantages, thereby saving herself many precious months of time in the race against Axis scientists. Britain in turn eventually gained the invaluable aid of the peerless engineering capacity and mass production of the United States. Canada, as a full partner in the joint venture, was suddenly launched into the full stream of Allied scientific investigation, and invited to play such a part as her natural advantages and available resources should suggest or determine.

The desirability of a free exchange of war secrets between the United Kingdom and the United States had occurred to several people in high positions soon after hostilities began, but it needed the shock of Dunkirk to open the flood-gates. Professor Archibald Vivian Hill, Secretary of the Royal Society and Scientific Attaché to the British Embassy in Washington, and his chief, Lord Lothian, were urging it as early as May 1940. After the fall of France, Britain was ready and even eager to act, and in July 1940, President Roosevelt endorsed such an exchange. Sir Henry Tizard, chosen to head the Mission, was perhaps the outstanding veteran executive in war science research in Britain, having been Assistant-Controller of Experi-

ment and Research to the R.A.F. in World War I, and the
first Chairman of the Committee of Research on Air Defence,
created in Britain in 1935. This group had developed radar,
and made victory in the Battle of Britain possible. The Canadian government was invited to nominate three members to
join the mission. The late Lieutenant-General Kenneth Stuart,[5]
Air Vice-Marshal E. W. Stedman, and Dr. C. J. Mackenzie
accordingly went to Washington for the series of fateful scientific conferences which followed the arrival of the Mission there.
The Tizard Mission brought to North America not only information about British secret devices and equipment, and
prototypes of such brilliant new discoveries as the cavity magnetron, referred to in detail in a later chapter, but also a list
of the most urgent military and scientific necessities, such as a
proximity fuse for shells, a cheap and safe means of producing
RDX, a new electrical predictor for fire-control against aircraft,
and an exploration of the possibility of developing an atomic
bomb. All of these and many other investigations were promptly
begun as a result of the visit of the Mission and the cooperation
which ensued.

Besides Sir Henry Tizard, the Mission included Colonel F. C.
Wallace, whose valuable contribution to radar development in
Canada is mentioned in later pages, J. D. Cockcroft, who was
to return to Canada later as Director of the Atomic Energy
Plant at Chalk River, R. H. Fowler, First Liaison Officer in
Canada for the British Director of Industrial and Scientific
Research, and Dr. E. G. Bowen, who joined the U.S. Radiation
Laboratory at its inception as British Liaison Officer. Captain
Faulkner, R.N. and Group Captain Pearce, R.A.F. made up,
with Col. Wallace, the trio of Serving Officers of the Mission.

The results of the Tizard Mission on the whole course of
the war were prodigious, and no summary will be attempted
here. It sparked the whole scientific research programme of
the Allies in practically all aspects. What it meant in the
critical field of radar, and in particular in Canadian radar,
cannot be more concisely stated than in the language used by

---

[5] General Stuart's alternate was Maj.-Gen. H. F. G. Letson, then Military
Attaché at Washington; and as Stuart was unable to attend more than one
or two meetings, Letson became a regular delegate to the conferences.

a Canadian radar pioneer, Dr. Frederick H. Sanders, in the *Proceedings of the Institute of Radio Engineers,* Vol. 35, No. 2, February 1947:

"(1) It marked the beginning of a pooling of British and American knowledge of the art. Britain contributed some revolutionary devices, such as the cavity magnetron and the 'micropup' pulsed triode, plus a vast store of practical operational experience. The United States had the radar knowledge of the Naval Research Laboratory and Camp Evans Signals Laboratory, plus such outstanding figures in high-frequency research as Southworth and Friis of Bell Telephone Laboratories, Barrow of the Massachusetts Institute of Technology, Hansen, the Varians, and many others.

"(2) A 'Radiation Laboratory' was to be established at the Massachusetts Institute of Technology, an institution which was to expand until ultimately over 2000 workers were engaged in microwave research and development.

"(3) The British were to obtain the aid of the United States' vast mass-production capacity.

"(4) From the Canadian viewpoint it marked the start of a really large radar effort, as the British asked specifically for the National Research Council to develop—and Canada to build in quantity—a new anti-aircraft set for the defence of Britain. As a result, the newly formed crown company, Research Enterprises Limited, intended originally to build only optical equipment, was expanded in scope to take care of radar manufacture in Canada."

The Private Gifts

The fearful military explosion which began with the Nazis' lightning occupation of Denmark and Norway at once transformed, as has been said, all Allied thinking about the war. The Tizard Mission was one of the fruits of this new attitude. Another interesting and profitable consequence in Canada was the spontaneous gift of over a million dollars by a few public-spirited Canadians, which, without strings of any kind, was made available to the National Research Council for war research. The timing of the gift was most fortunate and multiplied its value, so that the final results were out of all proportion to its magnitude. This gift, coming about the time of the visit of the Tizard Mission, rapidly altered the whole face of Canadian war research in a few weeks.

The original offer by a small group of Canadian business men to contribute toward the prosecution of the war a sum totalling about a million dollars seems to have been first made to the Acting Deputy Minister for Air, J. S. Duncan. He at once called a meeting of high departmental officers to discuss with representatives of the donors the best way of applying these funds. Dr. C. J. Mackenzie, then Acting President of the National Research Council, outlined to that meeting some objectives of Canada's war research, and as a result it was unanimously agreed that the money gifts could be used to the greatest advantage on war research projects proposed by the National Research Council.

On August 27, 1940, by P.C. 4260, a War Technical and Scientific Development Committee was set up. The members included Dean Mackenzie, Sir Frederick Banting, Dr. Otto Maass of the National Research Council, and representatives of the government departments directly concerned with the prosecution of the war, and of the private donors. The Committee was authorized to receive funds from private sources and allocate them to the National Research Council for projects proposed by the Council and approved by the Committee.[6]

The period from midsummer 1940 to midsummer 1941 has been described by Dr. Mackenzie as the year of the most spectacular development in war research in Canada. "From the fund of 'free money'," he told the Royal Canadian Institute in 1946, "we were able to start work immediately on any problem, without further reference. It was 'adventure capital' which enabled us to start all sorts of projects long before there was time to establish a sound 'case' for their worth."

At the first meeting of the Committee a list of over thirty projects involving the expenditure of about $600,000 was submitted for approval: sixteen of these were immediately accepted

[6] In July 1941, after the death of Sir Frederick Banting in an air crash in Newfoundland, the fund was re-named the Sir Frederick Banting Fund. By February 1943, the sums made available to the National Research Council through the Fund had aggregated $1,300,000.

and the sum of $262,700 allotted for the purpose. The grants made on that first day make interesting reading now, for most of them flowered out into major enterprises. In Chemistry, grants were made for fundamental research in chemical warfare, to form an explosives laboratory, and for a study of the impregnation of service uniforms with anti-gas chemicals. In Medicine, grants were made for physiological studies of high-altitude flying and biological warfare. In Physics, grants were approved for work on the proximity fuse and for research in predictors, gun sights, chronographs, sound-ranging and anti-submarine devices. In Aeronautics, sums were voted for research in de-icing and defrosting, radio navigation, and wooden aircraft.

Especially important was the help given to early research in radar from this "Santa Claus" fund. By the beginning of September 1940, an appropriation of $330,000 for this purpose alone had been endorsed; and this grant carried the experimental work in the early development stages of the gun-layer radar—a massive programme described at length in Chapter II—the anti-submarine (ship-borne) radar developments, the Coast Defence sets, and the ASV or airborne radar sets destined for protecting Canada's shores and detecting enemy surface vessels and submarines.

At the end of the first year, Dr. Mackenzie, reporting to the Committee, was able to announce that grants covering about thirty projects and amounting to nearly a million dollars had been made. The sum of $85,000 had been allotted for "extra-mural work of a fundamental value at the various universities, and over thirty-six projects of importance are now being worked on." Radar projects, Dr. Mackenzie said, had been given the highest priority, and as a result the Council had a staff of 200 engaged in this work. He announced that their success in producing a prototype of certain radar equipment had led to an order being received by Research Enterprises Limited through the American government for $30 millions of equipment.

After reciting further accomplishments, Dr. Mackenzie summarized the value of the gifts: "By having available such a fund, the Research Council during the past year has been able to start investigations immediately on any promising problem, and it has been repeatedly found that by having such 'free money' we have been able to get on with months of valuable planning and investigations before official acceptance of and financial support for a project could be obtained." Great returns flowed in from this free money donated by public-spirited citizens. In later months the need declined, since government funds became available without any restriction, but in the meantime invaluable time had been won in several vital lines of war research.

"Canada," said Dr. Mackenzie in 1946, "is not a large country in the scientific sense, but for the first time she has operated as a nation in this field." He added that the name of Canada had become known scientifically in the Second World War as it had done in a military sense in the First World War. Beginning, as has been said, with 300 scientists, engineers, and mechanics, and a single massive laboratory at Ottawa, the scientific effort of Canada burgeoned rapidly and strongly under the impetus of war. Six years which were both intensely interesting and profoundly significant in the scientific story of Canada followed the outbreak of hostilities in Canada in 1939. In the pages which follow an attempt has been made to depict some of the highlights of those eventful years. Without seeking to anticipate unduly what those pages contain, a few words may serve to introduce the theme. Canada was the first nation in the world to achieve mass-production of microwave radar fire-control instruments, "a venture," in the words of the official British history, *Science at War*,[7] "which turned out highly successful and most valuable." Canadian physicists did brilliant early work on the proximity fuse, ranked by James Phinney Baxter 3rd, U.S. war science historian, as "amongst the three or four most extraordinary scientific achievements of the war."[8] The basically new methods which made it possible to convert RDX from an impractical luxury to a mass-produced explosive widely and effectively used as an ingredient of victory on land and at sea by the forces of the United Nations, were evolved in Canadian laboratories by Canadian chemists. Of the work in chemical warfare and smokes, American scientific historians testified to the "very efficient and

7 J. G. Crowther and R. Whiddington (Philosophical Library, New York, 1948), p. 77.

8 *Scientists Against Time* (Little, Brown and Co., Boston, 1946), p. 241.

WARTIME EXPANSION OF THE RESEARCH COUNCIL'S WORK

The entrance to the 85-acre plant near Ottawa, one of several laboratories which have grown out of wartime activities

FOUR OF THE MANY WHO WORKED FOR THE COUNCIL

(*top left*) Dr. R. W. Boyle, Physics and Electrical Engineering; (*top right*) Dr. O. Maass, Chemistry; (*bottom left*) Dr. J. H. Parkin, Mechanical Engineering; (*bottom right*) Dr. J. D. Cockcroft, Atomic Energy

high-grade groups of scientists" working in Canada on war problems. Numerous conferences, they reported, were held on both sides of the border, and "these contacts were invaluable." Dr. Otto Maass, in their opinion, "had under him in Ottawa and at the Experimental Station, in Suffield, an exceptionally able group of scientists both in and out of uniform."[9] In aviation medicine, Canadian physiologists, biochemists, and others broke new ground, and research facilities were created second to none in the world. While a determined effort has been made to keep out of this record anything that smacks of national boasting, it is difficult to add up the achievements in many fields without experiencing a new sense of national pride.

[9] W. A. Noyes, Jr., *Chemistry,* Science in World War II, Office of Scientific Research and Development Series (Little, Brown and Co., Boston, 1948), p. 154.

CHAPTER II

RADAR

THE task of defending Canadian soil in September 1939 seemed to boil down to a job of helping Britain and her allies defeat their common enemies in other parts of the world, as far away as possible from Canadian shores. Canada's defence strategy reflected this situation. Between Nazi Germany and the Atlantic shoreline the fleets of Britain and France were interposed. Between Japan, a potential but not yet actual enemy, and Canada's west coast, lay much of the naval strength of the United States. The threat from across the Pacific was such as to lead the Canadian government to take preliminary steps toward strengthening the defences of the British Columbia coast. Air bases and coastal defence batteries were established there. The rapid deterioration of Britain's relative strength at sea (as France fell and as Hitler seized the European coastline from North Cape to the Bay of Biscay) drastically altered the earlier conception of Canada's defensive position after April 1940, and there was increasing anxiety over the threat to Canada's north-eastern approaches. Attention thus shifted to the eastern ports, to Newfoundland, and, after 1941, to Labrador.

Under these circumstances there was growing concern over the passive defence of Canada's shores. Among other activities, this led to new stress on better instruments for early warning, and to more accurate and dependable fire-control instruments on coastal guns.

When hostilities broke out in 1939, coastal batteries everywhere were still aimed by *optical* instruments which determined the range and bearing of the enemy vessel. The data so obtained were then fed to a fortress plotter, or some similar instrument, which rapidly calculated where the guns required to be aimed. As in duck-hunting, the aim had to "lead" the moving target so that the shell would reach the point where the vessel would be when it arrived, not where it was when the sight was taken, nor when the shell left the gun. A moment's reflection will suggest some of the ever-present complexities of fire-control. Even against a sitting target it is necessary to take into account such variable factors as the temperature and density of the atmosphere, and the fact that the propellant or charge of powder which projects the shell burns a little differently with each shot. A field gun firing at a fixed target may register no better than one hit in a hundred rounds. Against a moving target such as a warship, the battery commander must be able to ascertain the precise position of the target and its exact rate of change of position in two dimensions, namely, range and bearing. These figures must then be translated into a forecast of the expected position of the ship by the time the shell has travelled five, ten, or fifteen miles to its destination.

The use of gunnery against aircraft introduces further formidable problems. Since the aircraft is free to move in three dimensions, its precise position in these three dimensions in relation to the battery—its range, bearing, and elevation, in other words—must be accurately and speedily obtained, and these figures must be continuously fed to the uncanny mechanism known as the predictor, along with allowances for wind and temperature. An aircraft may well travel two miles or more while an anti-aircraft shell is hurtling toward the target, and since the chance of actual physical contact of a shell with a vital part of the aircraft is remote, the fuse must be set to explode the shell into a cone of numerous lethal steel fragments a few feet (50 to 100 feet is the optimum distance) before reaching the flying target. A small error anywhere in the chain will defeat the gunner. It follows from this casual examination of the problem that accurate fire against surface vessels, still more against aircraft, is a very complex matter, and that a high percentage of hits can result only from instruments of exquisite refinement. A great deal of scientific effort was expended between 1939 and 1945 in grappling with this problem, and very substantial progress was made, though it should be remembered that the problem itself was growing more difficult every year as the speed, altitude, and manoeuvrability of aircraft were being increased, and as the enemy's own scientific counter-offensive developed. The fact that the problem was thus growing steadily in magnitude made it all the more imperative that new and more effective means of fire-control and more deadly weapons against flying craft be devised. The two most spectacular answers were the proximity fuse and radar-activated fire-control instruments.

Radiolocation, as a practical weapon of war, was born in Britain. It was first conceived as a sort of electro-magnetic burglar alarm, to warn against the intrusion of Goering's bombers. Secretly designed, its production prosecuted with a sense of desperate urgency in an era of mounting Nazi menace, radar and allied electro-magnetic devices branched out amazingly in Britain and elsewhere until by 1945, they had transformed every major aspect of war. Radar ranks as probably the outstanding discovery in an age of military marvels. British scientists pioneered radio-location and made it possible for the R.A.F. (with some aid from the R.C.A.F. and strengthened by hundreds of Canadian-born fliers) to win the critical Battle of Britain.

Canada (which, it should not be forgotten, was Britain's senior Ally during the darkest period of the war, from the capitu-lation of France to Hitler's invasion of the Soviet Union, and at a time when the United States was still filling the role of a friendly neutral) was invited at an early date to share Britain's super-secret location device, and after the fall of France was fully admitted, along with the United States, into a three-way partner-ship of scientific effort. The story of Canada's contribution in the scientific development of military radar is one of the brightest chapters of our war story. Much of it could not be told at the time because of security considerations; but it deserves to be remembered now, not only by military men and scientists, but by all the people of Canada.

A word or two of background may be useful for the non-technical reader. Radar's first application took the form of an electro-magnetic searchlight combined with a precise means of ascertaining range or distance. It was operated by projecting, and focusing to some extent, pulses of energy of great power but staggeringly short in duration—as little as one-millionth of a second—in the direction of the object to be detected. The object illuminated by the radar searchlight—originally a hostile aircraft, later the superstructure of surface vessels, the decks of submarines, the submarine's periscope, buildings, cliffs, shores and so on—reflected back these brief pulses of energy, and ultra-sensitive receivers not only registered the echoes but displayed on a cathode ray screen the precise length of time taken for the pulse to be transmitted and the echo to be received. Since the pulses of electro-magnetic energy travelled at the same speed as light, and since this was constant and known, the distance of the object "illuminated" by the electro-magnetic searchlight could be read off on the radar screen, once a suitable scale had been built into the set. Accuracies as close as a few yards on objects twenty miles away were possible before the end of the war. To the earliest discoveries of methods of measuring range, there were rapidly added highly accurate methods of measuring the other two dimensions: bearing (or azimuth) and altitude (or elevation).

The word "radar" comes from "RAdio Detection And Ranging". As soon as the device was available it supplemented, even where it did not supersede, most of the earlier optical and auditory methods of searching for hostile aircraft and surface vessels. Radar could do many things better than the older methods and some things impossible for them. Optical direction-finding is sharply limited by atmospheric conditions and it fails in total darkness; radar rays pierce fog and cloud and are independent of daylight. Auditory sound-ranging had been brought to relative perfection in the search for anti-aircraft protection, but further progress was barred by the physical nature of the medium. Sound waves in air travel slowly, less than 1200 feet a second, while the radar pulse is travelling 186,000 miles. As aircraft speeds moved forward to approach the speed of sound the efficiency of auditory detection rapidly declined. And the distraction of other noises as well as enemy "jamming" further limited the value of the bi-aural detecting-and-ranging instruments. The range of radar was, moreover, far greater than any optical or auditory device. Even before the war, radar sets in Britain were regularly following commercial aircraft while still flying above Holland and Germany.

Britain was, indeed, saved from subjugation in 1940 partly because her scientists and military engineers had been "on the job" years earlier. A few lines must suffice here to sketch in Britain's pre-war achievement.

In February 1935, Watson Watt, then Superintendent of the Radio Department of the National Physical Laboratory in Britain, officially demonstrated the reflection of radio waves originating in the transmitters of the Daventry broadcasting station and bouncing back from an aircraft which had been set to flying a course in the vicinity. By June 1935, a radiolocation laboratory had been constructed on the Suffolk coast and radar apparatus was following aircraft more than 40 miles. A larger laboratory was rapidly built at Bawdsey Manor, near Felixstowe, where in March 1936 an aircraft flying at 1500 feet was successfully located at a distance of 75 miles. In September 1936 the first Air Exercise was watched by radiolocation. In 1937 preparations were begun for the construction of twenty watching stations, stretching from the Solent to the Firth of Tay, covering the British coast and forty miles out to sea. The five stations already erected to watch the Thames Estuary were able to follow the aircraft which bore Mr. Chamberlain on his historic "umbrella" flight to Munich in September 1938, and a continuous twenty-four hour watch for hostile aircraft was then begun. On Good Friday, 1939, the day Mussolini invaded Albania, the whole chain of twenty stations opened a continuous watch. It was at about this date that Canadian radio scientists first came into the British picture.

The Air Ministry in Britain had invited Canada to share with them "information respecting a most secret device which they had adopted for the detection of aircraft", and Canada responded to the British invitation by sending over the chief of the Radio Section, Dr. John T. Henderson. He sailed on March 18, 1939, for Britain, where he was met by Squadron Leader F. V. Heakes, R.C.A.F.; and to these two Canadians, and to representatives of the other Dominions, the first official disclosure of Britain's "most secret device" for the detection of aircraft was duly made.

The illusion of security induced by Canada's geographic isolation from Europe had tended to leave this country relatively apathetic about the development of new early-warning devices, a state in rare contrast with the feverish urgency prevalent in Britain. A good deal of work had been done in Canada, however, on the propagation and reception of radio waves and their application to *peacetime* uses. As early as 1926, Colonel W. A.

Steel and Major-General A. G. L. McNaughton had patented a method of using the cathode ray oscilloscope for direction finding, using two sets of antenna carefully oriented, one N-S, the other E-W. Dr. Henderson's early work had been connected with a project to find the bearing (location) of atmospherics (distant thunderstorms creating radio static). In 1939, he and his associates of the small Radio Section of the National Research Council were engaged in the development of Cathode Ray Direction Finding equipment suitable for marine and aircraft use.

Accordingly, the detection of objects by the use of radio waves did not come as a completely revolutionary idea to Dr. Henderson and his colleagues. The success of Appleton in Britain, of Breit and Tuve in the United States, in getting echoes back from the ionosphere and thus measuring its height (either by modulating the wave-length or by using short bursts of energy and timing the echo), was well known. Six months before the invitation to visit Britain, there had been discussions at Ottawa between the National Research Council and the Department of National Defence over the possibility of using radio waves for the detection of aircraft. Dr. Henderson, on his arrival in Britain in March 1939, was, therefore, not unduly amazed to learn from the British that echoes from aircraft had been obtained by radar, but the actual existence and performance of a chain of twenty early-warning stations already erected and guarding Britain in the spring of 1939 was staggering enough.

The revelation of what was possible in this field, and of what Britain had already accomplished, led in subsequent months to a series of recommendations for immediate activity in Canada, including the manufacture in Canada of British radar equipment. Dr. J. T. Henderson himself, Dr. R. W. Boyle, Chief of the Physics Division, who was in Britain on a mission chiefly connected with this field shortly after the outbreak of war, Major-General A. G. L. McNaughton, President of the National Research Council until he left to take the Canadian Corps overseas, and Dr. C. J. Mackenzie, who succeeded McNaughton as Acting President at that time, all put forward over the next few months a series of plans, including financial appropriations and recommendations for adequate staff for an immediate attack on a Canadian radiolocation programme. Unfortunately, in the immediate pre-war months and until the fall of France, these proposals met with considerable frustration for reasons already related in Chapter I (p. 16).

Despite these obstacles, some headway was made even during the months of the so-called "phoney" war—a frustrating and disturbing era which ended abruptly and ominously on the day (April 9, 1940) when Hitler overran Denmark and invaded Norway.

When war actually broke out in Europe in September 1939, Dr. J. T. Henderson was in New York inspecting commercial radio equipment, which had not been developed with military requirements in mind but which, he thought, might be adapted or modified in Canada into early experimental service sets. This U.S. equipment included television receivers, a new type of direction finder made by Western Electric, and a new instrument developed by the Bell Laboratories for ascertaining the altitude of aircraft in flight by the measurement of the time taken to transmit a modulated radio wave groundward, and to receive again the "echo"—the same principle as the measurement of the height of the ionosphere but with the wave aimed downward instead of upward. This last, a radio altimeter, offered some promise of rapid modification into a radar set that might be used on an aircraft to detect enemy shipping or be built into a surveillance set for guarding Canada's coasts and harbours. On September 2, 1939, with this in mind, Dr. Henderson placed an order for a Western Electric altimeter; and also, with a view to constructing new sets from scratch, orders were placed for certain high-frequency radio tubes (including some low-power 10 centimetre tubes) commercially available in the United States. This equipment began to arrive in Ottawa two months later.

November 1939 was a month of significant beginnings in Canadian radar. Dr. Henderson and three of his colleagues, with the aid of four men assigned to the National Research Council by the Army (R.C.C.S.), built an experimental set modifying the Western Electric altimeter to emit brief pulses of energy, from which radar echoes could be received and displayed on a cathode ray tube. "By the end of November we had observed our first echoes over short distances from aircraft and buildings," wrote Dr. Henderson in an early Progress Report.

This quiet language masks the historic significance of the event. It was the first time such radar echoes had ever been observed in Canada—in its own way as notable an occasion as the first sentence spoken into the telephone at Brantford by Dr. Alexander Graham Bell, or the first brief flight by a heavier-than-air machine at Baddeck, Nova Scotia, in 1909.

During the winter of 1939-40, the nucleus of scientists and technicians in the Radio Section was slowly but steadily augmented (by March 1940 the number had grown from twelve to twenty-two) and day by day these few pioneers of Canadian radar began to tackle one after another a few of the vast and enormously baffling problems which had to be met and overcome if this challenging and revolutionary new technique was to be mobilized in the defence of Canada and used against the looming Nazi threat to world freedom.

By now Dr. Henderson and his colleagues were in possession of considerable theoretical knowledge of radiolocation, some practical experience in using several types of equipment, and a sufficient awareness of what had already been done in Britain, to see in a general way what direction Canadian development ought to take. The obstacles to rapid progress were, however, still very formidable. Prototypes and exact specifications from Britain would have been most useful, but in the early months of the war these were difficult, if not impossible, to obtain. The fruits of military research in this field in the United States (still a neutral country) were inaccessible. Commercial tubes and components made for other than military purposes were of limited value. Canada possessed no radar industry and only a handful of research scientists in the field of radio.

Yet these handicaps had to be overcome. The defence of Canadian shores and skies, the imminent menace of the Nazi submarine, the growing threat to Britain from the *Luftwaffe* as the months went by all called for swift and effective action in Canada. Staggering scientific and technical problems had to be quickly mastered in Canada if radar sets were to be built in time for the protection of Canadian harbours, the equipment of coastal planes against submarines and surface craft, the erection of warning sets against possible aircraft raids upon strategic spots in Canada, and the construction of fire-control units employing radar to supplement optical or auditory instruments for use in Britain and elsewhere. To make a successful radiolocation set for any of these purposes raised questions never before answered in Canada. Transmitters had to be designed and built capable of delivering powerful bursts of electro-magnetic energy lasting as short a time as one-millionth of a second, which, when aimed at aircraft many miles away, would reflect an "echo" strong enough to be recognized and measured on its return. What radically new types of tubes could be made to emit such pulses? What wave-lengths would provide sharp focusing and yet allow adequate power? What types of antenna, array (billboard), horn, or parabolic mirror would best serve to project and focus a radar beam toward its distant objective? How could receivers be built sensitive enough to register and measure the almost infinitesimal quantities of energy which constitute the echoes bounced back from the target?[1]

The wave-length or frequency to be standardized for Canadian radar was one of the more critical matters for early decision, and because the whole problem led in Britain to one of the most brilliant and far-reaching inventions of the war—the *cavity magnetron*—it needs some comment here, even in connection with the very earliest Canadian sets. The Western Electric altimeter, already mentioned, operated on a 67 centimetre wave-length—a radio wave a little over two feet long. British development up to then had been made mainly in the wave-lengths 1.5 metres and above, and there were considerably more data available in Canada for sets built in that region. On the other hand, the shorter wave-lengths promised outstanding advantages if sets employing them could be made powerful enough. For one thing, there was a direct ratio between wave-length and the optimum size of aerial array (or antenna system); and if radar was to become airborne or even be fitted to light naval vessels, the need for large, heavy, and unwieldy antennae would be a sharply limiting factor. The 1.5 metre radar set, for example, required an aerial array which was really too large to fit properly on an aircraft; indeed, first-class results from airborne radar using so long a wave could not be expected.

[1] In a device which will send out a pulse of a million watt power, and get back one-ten-millionth of a watt power as an "echo"!

North America the remarkable new radar valve, the cavity magnetron, which made it possible to leap almost at once over the hurdles which had long been standing in the way of the use of extremely short radio waves for radiolocation.

It would not be easy to exaggerate the role played in the history of the war by this simple but finely turned squat cylinder of brass about the size of a flat tin of pipe tobacco.[3] The whole future development of Allied radar in both defensive and offensive aspects turned upon its employment. Microwave radar using the cavity magnetron and subsequent refinements constituted a large part of the lead or margin which British, Canadian, and American radar persistently enjoyed over that utilized by Germany, Italy, and Japan. Built into airborne sets, microwave radar helped turn the tide of the anti-submarine warfare at the most critical hour of the war. As an offensive weapon it vastly increased the accuracy and effectiveness of the Allied bombing of Germany. Indeed, the British war-science historians, Crowther and Whiddington, say: "It [the cavity magnetron] probably had a more decisive effect on the war than any other single new weapon."[4] But quite as remarkable in its own way was the fact that as early as the summer of 1940, long before a single microwave radar was in active service, the very disclosure to U.S. scientists of the existence of the cavity magnetron played a large part in convincing them that the British possessed valuable new war secrets which would greatly enhance the war potential of the United States, and which of themselves justified the wisdom of a policy of full cooperation. Of the cavity magnetron, the official U.S. historian of war science, James Phinney Baxter 3rd, wrote: "When the Tizard Mission brought one to America in 1940, they carried the most valuable cargo ever brought to our shores. It sparked the whole development of microwave radar and constituted the most important item in reverse Lease-Lend."[5]

[3] Though it has had much less publicity, the Sutton tube (the reflection oscillator), developed at the Wills Physics Laboratory in the University of Bristol by a team directed by R. W. Sutton, was in its own way quite as remarkable an achievement; the two together made microwave radar an early triumph.

[4] *Science at War* (Philosophical Library, New York, 1948), p. 39.

[5] *Scientists Against Time* (Little, Brown and Co., Boston, 1948) p. 142. Churchill regarded the cavity magnetron as so vital that for many months aircraft using it were not allowed to fly over the continent lest the Nazis learn its secrets.

Dr. Baxter added that the valve was first shown by Professor
J. D. Cockcroft and Dr. E. G. Bowen to members of the U.S.
Microwave Committee on the week-end of September 28-29,
1940, while guests of Alfred Loomis at Tuxedo Park. Canadian
scientists who were invited to attend conferences connected with
the Tizard Mission's visit to the United States recall that U.S.
scientists set to work within twenty-four hours to test the operation of the cavity magnetron, and that more than anything else
its superb performance won them around to recommending
immediate and full cooperation with the British and Canadians
in secret war research.

One is tempted to dwell unduly upon this remarkable valve,
but a few words must serve. The principles of the construction
of the early or traditional radio tube employing electrical voltage,
and consisting essentially of a cathode, an anode, and a grid
within a glass tube, are known to all amateur radio enthusiasts.
Electrons are made to move from cathode to anode under the
influence of an *electrical* field. The magnetron, however, applies
in addition a *magnetic* field so as to make the electrons move
in a curved path sweeping out from the cathode to the anode.
If the magnet is strong enough some of the electrons never reach
the anode but curve back again to the cathode. If these curving
electrons are made to pass by the right kind of circuits, oscillations
can be set up and maintained in those circuits. The cavity
magnetron (or Cavitron) as invented by Dr. J. T. Randall at the
Physics Laboratory at Birmingham, working with Mr. H. A. H.
Boot, employed this principle in a radically new yet strikingly
simple manner: a rotating wheel of electrons, as Crowther and
Whiddington so aptly put it,[6] is made to blow a sort of electrical
note, like a siren, on the eight resonant cavities of the magnetron,
setting up oscillations of ultra-high frequency within them, so
that brief pulses of great power can be taken out by inserting
a suitable loop.

The first cavity magnetron had been produced in July 1940,
just in time to be displayed by the Tizard Mission—just in time,
historians may decide, to constitute one of the turning points of
the war. The urgent problem of producing tubes or valves
suitable for microwave radar had been posed only as recently

[6] *Op cit.*, p. 37.

as the autumn of 1939 to Professor Oliphant at Birmingham:
Randall and Boot had fortunately found a brilliant and novel
answer almost immediately in the resonant cavity magnetron.
The General Electric Company Limited then designed an industrial model, and produced the first one in July 1940. The Tizard
Mission sailed for North America in August 1940 taking a
priceless prototype along.

It is an interesting sidelight for Canadians that the Tizard
Mission did not at first intend to visit Canada at all, or to seek
the assistance of Canadians in solving some of the most pressing
problems of the scientific front. But while in the United States
they became impressed by reports of the progress already made
in Canada in 1½ metre radar, and in microwave radar techniques,[7] as well as in other scientific research; and as a result
they not only visited Canada but laid upon the shoulders of
Canadian scientists and industrialists several of their major
burdens and anxieties, all of which were resolutely tackled here.

One of these assignments led to the mass production in Canada
of a microwave gun-layer or fire-control radar for anti-aircraft
batteries—perhaps the most impressive single performance by
Canada in the field of radar during the war.

The Battle of Britain, it should be remembered, had begun in
August 1940. To the Tizard Mission (representing as it did the
top-ranking war scientists of Britain) there was no problem
more vital at the moment than that of finding new and better
ways of shooting down Nazi aircraft from the sky. Indeed, it
seemed then that unless an answer could soon be found to this
problem, all other British military problems would soon cease
to have significance, for aerial mastery would devastate shipping
in and out of Britain, and she would be beaten to her knees
by starvation. Anti-aircraft fire had never been very effective,
even in the days of slower, clumsier planes of lower operational
ceilings. Now Nazi bombers were faster, more manoeuvrable,
carried heavier bomb loads, possessed new navigation instruments.
Somehow or other ground defences against them had to be vastly
increased in efficiency, and an answer found to the night bomber.

[7] As early as February 1940, Dr. J. T. Henderson and Dr. F. H. Sanders
had been doing some work on 10 centimetre radar in the National Research
Laboratories at Ottawa.

Was radar the solution? At any rate, the Tizard Mission came
to North America urging the highest priority in a search for
better anti-aircraft equipment, faster and more accurate gun-
layers, better predictors, and a proximity fuse also, if the latter
was humanly possible. It was into this programme that Canadian
effort was to be fitted: among other things, Canada was
specifically asked to develop in mass production a microwave
gun-layer, while U.S. effort was to be concentrated on radar
for air interception.

The first discussions between the Radio Section and Colonel
H. A. Taber of the Canadian Army on the construction of a
gun-laying set had begun in May 1940. Cables were exchanged
with Britain, and Canada was advised what stage the development of a satisfactory fire-control set had reached there. Some
preliminary plans were laid in Canada to construct a gun-laying
set on a wave-length of 50 centimetres; and on October 7,
1940, the Department of National Defence made a formal
request to the National Research Council to set about such a
project. Advice from Britain had made it clear that if Canada
succeeded in making an acceptable gun-laying set, large orders
could be counted upon for British use also.

Before this programme got under way, however, the implications of the invention of the cavity magnetron and other
new radio discoveries had changed the whole thinking of
British and Canadian scientists; and when the Canadian programme did get rolling almost immediately afterwards, it was
directed toward the mass production of a *microwave* (or 10 centimetre) radar set which promised far more valuable results than
anything which had been produced or even laid on the drawing-
boards up to that time.

To see the full value of Canada's mass production of this
microwave gun-laying set (G.L. Mark III C, as it came to be
styled) it will be useful to look across the Atlantic for a moment
to see what had been going on there.

The great superiority which a radar-activated gun-layer
would have over the earlier methods of fire control by sound
or optical means had been foreseen as far back as the first
demonstration at Daventry in February 1935. Work had begun
on a radar gun-layer in 1937 at Bawdsey, and by October of

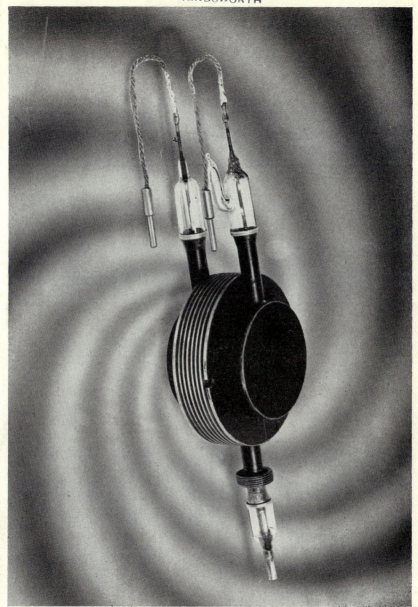

THE DEVELOPMENT OF RADAR

The Cavity Magnetron—"this . . . simple but finely turned squat
cylinder of brass about the size of a flat tin of pipe tobacco"

RADAR IN USE

Long-Range Early-Warning Tower at Metcalfe Road Field Station developed for the R.C.A.F. by the Council. The antenna at the top finds the range and direction of aircraft out to 100 miles. Antennae up the side of the tower give the height of the aircraft

that year trials of a "lash-up" system had given rich promise of accurate range-finding. The first experimental G.L. Mark I underwent trials in the early summer of 1938. It measured range out to about 30,000 yards with an accuracy of ±50 yards up to about 15,000 yards. It indicated bearing to an accuracy of ±1 degree. But it could not measure elevation at all.

A further serious weakness was that the information it did provide could not all be fed to a predictor except by a series of discontinuous readings. As every student of anti-aircraft gunnery will know, it is not enough to be able to tell a gun crew exactly where its target is at any given moment. It is necessary, as in duck hunting, to aim well ahead of the target. However, the amazing instrument known as the "predictor" will work out exactly where an aircraft should be in, say, twenty-five seconds, given its present position and the rates at which it is changing its range, elevation, and bearing. What the British military authorities wanted was a radar set which would continuously feed to a predictor in a smooth fashion exact data about the bearing, range, and altitude of an aircraft, so that "continuous following" of the target by the battery of anti-aircraft guns could be achieved.

G.L. Mark II was Britain's next answer to this problem. Development contracts for it were placed with selected British manufacturers in the autumn of 1939. The first working prototype of G.L. Mark II was delivered in the summer of 1940. The first Canadian proposals had in mind the construction in Canada of an improved version of this gun-laying radar for the defence of Canadian key points. G.L. Mark II had three new features: it could measure elevation; it provided "continuous following"; and in addition, it employed a device which enabled the range operator to select the target so that the other two operators (who were regulating bearing and elevation) could subsequently see only the one target, and hence would not be distracted by the appearance of other aircraft within their field of vision.

The manufacture in massive quantity of G.L. Mark II was a very large industrial undertaking, especially since it was still operating on relatively long radio waves, which in turn required an aerial array of considerable size; and consequently full production did not get going in Britain (loaded up with other commitments) until 1941.

Meantime, as we have seen, the cavity magnetron seemed to promise facilities for a gun-laying radar of much greater accuracy and resolution of the target, together with much smaller aerial arrays, such as paraboloid reflectors, so compact indeed that they could readily be built on to a truck or van and be transported swiftly about the countryside in company with mobile anti-aircraft batteries. The result was that, parallel to the work being done on G.L. Mark II, the British also began planning experimental models of G.L. Mark III in the microwave band. The first precursor of such was made in Britain by a commercial firm in the summer of 1941.

Canada came fresh and already well armed into the radar research and production field just as it was becoming apparent that microwave radar was possible, so that, happily, instead of repeating or retracing any of the course pursued in Britain, the National Research Council, in October 1940, was able to begin at once to work toward a version of G.L. Mark III, a model which was distinguished from its British counterpart by the added initial "C". And with such enterprise and resourcefulness was the Canadian project pushed along, that to the amazement of the British, the Canadian version, G.L. Mark III C, began to be available in quantity several months before the British version, despite all the advantages of the British early start in radar. It is hardly necessary to add how welcome, under the circumstances, the addition of this early Canadian equipment was to the anti-aircraft defenders of London and of the great industrial towns of Britain.

The chronology of those first months in Canadian microwave radar is interesting. Professor J. D. Cockcroft, who had become the head of the British Scientific Mission when Sir Henry Tizard returned to England earlier in the month, laid down for the benefit of the National Research Council, on October 28, 1940, the general outline requirements for a G.L. radar, and gave the Radio Section what amounted to a General Staff specification for the instrument. The specification called for a range accuracy of ± 50 yards up to 18,000 yards, with bearing and elevation accuracies of plus or minus one-quarter of a degree.

These fire-control data were to be provided smoothly to permit "continuous following" of the target, so that they could be used by existing mechanical anti-aircraft predictors. The set was to provide its own "early-warning" system up to 60,000 yards. (In a layman's language, all aircraft coming within a range of about 35 miles were to be clearly visible on the early-warning display, so that long before enemy aircraft approached the gun position, a suitable target could be selected, and the predictor given time to settle down to a smooth rate of following by the time the aircraft was within range of the gun.)

Rather than seek to build both an early-warning set and an accurate position-finder into the one instrument, the Canadian designers elected to design two separate trailers or vans, each with its own separate aerial, transmitter, and receiver. As nothing was known about the feasibility of putting microwaves through a rotating joint, and as the aerial system would have to be capable of swinging around through 360 degrees to focus on the oncoming aircraft, it was decided to rotate the whole cabin of the accurate position-finder (or APF as it became known to radar scientists at Ottawa). The APF thus became a power-driven rotatable trailer, housing all the radio gear and supporting the antennae. The other portion of the set, the early-warning radar or zone-position indicator (ZPI as it became), was a set using much longer waves (175 megacycles or about 1¾ metres wave-length), built in a fixed trailer with an antenna capable of rotation. Three heavy trucks completed the convoy, used for towing purposes and for housing the Diesel power unit, cables, and spares.

Decisions about these and other details and early experiments in the performance of the tubes and components occupied the month of November 1940, by the end of which month many of the main features had been "frozen".

Research Enterprises Limited, Leaside, Ontario, which had come into being only a few weeks before, had by this time taken on its staff some mechanical engineers, and their chief of mechanical work, William Vrooman, together with F. S. Mac-Kay on the electrical end, came to Ottawa to assist in the design. Research Enterprises Limited gradually assumed responsibility for the mechanical details of the trailers. Meantime, before the end of 1940, the radio scientists of the National Research Council were at work designing the transmitter, receiver, antennae, transmission lines, sweeps, displays, integrators, and electro-mechanical controls. Specifications had to be laid down and contracts awarded for such matters as the building of the fixed and rotating trailers, and for the Diesel generator needed for the supply of power. Delicate amplidyne and thyratron controls for driving the aerials had to be investigated and ordered. Special condensers had to be procured from Boston for the range system. A great deal of time had to be given to advising Research Enterprises Limited and their sub-contractors, so that a supply of high-sensitivity tubes would be available in time. In particular a supply of the cavity magnetrons had to be assured. "Satisfactory magnetrons from the Northern Electric Company were received early in February 1941, and considering that no one in Canada had any knowledge of 10-centimetre magnetrons until September of 1940, this was a fine achievement," notes Dr. John T. Henderson, chief of the Radio Section. "Similarly, local oscillators were obtained by copying, with slight modifica-tion, a British Sutton tube, and first samples were received in April. This tube, with minor improvements, has been standard-ized in the G.L., and again great credit is due the manufacturers, Rogers Radio Tubes, and in particular to Mr. H. Parker, for their rapid development in Canadian production."

It is not difficult even now, years later, to reconstruct the air of urgency and excitement which prevailed during that winter around the National Research Laboratories on Sussex Street and out at the Metcalfe Road Field Station. There was one basic point of persistent anxiety: microwave radar was still in the theoretical stage. Was it prudent to go full steam ahead on 10 centimetre gun-layers when no one in the world had yet proved the new theories in actual performance? In Britain and in the United States, as in Canada, the cavity mag-netron and other new equipment and designs were being feverishly tested. It was a race to see who could be first, and much was at stake.

Research on microwave radar had begun in the United States on November 10, 1940, at the Radiation Laboratory in the Massachusetts Institute of Technology at Boston. Dr. Baxter has related[8] how the first American microwave pulse radar was put together in about two months of intense activity in a laboratory on the roof of the main M.I.T. building. The first operation, on January 4, 1941, showed echoes from buildings on the Boston skyline, but the first American attempts to pick up aircraft echoes were failures.

Canadian scientists, grappling not only with microwaves never before harnessed but facing the rigours of heavy snowfall and intense sub-zero weather at the Metcalfe Field Station, were also without definite results on echoes as late as March 6, 1941. But both at Boston and at Ottawa the month of March 1941 was a month of triumph. In its first airborne test on March 10, a Boston set detected planes up to five miles; and during the latter part of March, Ottawa scientists came through with very encouraging echoes on approaching Hudson aircraft at ranges up to 17,000 yards. This was done using a purely experimental set-up consisting of a 6-foot reflector or paraboloid mirror for transmitting and a 30-inch paraboloid for receiving.

Just in case 10 centimetre radar proved a failure, development had been carried on simultaneously with 65 centimetre sets, and in order to be on the safe side, some work on that wave-length was continued as late as the end of April.[9]

"During the spring of 1941," Dr. Henderson summarized, in his Progress Report of May 1942, "the picture changed rapidly from one where we had little knowledge of 10 centimetres, to one where we had sufficient confidence in the expected performance to drop the parallel work on 65 centimetres."

Rapid progress on G.L. Mark III C was made during April and May of 1941, so that it was possible to schedule and hold a successful demonstration of the complete G.L. convoy, both the early-warning instrument and the accurate position-finder, as early as June 17, 1941, barely seven months from the day when the first statement of detailed requirements had been received. Canadian, British, and U.S. Services were present.

The manufacture of the gun-layer radar convoy in quantity, consisting as it did of two massive trailers with attached antenna

---

[8] *Op. cit.,* p. 146.

[9] A note on some of the contributions made to radar research by Canadian universities, and a list of several of the outstanding pioneers in Canadian radar, will be found in Appendix A (p. 267).

plus three large trucks for towing and housing the Diesel power unit and spares, was of course essentially a large industrial production job, and as such was turned over to Research Enterprises Limited. But with the assistance of some R.E.L. staff, the scientists and technicians at Ottawa themselves built five such complete convoys of G.L. Mark III C in 1941. The first model was tested, as has been said, on June 17. The second was built but never assembled, the several chassis being sent to Research Enterprises during the summer and early fall to serve as models from which the final production prototype could be evolved. The third was forwarded to the U.S. Army Signal Corps (it had been requested by them in December 1940), so that they could become acquainted with the design and make any use of the circuits in it for their own purposes. The fourth was shipped to Britain in December 1941, where it arrived in the same month as the first British experimental model was being delivered, and actually nine months before the first of the British "pre-production" models was ready. The fifth constituted the National Research Council's standard model.

The armed services in all three countries followed keenly the progress of the Canadian programme. Naturally they were most intensely interested in the accuracy of performance which could be expected from anti-aircraft fire when the microwave radar device went operational. Dr. Henderson has told how, to test the accuracy of the first set, it was arranged to obtain precision-testing instruments (kine-theodolites) through the courtesy of the United States Coast Artillery Board. These were brought to Ottawa by an officer and crew from the United States Army, and used to measure the accuracy of the G.L. in the three dimensions—range, azimuth, and elevation—which gun-laying requires if it is to be effective. In general the range accuracy of the first set was ±19 yards, and the accuracy in elevation and bearing slightly better than plus or minus one-sixth of a degree. This remarkable precision will be fully appreciated by any student of gunnery, and for the layman it is only necessary to interject that the reach far surpassed anything attainable by pre-radar methods. It could follow a target very smoothly, and the data supplied were, of course, equally reliable and available in fair weather or foul, in broad day or the middle of the darkest night.

All this time Research Enterprises Limited at Leaside, Ontario, were being promptly supplied by the Radio Section with interim specifications so that they could speed up preparations for mass production at the earliest possible date. At the beginning of August 1941 the Radio Section began to forward such specifications on the construction of G.L. units, and by the end of November these were all in the hands of Research Enterprises Limited, sufficiently complete to define construction and performance of the unit.

The rest of the story of the G.L. Mark III C belongs for the most part to the history of the "industrial front"[10] in Canada, and to the story of "Operations Overseas". The achievement of Research Enterprises Limited is itself a notable page of Canadian story: nearly $200 millions of radar equipment was produced there and shipped to the fighting fronts of the world; and among the dozen or more types of Canadian radar mass-produced there, the G.L. programme, consisting of 665 complete convoys, was in some ways the leading achievement. No one can sift out from the incredibly complex story of the winning of the war just exactly what contribution the Canadian G.L. radar made. Accurate anti-aircraft fire depends on many things besides accurate position-finders—on gun barrels, explosives, fuses, and predictors, for example—, and Canada had a share in the development of several of these.

It is interesting to recall that at the outbreak of war, indeed as late as August 1940, Anti-Aircraft Command in Britain found it necessary on the average to fire 20,000 rounds to bring down a single unseen aircraft, and seldom damaged more than one or two per cent. of the enemy airfleets, whereas, against the flying bomb attacks of 1944, using radar gun-layer with automatic following, a new U.S. predictor, and the proximity fuse, 70 per cent. of all the flying bombs were shot down, and for limited periods gunners were shooting down 100 per cent. of the missiles coming within their range.[11] This extraordinary

---

[10] A phrase used as the title of a brochure prepared by the Department of Munitions and Supply (The King's Printer, Ottawa, 1943).

[11] Crowther and Whiddington, *op. cit.*, p. 78.

performance owed a great deal to U.S. scientific ingenuity, since the equipment used was of American design (except the anti-aircraft gun itself, which was British). But Canada also had a hand in this brilliant achievement. The U.S. gun-laying radar (styled SCR-584) was developed in the closest collaboration with Canadian and British work on G.L. Mark III: each owed a good deal to the other's discoveries. And, as related in the next chapter, some of the most novel attacks on the problem of the proximity fuse were originally proposed by Canadian scientists.

Radar for Canadian Coastal Defence

The problem of adapting radar to Canadian coast defence was by-passed on an earlier page, to pursue the fortunes of the more massive gun-laying project at the point where experiments were being made with the Western Electric altimeter in the winter of 1939-40.

Following the comparisons made at Kingston in May 1940 between the 67 centimetre set built around the Western Electric altimeter and a 1.5 metre set constructed at Ottawa from scratch, a decision was made in June to build the Canadian coastal defence sets on the latter wave-length. It is hardly necessary to remind the reader again that the fall of France, the declaration of war by Italy, the loss of the French navy, and the occupation by Nazi military forces of the whole north-western coast of Europe from the northern tip of Norway to the south of France, had greatly increased the possibility of enemy raids on the east coast of Canada. Even after Britain's naval position had again been improved somewhat by her naval actions at Oran and Dakar, and the acquisition of the fifty U.S. "over age" destroyers, there was always the chance that the Nazis, fully aware of the strategic importance of Halifax as the western end of the life-line to Britain, might make a "suicide" attack upon it with such naval units as they could spare for the purpose. Accordingly, the first coastal defence radar sets ordered by the services were for the protection of Halifax. Two powerful detection units were planned and built as rapidly as possible, the first for installation at Duncan's Cove, just south of Chebucto Head, and about ten miles south of Halifax, and the second for Osborne Head, abo

eight miles east of Halifax. First requirements from the services
called for warning or detection sets only, to advise of the approach
of surface vessels, but the work going forward on fire-control
against enemy aircraft demonstrated that ship positions also
could be located by radar with sufficient accuracy to direct
the fire of coastal artillery guns. Equipment was accordingly
requested and promptly built by the National Research Council
for this purpose also. The next advance was based on the
discovery that with microwave radar echoes were obtained even
from splashes of shells in the water, and that these could be
accurately located for range and bearing without interrupting
the smooth tracking of the target, thus greatly aiding artillery
fire. One after another these refinements were added to Canadian
coastal defence.

The first set, installed at Duncan's Cove in the summer of
1941, operated on 1½ metres and with an output ranging from
50 to 75 kilowatts. The antenna array was large and elaborate
(16 feet by 24 feet) and mounted on a 90-foot tower. It had
a range accuracy of ±100 yards and a bearing accuracy of
plus or minus one-sixth of a degree. The antenna height was
168 feet above sea level. With it, large passenger vessels were
visible up to about 20 miles, average freighters to 12 or 13
miles, destroyers to 10 miles, corvettes to 8 miles, and motor
torpedo boats up to 7500 yards. The Osborne Head Station,
built somewhat later, was turned over to the Army in June
1942 and extended these ranges by about 20 per cent.

Duncan's Cove station operated continuously during the
autumn of 1941 and was, indeed, one of the few radars guarding
North America at that time. Both Duncan's Cove and Osborne
Head stations followed the course of shipping in the vicinity
of Halifax every night, and, in poor visibility, by day also.
Ship positions were relayed to the naval plotting board at
Camperdown. The Royal Canadian Navy officially credited
the Duncan's Cove radar set with saving six million dollars
worth of shipping in the first six months of its operation, and
though the following of friendly aircraft had not been prominent
in the minds of the designers, on more than one occasion lost
R.C.A.F. aircraft were safely guided back to their base at Dartmouth.

The next step taken by the Canadian Army was the request for fire-control sets for the coastal defence of Canada, and originally, on April 9, 1941, a total of forty-one such units was ordered. The progress being made by this time on the mobile anti-aircraft radar G.L. Mark III C, employing microwave techniques, suggested the provision of similar 10 centimetre equipment for controlling the fire of Canadian coastal batteries. Indeed, many of the components developed for the gun-layer could be directly incorporated in such a set. Performance specifications, as received by the National Research Council in May, called for accurate measurement of range up to 30,000 yards, with a maximum allowable range error of only ±25 yards, and a provision for accurately spotting shell splashes within a thousand yards of the target vessel. The set's primary purpose was of course the feeding to coastal batteries of a continuous flow of data about the position and movement of enemy warships, with this additional refinement, that the actual performance of the coastal guns against the enemy target (as evidenced by shell splashes) could be checked constantly against the elevation and bearing data being fed to the guns. The construction of the experimental model (called CDX, the CD for Coast Defence, and the X indicating microwave frequency) began in April 1942, and by the following month the transmitter housing had been designed and completed. In June, antenna rotators were planned. In July the display racks were designed and built, and by August the electrical design of the range-measuring equipment was complete. In that month, also, preparation began of a "lash-up" CDX unit for performance trials off Osborne Head, Nova Scotia. In September 1942 this lash-up unit was thoroughly tested at Ottawa and then shipped to Halifax early in October. Preliminary trials, held between October 15 and 20, on what was then only the second microwave coastal set operating in North America, proved conclusively its superiority to earlier longer-wave models. Although mounted at only about half the elevation of the 1½ metre radar at that site, it could "see" further across the water, while there was a most gratifying absence of the "clutter" and spurious echoes which had been prevalent on the display screens of the longer-wave sets. Discrimination of targets was good. Ships only 150 yards from one another, and separated by only a quarter of a degree in bearing, could be readily told apart.

The prototype set was completed early in 1943 and put into operation in the last week in March. The set fulfilled the specified accuracy of 25 yards in range and one-sixth of a degree in bearing; while the fall of shot could be measured up to 50 yards in range and the same error in bearing. A maximum detection range of over 40,000 yards (23 miles) could be obtained on larger passenger liners, and typical freighters could be followed consistently up to 35,000 yards. There was no interference from aircraft echoes, and the radar display was quite free from false echoes of atmospheric origin. Though it never saw service against Hitler's navy, the very existence of such powerful new coastal gunnery fire-control instruments may have served as a deterrent to hostile raids. As the war progressed, and the menace of attack on Canada's coasts by surface vessels diminished, the original order of forty-one equipments was reduced to fourteen. These were built at Research Enterprises Limited, together with five additional CDX equipments on order of the Soviet Union.

The value of the "fall of shot" information picked up by such radars as CDX suggested additional refinements in this field, and before the end of the war much further progress was made by National Research Council scientists and Army engineers in developing radar sets which would permit rapid and accurate correction of range and bearing errors based on actual detection of the fall of shells aimed at a distant target.

Perhaps it is not necessary to document at length the revolution brought about by radar-directed gunnery used against shipping at night. The first and thus most spectacular demonstration was in the battle of Cape Matapan. The first radar-directed broadside from H.M.S. *Warspite* on that occasion consisted of six 15-inch shells. Five of the six secured hits. Three Italian cruisers and two destroyers were sunk.[12]

Mass production of all-Canadian radar sets designed by National Research Council scientists was not the only service provided by Research Enterprises Limited in this field. They built, for example, a total of 670 sets of an adaptation of a British

[12] Crowther and Whiddington, *op. cit.*, p. 73.

light-warning radar for the United States Army. The American forces used this set extensively in the Pacific during the period when U.S. manufacturers were striving to expand their own production facilities to meet the urgent requests of the Army and Navy.

An order from the British Ministry of Aircraft Production for a mobile radar set for ground interception of aircraft resulted in another important contribution by Research Enterprises Limited. This was a 50 centimetre interception-control radar which used tilting 10-foot parabolic mirrors mounted on a small steel tower. The entire equipment of a single set, including transmitter, receiver, displays, equipment for interrogation of aircraft to ascertain whether friend or foe, antenna mountings, dual power units, and spares for six months' operation, required an impressive convoy of eight trucks. Seventy of these massive convoys were assembled at Leaside and some of them reached Burma early in 1945.

The radar sets so far described were built for British use, or at the request of the Canadian Army. We now turn to those designed and built for the R.C.N.

The Night Watchman

In March 1940, the Royal Canadian Navy asked the Radio Branch of the National Research Council to devise and install a simple radar system which could be employed in conjunction with the buried guard-loops used to protect harbour entrances. The first installation was needed for Herring Cove, where the ship channel is about a quarter of a mile off shore, and the far shore is about two and a half miles away. What was wanted was a guard beam of the so-called "burglar alarm" type, the principle of which is familiar to the public now because of numerous photo-electric devices. Any ship crossing the guard-loop would instantaneously show up on the display tube, and of course this would occur no matter how dark the night or how foggy the day, since radar beams operate independently of night or fog. The radar beam was fixed to bear in a pre-determined direction, and when it struck the hull or super-structure of a passing vessel, an "echo" of electro-magnetic energy would be reflected which would show up on the cathode ray tube of the Night Watchman panel.

In actual practice, a "pulse" or short beam of energy, lasting one-half of one-millionth of a second, was produced at uniform intervals. The "echo" coming back from a ship in the channel one-quarter of a mile away would be received about three-millionths of a second later—for all practical purposes, simultaneously! The power output used on the first Halifax Night Watchman was about 1 kilowatt.[13] The principle is similar to that of the use of a short blast from a ship's horn when a vessel is feeling its way through fog near shore or amidst suspected ice-fields, with the important difference that radar waves travel 186,000 miles a second and sound waves only about a fifth of a mile in the same time. The duration of the "burst" and of the succeeding pause can both be correspondingly shorter when electro-magnetic waves instead of sound waves are used.

The Halifax installation was complete in July 1940, and naval staff detailed to operate the equipment was then trained and placed in charge. Nine months later an improved form of receiver was installed. In December 1940, the U.S. Army Signal Corps ordered a duplicate of this equipment, which they had seen in operation. This was forwarded to the United States the following February. The Night Watchman sets were a minor achievement in the radar field, but the experience acquired by Canadian scientists in designing and installing them came in handy in fulfilling the next request from the Royal Canadian Navy, which was a set to be installed on ships for the detection of Nazi warships and submarines.

In February 1941, Commander Pressey of the Royal Canadian Navy proposed that Canadian scientists develop a small shipboard radar set which could be used for the detection of submarines on the surface. There was a model already to hand: the Royal Navy's set known as the "286 type". The wave-length to be used was relatively long—about 1½ metres. Research in Britain had already indicated that a much more powerful and

13 This may be compared to the strength of signal of a small community radio broadcasting station, with this important difference, however, that the broadcasting station emits a "continuous wave", whereas the radar transmitter operates in very short pulses separated by comparatively long periods of inactivity.

accurate search set was possible if far shorter wave-lengths could be employed,[14] but there were still many technical obstacles to be overcome before this was possible, and something was urgently needed as a stopgap. The Battle of the Atlantic had taken an ominous turn, and the Allied anti-submarine forces needed at once all the radar vision with which they could be provided. If still sharper eyes were being promised in laboratories and on drafting boards, well and good, but meantime Canada required the best possible existing apparatus for her growing anti-submarine navy.

The National Research Council began at once to build such a set. The first unit was completed in May 1941, installed on a corvette, and given a sea trial before the month was out. The work already done on other types of radar speeded up the production, since the transmitter used was a copy of the unit already developed for use on patrol planes, and the receiver was a modified copy of the Night Watchman equipment. As was common in the early stages of radar development, the scientists had to make do with the best radio tubes and components available on this side of the Atlantic at the time, though well aware that far superior equipment was already in existence elsewhere, or about to be available. But even with makeshift tubes, this early set reached a power output of 4 to 5 kilowatts, and this was doubled when better tubes came to hand.

This first Canadian shipborne radar performed well by the standards of the time. From a typical corvette installation, the operator could expect to see from three to four thousand yards on surfaced submarines and about five thousand yards on other corvettes. Aircraft were usually visible up to 25,000 yards. At the request of the British Admiralty, a set was installed in June 1941 on H.M.S. *Malaya,* which had crossed the Atlantic before Admiralty radar equipment could be completely fitted and which needed more protection before it returned to dangerous waters. The installation of a Canadian radar on the *Malaya* was completed on July 17, 1941. Canadian scientists followed with interest the performance of this set, partly because the aerial on the British warship was fitted at a greater height than was possible on the corvettes which were

[14] See pp. 32-3.

being equipped in Canadian shipyards. Swordfish aircraft could be followed by it to 20,000 yards when flying 500 feet above the sea, submarines to 4,000 yards, and excellent echoes could be obtained from cruisers at twelve to fourteen thousand yards. Two more British ships were supplied with Canadian shipborne radar sets under similar circumstances later in the summer of 1941.

By this time microwave models were beginning to show distinct promise, thus rendering the early 1½ metre sets such as these largely obsolete, but they remained in service until the new 10 centimetre sets were ready and they rendered useful interim service, if no more. A modified version of these early 1½ metre sets was fitted to Motor Torpedo Boats for the Royal Canadian Navy, and continued to give good service until the end of the war.

By June 1941 the Royal Canadian Navy had become so convinced of the superiority of microwave radar that they formally requested the National Research Council to develop a 10 centimetre set for use on corvettes, Algerines, and frigates, the basic purpose being the detection of enemy submarines and surface warships, coupled, if possible, with aid to naval gunnery.

In August 1941, one of the new 10 centimetre units built in the United States for airborne interception was set up side by side with one of the older 1½ metre naval models at Duncan's Cove, just outside the entrance to Halifax Harbour. Directed toward the same ships proceeding out of the harbour, the 10 centimetre set gave a range double that of the older unit, and better discrimination of the target. This test confirmed the decision to go ahead on the microwave naval sets. The first Canadian-made unit was tested from a shore site overlooking the entrance to Halifax Harbour, was subsequently installed in an Algerine type mine-sweeper, and given sea trials off the Halifax coast. Again it proved far superior to a 1½ metre set operating alongside. A production order was thereupon given to Research Enterprises Limited, and seventy sets were built, the later models incorporating a series of improvements suggested from time to time by naval authorities. Production models were in service in the Royal Canadian Navy

from early 1943—in time to play a part in the most critical
months of the Battle of the Atlantic—until the end of hostilities.

The superiority of the 10 centimetre sets over the older 1½
metre search radar led to an immediate exploration of the possibility that even shorter wave-lengths might be worth developing.
For certain purposes one outstanding advantage of the shorter
wave was the reduced size of the antenna to be employed (there
is a direct ratio between the wave-length and the dimensions
of the antenna). This at once suggested the utility of microwave radar on motor torpedo boats, motor gun boats, and other
small craft of the Coastal Forces, where weight and size were
severely restricted. In May of 1942 the National Research
Council was asked by the Admiralty to undertake the development of a small high-resolution surface-search radar to operate
on a wave-length of only 3 centimetres or thereabouts. What
was wanted was a compact but powerful set, capable of being
mounted on small craft and yet with range and resolution not
inferior to those in use on destroyers and other warcraft. This
posed new problems of space, weight, ability to stand mechanical
shock, water-proofing, low power supply, easy removability so
that sets could be taken out readily and serviced ashore, and
ability to continue working through long periods of high temperature and humidity. These specifications were all super-
imposed on the already formidable scientific problems of developing a satisfactory radar set in the new 3 centimetre wave
band.

By April of 1943 the first of these new sets had been built
and was flown over to the United Kingdom and demonstrated
there before an aggregation of "heavy brass" at Portsmouth. Dr.
K. C. Mann, of the National Research Council, was in charge
of the equipment. The results were in general quite satisfactory,
but a number of further refinements were suggested, and an
active programme at Ottawa and Research Enterprises Limited
was kept moving all that summer. In the autumn, the British
placed an order for 2000 of these sets. The production model
was a compact but powerful search radar for small craft. Its
antenna had an aperture of only thirty by five inches, but its
transmitter developed 50 kilowatts at peak output (equivalent
during the brief "pulse" to the power output of the most

A RADAR SET

Canadian Type 268 Radar

A RADAR STATION

Coast defence station (1½ metres) near Halifax

powerful radio broadcasting stations then in Canada!). It met the rigid requirements listed above, and its performance as a searching device compared favourably with those on much larger warships.

Early sets were used in the Channel and on larger craft for convoy runs to North Africa. Equipped with a larger antenna, a number of them proved effective in picking out Nazi submarines equipped with the new *Schnörkel* breathing tube and thus running virtually submerged.

When the war was over it was decided to use some of these 3 centimetre sets as safety devices on merchant shipping, and during 1946 the National Research Council installed nearly one hundred of them on Canadian vessels. Except for the multiplicity of controls, they are nearly ideal for merchant shipping and have given invaluable service pending the development of a civil marine radar.

Miscellaneous Radar and Radio Contributions

Between 1939 and 1945 the whole field of detecting, ranging, signalling, plotting, and communicating by use of short-wave electro-magnetic devices grew so prodigiously that any record which pretends to be reasonably complete must mention scores of relatively minor achievements as well as those on which public attention has been focused. For example, early in 1941 the Royal Canadian Navy asked for shore beacons operating on a radar principle. The idea was that a short pulse of energy from a ship's radar would "trigger" a beacon located on the nearby shore. This would set off a mechanism within the beacon which would return a coded reply: coded so that the vessel, possibly off its course or beset by fog or heavy weather, could at once identify which beacon it had interrogated. The "blip" or flick on the radar display aboard ship would also give the captain some information about his distance from the beacon. If he could get responses from two beacons at once he could locate his position by triangulation.

The National Research Council met the request by adapting some of the earlier search radars which had become obsolete through the production of more powerful transmitting tubes. The receiver of these beacons was geared up so that it "triggered" the transmitter, while a coding wheel permitted the resulting emission to be readily identified.

The first of these radar beacons was set up on the shore near Chebucto Head at the entrance to Halifax Harbour. The shore installation included an aerial 125 feet above the water, and trials showed that corvettes as far out as thirty-five miles could "trigger" the beacon with their radar signals and obtain a coded response which showed up on their own cathode ray display. The beacon could respond simultaneously to five different interrogating signals with no difficulty.

Another naval request came on March 19, 1941. Nazi submarines were now known to be using radar, and this suggested a supplementary means of detecting the presence and roughly the range and bearing of such enemy warships. A sensitive receiver on a Canadian corvette or destroyer would first reveal that an enemy radar beam or "searchlight" was "illuminating" it: then "direction finding" could be applied to the enemy signal and the anti-submarine craft set on a course toward the U-boat. The National Research Council undertook the development of such a receiver, engaging a New York firm to build the actual apparatus, but reserving all final testing to Canadian territory as a security measure.[15] By the time the first two models had been received from New York, Research Enterprises Limited was in a position to handle further production, and altogether about twenty sets were delivered to the Royal Canadian Navy. The apparatus itself was relatively simple, consisting of a wide band receiver tuned slowly over the entire range to be searched. Should an enemy radar signal be detected, it would show up on a cathode ray tube and ring an alarm bell in the radar operator's cabin, where it would serve as an additional or early-warning aid to the usual means (Asdic and Radar) of detecting the presence of Nazi submarines.

An urgent call for help reached the National Research Council in February 1944. A few months before, the Germans had loosed one of their most ingenious secret weapons, a radio-

[15] It will be recalled that the United States was not yet at war, and it was not desirable to risk radar secrets unnecessarily within an area where enemy agents were still free to operate.

controlled glider bomb, first in the Bay of Biscay and in the neighbourhood of the Azores, later in the waters about Italy. This was so effective in the early stages that it made the area unhealthy for Allied surface craft and hampered the naval operations connected with the campaign in Italy. The best answer to the radio-controlled glider bomb—which was directed from an enemy aircraft flying at a great altitude—appeared to be the "jamming" of the wave-length which the Nazi aircraft was using to guide the glider bomb. Such jamming, if powerful enough, would cause the enemy airship to lose control of the missile, which then crashed harmlessly off the target.

The Radio Branch of the National Research Council went into immediate action to produce five such "jammers" in a crash programme, and the first of them was actually shipped to Halifax on March 29. It gave out a powerful wave (1 kilowatt output) which was modulated over the entire frequency range likely to be used by the enemy in guiding the bomb. When in the course of such rapid modulation the "jammer" radio wave coincided with the frequency being used in controlling the glider bomb, it would obstruct or temporarily "take over" the guiding of the Nazi bomb, which would then glide off course and out of the pilot's control. A ship installation was made at Halifax and tests showed the equipment to be effective.

The use of microwave radar equipment as a convenient and relatively secret means of communication between the ships of a convoy at times when weather conditions made communication by flag or loud-hailer impractical was suggested by the Navy in May 1943. The Radio Branch proposed a slightly different solution for the same problem and with the approval of the Navy built two units using a voice-controlled carrier wave and a call signal. The field tests showed the equipment to work satisfactorily up to a line-of-sight range of four miles. A change in Naval Convoy procedure shortly after the tests were made, however, discouraged further work on this device, in view of the many high-priority problems then being tackled by radar scientists and engineers.

Radar equipment detected with increasing efficiency the approach of aircraft or ships, but in the very early stages could not identify them as being friend or foe. It was necessary to devise equipment which, when challenged by a radar signal, would give out a properly coded reply so that friendly ships and aircraft would not be molested. Early in 1943 the National Research Council was asked to develop and install such identifying equipment as part of the radar instalments on Canadian naval craft. By this time all allied shipping and aircraft had been equipped with a "transponder", which gave out an appropriate response when interrogated by a friendly radar search unit. This response showed up on the cathode ray tube of the Canadian corvette or other naval craft. Seventy-five of these identification equipments were constructed by the National Research Council and turned over to the Navy in the autumn of 1943.

Radar for the R.C.A.F.

When hostilities broke out in 1939, the R.C.A.F. enlisted scientific aid to provide early warning against possible aerial raiders. Knowing how far Britain had already gone in ringing the British Isles with a chain of early-warning stations of high efficiency, the R.C.A.F. first approached the authorities in the United Kingdom to see if similar equipment could be procured for installation at strategic points in Canada. The menace to Canada in the early months did not seem to be very great, and during the period described by Neville Chamberlain as the "twilight war", this dependence on Britain appeared to be the the best solution, even if Canada had to wait for a time, until the most pressing needs in the British Isles had been satisfied. At the same time as the British were erecting their own East Coast chain of radar stations, they were planning similar early-warning installations for Malta, Aden, and other vital ports in the Commonwealth and Empire. As early as July 1939, the Chief of the Air Staff at Ottawa had asked the National Research Council to undertake the production of a radiolocation set with a maximum range on all aircraft at all heights and able to "see" completely around the 360 degrees. These early plans for Canada were based on such British C.O. (Chain Overseas) stations, which it was proposed to copy here with equipment largely obtained from the United Kingdom.

After the fall of France and the subsequent over-taxing of British resources, it became apparent that any radar protection of Canadian skies and shores would need to be provided wholly by Canadian effort, with, of course, some help from Britain in the form of blueprints, valve designs, prototypes, and "know-how".

A beginning was made in 1940 on the high-powered transmitter required for a Canadian early-warning station, but the greater urgency of such projects as the anti-aircraft gunnery control sets for beleaguered Britain occupied most of the available staff at the National Research Council at Ottawa. The progress made on the early-warning component of G.L. Mark III C could in any event be put to good use in building early-warning sets for the R.C.A.F., and when, in July 1941, work was again begun in earnest on them, the task had been simplified. The precise assignment actually given to the Radio Branch in 1941 was to build a set able to "see" 90 per cent. of all aircraft at a range of 100 miles over land or sea, with a range accuracy of a quarter of a mile and a bearing accuracy of one degree. To get echoes from such distances it was necessary to consider power outputs in the 500 kilowatt range, which, it may be remembered, would have to be five hundred times the output of the first radar set built in Canada in the early months of 1940.

Work began in January 1942 on the erection of a 200-foot wooden tower at the Metcalfe Field Station about eight miles south of Ottawa. This was finished in June. What is called a billboard array was mounted at the top of the tower, and other antennae were mounted on the sides. A device known as a "rotating magnetic field sweep", developed by an engineer of the National Research Council, and later used in many radar sets in the United States, made it possible to detect an echo from aircraft at very long ranges under circumstances which, in earlier models, would have been lost against the noise background.[16] So powerful was the new set when demonstrated in the late spring of 1943 that it could consistently locate and follow a high-flying aircraft 200 miles and more—the only station in Canada capable of such performance. A series of aircraft flights was arranged which proved that a small bomber was constantly visible out to 120 miles, and good tracking ob-

---

[16] Not static, but internal noise in the receiver, caused by the flow of electrons in the vacuum tube.

tainable to 150 miles at 15,000 feet. Official tests at higher altitudes could not be arranged, but random aircraft were frequently picked up and tracked well beyond 200 miles.

By 1942 the success attained in other fields with microwave radar led to an investigation of its use in high-power early-warning sets such as the one described above. On balance, microwave frequencies promised a much more efficient performance and less likelihood of enemy jamming, using lower antenna towers and more compact equipment. These gains were possible when the problem was solved of designing tubes and other components capable of supplying microwave pulses of sufficient power for ranges of the order of 100 miles or more. However, by this time cavity magnetrons capable of producing bursts of energy of 400 to 500 kilowatts were becoming available, and after the careful weighing of pros and cons, work was actually begun on a Microwave Early-Warning set (MEW) during the early summer of 1942. United States scientists had decided to explore the same field in the Radiation Laboratory at the Massachusetts Institute of Technology, and close liaison was maintained between them and the Ottawa staffs.

Some valuable theoretical and experimental work was done at this stage at McGill University by Professor W. H. Watson and associates.[17] This was connected with the problem of the best antenna design for a microwave set of such high power and long range. In Dr. Watson's own words: "We may characterize as the important contribution of the McGill research that it provided a simple way of extracting radio energy from the wave guide by means of slots cut in the wall of the rectangular tube constituting the wave guide, and also supplied an adequate theory to accomplish the design of the linear radiator." The layman may find it easier to follow the language by the analogy of the visual searchlight, and to think of the McGill contribution as a means of focussing the beam of electro-magnetic energy as powerfully and as sharply as possible upon the distant aircraft. The "slot" antenna offered so many advantages that it was immediately adopted in other fields.

The Radio Branch at Ottawa worked methodically on MEW from July 1942 to the spring of 1943, when the renewed penetra-

17 See also Appendix A, p. 269.

tion of the Gulf of St. Lawrence by Nazi submarines gave a sudden impetus to the MEW project as a possible weapon in the defence of Canadian convoy routes. The earlier radar sets using longer waves had provided inadequate warning against small objects moving on the surface of the water; but the new 10 centimetre equipment which was being built for MEW work could obtain echoes from submarines running awash or even from periscopes, and do so at a considerable range. The R.C.A.F. placed a rush order with the National Research Council for seven MEW equipments (later the order was increased to twelve) specially adapted for anti-submarine work, and this programme was accelerated to meet the growing threat of the Nazi submarine in the St. Lawrence.[18] So urgent was the call, that even the crash programme for seven "model shop" sets to be built at Ottawa was supplemented by a hastily assembled "string-and-sealing-wax" set (or haywire-and-bindertwine, in the Canadian idiom), which was thrown together for installation at Fox River, Quebec. The station itself was literally bulldozed into existence in the early spring, and the equipment set to watching the waters of the Gulf of St. Lawrence until such time as the model shop productions could be installed. The surveying of suitable sites for anti-submarine radar sent National Research and R.C.A.F. engineers scurrying around the coasts of Quebec, Newfoundland, and the Gulf of St. Lawrence area by train, light aircraft, small vessels, jeeps, skis, snowshoes, and just plain foot-slogging. There was a great upsurge of morale, however, at the knowledge that Canadian scientists were teaming up with the Services to counter the Nazi move against convoys from Canada to Murmansk and the ports of Britain.

The excellent performance of what was called MEW/AS (the anti-submarine version of the Microwave Early Warning) would have made it eminently suitable for the long-range low-angle detection of flying buzz-bombs (V-1), which began to fall upon Britain in June of 1944. As a matter of fact, the R.C.A.F. did receive an urgent request for some powerful microwave

[18] There had been a series of sinkings the previous summer, culminating in the torpedoing of 14 cargo vessels and two escorts within a few days in late August and September of 1942. Early in 1943 it was sensed that the German navy was putting forward its supreme effort to sever the sealanes between North America and Britain.

radars for this purpose, and two complete Canadian equipments were packed and made ready for shipment. However, the answer had already been found in Britain, thanks largely to the brilliant combination of British anti-aircraft guns, U.S. MEW, developed at M.I.T., the fire-control radar (SCR 584), their new electrical predictor, and the proximity fuse, designed in Canada and the United States and brought to mass production in the latter country. Since it was apparent that by the time the Canadian equipment would arrive the buzz-bomb would have ceased to be a problem, the Canadian sets were finally held in Canada.

The performance of the early-warning microwave radar, with an output of 300 kilowatts and operating on a 10.7 centimetre wave-length, gave excellent coverage from line of sight up to four degrees above the horizon and tracked aircraft up to 120 miles, frequently, indeed, as distant as 160 miles. A second antenna permitted the tracking of high-flying aircraft up to sixty miles.

The usefulness of these sets did not end with the conclusion of hostilities in 1945. Three of the installations were used by the Canadian Army Operational Research Group to study the phenomena of precipitation and the behaviour of storms. Another MEW set was assigned by the R.C.A.F. to Trans-Canada Air Lines and installed at Stevenson Field, Winnipeg, in the early summer of 1945, where it was used to study the problems of airport and airways control. Another wartime project for the R.C.A.F., the construction of a Microwave Height Finder, completed in 1944, was of even greater use in meteorology, since it provided research scientists with an excellent instrument for analysing precipitation layers in the lower atmosphere. Its ability to measure the cloud heights and in general to sample the atmosphere in a vertical plane (as against the resolution only in a horizontal plane supplied by MEW) was of particular value

The first radar sets to be mass-produced in Canada were those designed for detecting enemy vessels from aircraft, called ASV (Air-to-Surface-Vessel) by the British, while the Canadian version added the letter "C", and they became ASVC. Forty-five hundred of these ASVC sets were ultimately produced by Research Enterprises Limited: the first prototype was ready in

February 1941, and production models were shipped by the early summer of that year. Some of the early models were rushed down to the United States to serve as prototypes for U.S. producers, and the well-known Philco ASE (Army SCR 521) was a close reproduction of the Research Enterprises ASVC.

The story of this Canadian radar set for aircraft use illustrates some of the handicaps under which Canada's pioneer radar engineers worked in the early months of the war. As mentioned earlier, the first task given the Radio Section by the Canadian Air Force was the development of a radar suitable for mounting on aircraft used in patrolling ocean and gulf waters adjacent to Canadian soil. Lacking other models at that stage in the war, experiments were made with a modified Western Electric altimeter and a set was designed and built in Canada on $1\frac{1}{2}$ metres. The urgency of other assignments in the summer of 1940 led to the conviction that the soundest procedure would be to procure British equipment for Canadian aircraft or, failing that, to obtain from Britain a sample prototype from which a Canadian design could be copied. It was impossible to do this until after the arrival of the Tizard Mission, when a sample of the British ASV was received in Canada. This solitary model was, however, earmarked for Washington, and was available for study in the Ottawa laboratories for only forty-eight hours. It was hoped to get it back from the United States promptly for further examination, but actually it never did return, and the Research Enterprises radio engineers at Ottawa were compelled in the meantime to go ahead with the few measurements they had been able to make on it while it was in Ottawa, together with some data and sketchy manufacturing information which had been brought over by the British Technical Mission. Beginning in December 1940, a group of engineers and assistants who had been engaged by Research Enterprises Limited, using the shop facilities of the National Research Council and the advice and assistance of Radio Branch scientists, made a copy of the British set, with Canadian tubes and components. The overall performance proved to be equivalent to the British original, and Research Enterprises soon stepped up production, greatly aided by Canadian component manufacturers who undertook to supply tubes, cables, connectors, and other parts which were as far as possible duplicates of those used in the British set.

Another valuable contribution by Research Enterprises engineers was a Canadian version of the British radar used for coastal watching (RW), produced at the request of the Royal Canadian Air Force. The transmitter for this was the same as that developed for G.L. Mark III C. Another was a dual-purpose set (RWG) which combined the watching facilities with a radar for the ground-controlled interception of enemy aircraft. No less than 155 of the latter were produced at Leaside for the Royal Canadian Air Force and the United States Army Air Forces. Early in 1942 four of these sets were installed in the Panama Canal Zone by U.S. forces for warning and fighter-control use.

CHAPTER III

THE PROXIMITY FUSE

THE problem of hitting with shellfire a highly manoeuvrable modern aircraft travelling several hundred miles per hour at an altitude of, say, 20,000 feet is obviously, as has been suggested in Chapter II, one of enormous difficulty. The crew of the anti-aircraft battery must be able to follow or track the aircraft with incredible accuracy, to *lead* the "bird" by a distance varying with the plane's speed and course, and then fire a shell with a fuse cunningly timed so as to burst just before it reaches the future path of the plane, creating as it bursts a lethal cone of flying steel fragments which will coincide with the path of the aircraft at the right moment. The problem had grown measurably in complexity since 1918 because speed, altitude, and the effective range of aircraft had more than doubled.

To track a plane at all requires fire-control instruments capable of making, continuously and rapidly, the three separate measurements corresponding with the plane's position in three dimensions of space (elevation, bearing, and range). These data have then to be fed to a predictor, which, by extension of the path of the plane, can forecast the position where the aircraft may be expected to be by the time the anti-aircraft shell reaches it. The next stage is to set a time-fuse of the shell to the appropriate interval.

Amazing advances had been made in fire-control instruments even by 1940. Mechanical directors were being superseded by automatic electrical directors. Radar fire-control, as outlined in earlier pages, was proving under certain conditions to be a great improvement over earlier optical apparatus. But even with these marvels the efficiency of anti-aircraft fire remained unsatisfactory. As late as August 1940, the downing by Anti-Aircraft Command of one aircraft for an average expenditure of 20,000 rounds of ammunition was being reported. By the spring of 1941, this had been reduced to 4000; but it was still discouragingly low.

The part of the operation into which most of the error crept, and which was thus the major limitation on better shooting, was the problem of accurate range, tied up as it was with complete reliance on time-fused shells. Even when radar fire-control instruments came to give sensationally accurate answers for range, there were still factors of error left: the imperfections of fuse manufacture, the chance for personal error in the manual or mechanical error in the automatic setting of the fuse, and the elapsed, or "dead" time between the setting of the fuse and the actual firing of the shell from the gun. These errors, accumulated, might vary the point of burst as much as a thousand feet along the pathway of the high-velocity shell, thus rendering a hit largely a matter of pure chance.[1]

Some students of ballistics, aware that the time-fuse was the weak spot in the performance, had long dreamed of a radical new type of fuse, which would be detonated by the target itself! Not, of course, by actual impact—a hopeless prospect—but through some physical property of the aircraft itself, acting upon a shell as it approached, and detonating it at an optimum point in its path of convergence upon the plane, thus bringing the aircraft within the lethal cone of fire. Such a fuse, if it could be invented, would greatly increase the deadliness of anti-aircraft fire: it might indeed, if sufficiently accurate, revolutionize it. No wonder the British scientists, from 1934 on, faced with a growing menace of destruction from Nazi bombers, had given to the creation of a proximity fuse a high priority in their lists of imperative war inventions, and had begun to explore all possibilities.

Prior to 1940, when work began in Canada on a radio proximity fuse, the British had been working for some years on various new fuses for bombs and rockets. They had considered several possible principles for such proximity fuses: photo-electric,[2] acoustic, electro-static, and radar. They had

[1] "To bring about the destruction of a 'plane with anti-aircraft fire, the shell must burst within 50 to 100 feet from the target." *Roof over Britain: The Official Story of Britain's Anti-Aircraft Defences 1939-1942* (His Majesty's Stationery Office, London, 1943), p. 23.

[2] See Winston S. Churchill, *Their Finest Hour* (Houghton, Mifflin Co., Boston, 1949), p. 396.

reached the conclusion that the radar principle was much the most promising, but they had not got very far toward a practical fuse even for bombs or rockets, and were well aware of the prodigious practical difficulties inherent in any attempt to fit a delicate fuse of the sort they were contemplating into the nose of anti-aircraft shells to be fired at muzzle velocities and with spins already very rapid and constantly in the process of being increased.

It was at this point that the problem was picked up in North America. Canadian scientists were given a chance to try their ingenuity on some baffling aspects of this most glittering prize of scientific research. During the early experimental stages, Canadian and American scientists worked in close cooperation. Once the basic problems of development had been solved, the Canadian research group was reduced in number, and some of its personnel went to Britain and the United States to aid the production and operational efficiency of the new invention. The gigantic task of mass industrial production was taken over almost exclusively by the United States.

The story of the American development of the proximity fuse has been brilliantly and comprehensively told elsewhere.[3] Here, without ignoring that magnificent accomplishment, the stress will be laid upon Canada's contribution to a programme ranked as "among the three or four most extraordinary scientific achievements of the war."[4]

The challenge of evolving a radio proximity fuse was offered to Canadian scientists as a major incident in the visit of the important Tizard Mission of 1940 (see pp. 17-19). On August 15 of that year, Professor R. H. Fowler, liaison officer for the British Director of Industrial and Scientific Research, stationed at Ottawa, outlined the momentous problem to Professor E. F. Burton, director of the McLennan Laboratories, University of Toronto. On Burton's teaching staff at the time there was an assistant professor, Dr. Arnold Pitt, whose special field was electronic physics, and Burton at once discussed the project with him. Pitt soon satisfied himself that such a fuse was theoretically

[3] James Phinney Baxter 3rd, *Scientists Against Time* (Little, Brown and Co., Boston, 1948), pp. 221-242.

[4] *Ibid.*, p. 241.

feasible and plunged into the task. He asked that Dr. R. W. McKay, of the Ontario Research Foundation, be released to work with him on it; the National Research Council and the University of Toronto provided funds, and a "Toronto Group" to work on the fuse was soon assembled. The early research was done in the basement of the Physics Building, at Toronto, wedged in between the pressing duties connected with wartime classes of instruction on the new techniques of radiolocation. Later the National Research Council took over a four-storey stone building on St. George Street which had been previously occupied as a girls' dormitory. Active work by the Toronto Group began on September 15, 1940. The same problem had been proposed to the National Defense Research Committee in the United States, and work began at about the same time at the Department of Terrestrial Magnetism, Carnegie Institute, Washington. The work of the Canadian and American groups was closely coordinated from the beginning.

Pitt's group was rapidly confronted with a series of formidable obstacles which had to be overcome before a radio proximity fuse could be introduced into actual warfare. Some of these will occur at once upon reflection. A miniature broadcasting and receiving radio set of great delicacy had to be designed to fit into the nose of an anti-aircraft shell—to occupy, as historian Baxter so aptly puts it,[5] no more space than an ice-cream cone. Compactness was vital. (The more high explosives the radio set displaced, the less effective the shell would be in bringing down aircraft.) All components—antenna, circuits, tubes, battery, etc.—must be made so rugged as to withstand the almost unbelievable stresses which would be set up when the shell was fired from the anti-aircraft gun, at muzzle velocities up to 2750 feet per second and with a shell spin of as much as 475 rotations per second. Unless tubes, circuit, power supply, and antenna could be made to work perfectly after such a blast and spin, the shell would turn out to be merely a particularly costly and intricate dud.

What kind of tubes, for example, would continue to respond after subjection to a force equal to 20,000 times that of gravity? How could tiny circuits be designed so that the explosion in

[5] *Op. cit.*, p. 224.

the anti-aircraft gun would not cause even the slightest displacement or maladjustment? What kind of miniature dry cell would meet the power demands and still keep its vitality through months, perhaps years, of shelf-life? What radio-wave pattern would be emitted from the midget broadcasting station in the nose of the shell and what kind of echoes could be expected to "bounce back" from the fuselage and wings of an enemy aircraft? How could these echoes be made to trip the fuse and explode the shell? How could the fragmentation pattern of the exploded shell be linked up with these reflections from an enemy craft in such a way as to guarantee a lethal effect? Such were a few of the more anxious and formidable questions that had to be answered. All of these problems were wrestled with in many places, and by many minds, and it is not now possible, even if it were desirable, to single out all the individual achievements. The tube problem was tackled by Rogers Majestic Company in Canada, where H. Parker made some valuable contributions; in the United States the Western Electric Company, the Raytheon Company (whose flat hearing-aid tube looked promising), and the Hytron Corporation were prominent in this field. The Toronto Group seems to have been first in coming to grips with the battery problem, and they emerged with a radical new idea: they rejected the dry cell in favour of a wet battery which would be created by the actual discharge of the shell. The "set-back" or shock caused by firing broke a glass ampoule filled with liquid electrolyte, the spin of the shell drove the liquid into contact with battery plates, and within half a second the battery was "alive" and producing power. There were endless bugs to eliminate before this simple idea could be made effective, but it proved to be the best answer to the battery conundrum, and it was the device finally adopted by all researchers. It entirely disposed of the "shelf-life" problem, and the fact that a brief interval elapsed after the firing of the shell before the circuits were powered by the battery was an additional safeguard rather than a disadvantage.

The development of rugged components required, of course, repeated and extended tests under authentic and realistic conditions. The best proof was to fire them from guns and find out what happened. After futile experiments with parachutes attached to shells, it was found that they could be fired straight up in the air, that they would fall base-downward, and could be recovered by digging in the soil. The components thus received two "set-backs" under such conditions, both in the same direction: once on firing, once on landing. A firing range was set up at Camp Borden with the assistance of the Canadian Army. When a complete fuse was available to be mounted in the nose of a shell, the flight could be followed by a sensitive radio receiver with a phonographic recorder, the equipment being arranged in a panel truck and protected from falling shells by a large shelter.

Any proximity fuse which would explode as it neared such an object as an aircraft would also be detonated at the end of its flight as it approached land or water. To study this effect, observations were made at the Proof Establishment at Hamilton. Actual firing took place over Lake Ontario. (A good many American tests were conducted there, as well as Canadian.) Observation posts were set up on two points, about four and eight miles from the gun respectively, and the behaviour of the shell as it neared the surface of the water was recorded and studied. As the war developed, this characteristic of the proximity fuse tended to grow in importance to the point where it surpassed its value as an anti-aircraft weapon. Bombs, rockets, rifle and mortar shells which would explode at a set distance above land or water, "following the contour" of the ground, working against enemy ground troops with equal accuracy in sunshine, fog, or night, proved to be one of the most devastating new weapons of the war. General Lear, Chief of U.S. Army Ground Forces, called it "the most important innovation in artillery ammunition since the introduction of high-explosive shells."

The fuse was one of the most jealously guarded secrets of the war, and its use over land was long held back, because the devastation which the enemy could cause by getting wind of the secret was clearly seen from the beginning. "I think that when all armies get this shell, we shall have to devise some new method of warfare," wrote General Patton to General Levin Campbell, Chief of Ordnance, on December 29, 1944.[6]

6 Baxter, op. cit., pp. 235-6.

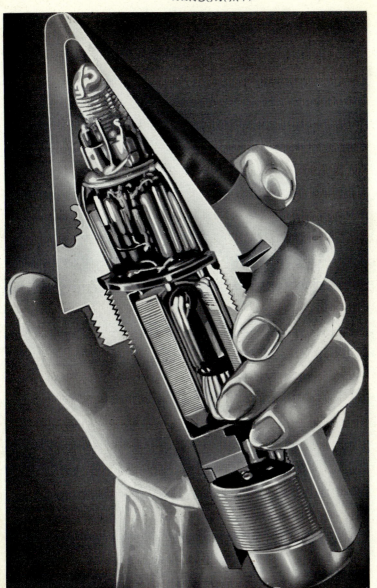

THE PROXIMITY FUSE.

In the nose is the transmitter. Below this is the amplifier and trigger unit along with the detonating condenser. The third unit holds the batteries and electrolyte container. Below the little finger of the hand are the safety switches, and at the base is the detonator

THE PROXIMITY FUSE IN USE

"Following the contour". Originally designed for anti-aircraft use, proximity fused shells were increasingly used against ground targets in the later stages of the war (*a composite photograph*)

A brief time-table of the work of the Toronto Group on the proximity fuse follows:

September 15, 1940: A preliminary survey of the problem began, together with some work on rugged fuse components.

January 15, 1941: Work began on a novel spin type of wet battery.

September 1, 1941: The personnel of the Toronto Group was increased and began the development assembly of a complete model of fuse.

February 1, 1942: Proofing of the complete model began.

October 1, 1942: Work began on a smaller type of fuse for the British 4-inch Naval, 3.7-inch A.A., and U.S. 90 mm. shells.

April 1, 1943: The engineering personnel of the Toronto Group were reassigned, three going to England to assist the British on tests of U.S. fuses from U.S. production. Two research workers went to Washington, one to assist the U.S. group on development, the other to act on liaison work. One went to Ottawa, and another to the Inspection Board in Britain. By this time the basic problems in development had been overcome and the burden of mass production had been assumed by the United States. No quantity production was attempted in Canada.

August 15, 1943: Proofing of the Canadian small-model fuse was completed. This virtually concluded Canadian research on the proximity fuse, though official tests and other help were continued. The investigation of a valuable new method of measuring the stability of projectiles during flight by recording the signal of a proximity fuse transmitter was continued until May 1944. Some of the studies were made at the Suffield (Alberta) Experimental Station.

Most of the Canadian work on the proximity fuse was done by the Toronto Group. But at least one interesting contribution came from the National Research Council staff at Ottawa. The Mechanical Engineering Laboratories were asked to design a reliable mechanism which would prevent arming of the fuse until half a second had elapsed after firing from the gun. A simple centrifugal shutter, controlled by a centrifugally driven clockwork, was designed. A spring lock held the clockwork in-

active until it was released by high spin. Shutter and clockwork
were made strong enough to withstand the shock of being fired
from a gun—indeed, of withstanding a force equivalent to
50,000 times the force of gravity applied in any direction. Fifty
assemblies were made and tested on a centrifuge. They were
then mounted in projectiles with an arrangement which fired
a smoke puff as soon as the shutter opened, which it did after
0.5 seconds. All assemblies functioned correctly when the projectiles were fired. Complete drawings and several samples were
sent to the Toronto Group.

So valuable did the scientific and military leaders in the
United States deem the proximity fuse that toward the end
of the war a quarter of all the facilities of their electronics
industry and three-quarters of their facilities for moulding plastics
were being devoted to the programme. Production of the tiny
rugged tubes alone required staffs of 10,000 persons. At the
peak of production nearly two million fuses a month were being
made.

The proximity fuse proved sensational in several theatres of
war, and one is tempted to dilate on it far beyond the proper
proportions of this chapter. It helped turn the tide of battle
against the Japanese naval bombers and "kamikazi" or suicide
fliers in the Pacific. When it was thrown in against the dangerous
Nazi thrust through the Ardennes in December 1944, it blunted
the offensive and may even have been the factor that brought
the thrust to a halt. More than any other single weapon, it beat
back the "buzz-bomb" or V-1 bombardment of London. Fortunately for Britain, intelligence had warned them months in
advance of what the Nazis were preparing to launch. Models
of the V-1 were hastily constructed and the proximity fuse shell
tried against them. When the offensive actually began, a combination of the latest gun-layer radar, the new predictor, and
anti-aircraft guns firing shells with proximity fuses soon achieved
an amazing record. In the last week of heavy V-1 attacks on
London, nearly 80 per cent. of all targets engaged were destroyed,
and on the very last heavy day, only 4 out of 104 bombs detected
by early-warning radar actually reached London, 68 of them
being blown up by anti-aircraft fire and 32 failing for other

reasons. This was a far cry from the days when it had required thousands of rounds of ammunition to bring down a single aircraft, or when—as in 1940—all the anti-aircraft batteries in Britain combined were averaging only slightly over 8 Nazi aircraft destroyed a month.

CHAPTER IV

NEW EXPLOSIVES

CYCLONITE or RDX (standing for Research Department Explosives) is an explosive from one and a half to two times as powerful, volume for volume, as TNT. Indeed, it is not far from being the most powerful chemical explosive known to man. It was the only outstanding new chemical explosive to be introduced into World War II, and it was used with telling effect in at least two theatres of war—against Nazi submarines, and to fill the aerial bombs known as "block-busters". The first mass production of it anywhere in the world took place in Canada: the method employed in making it there was evolved by a cooperative group of Canadian, American, and British research workers, in which the Canadian contributors brilliantly distinguished themselves. The international team-play which finally cracked the problem of commercial mass-production of the explosive owed a great deal to a novel synthesis devised at McGill University as early as October 1940 by Dr. J. H. Ross and associates (notably Dr. Robert W. Schiessler). This research had been assigned and was being financed by the National Research Council. Outstanding also were the subsequent contributions made in N.R.C. projects at the University of Toronto directed by another distinguished Canadian chemist, Dr. G. F. Wright.

RDX is a synthetic compound which had been known to chemists as far back as 1899. Its superior destructive power naturally interested military scientists, but in its early form it was not a practical substance for warfare. In order to compete with TNT, a new explosive had to go a long way toward matching it in other desirable qualities: in cheapness of production,[1] in stability even at relatively high temperatures, in having

---

[1] Since 60 aircraft using RDX bombs could carry as effective a payload as 100 aircraft carrying bombs loaded with TNT, it was not necessary for the two to be on all fours in cost of production, i.e. this was not the critical factor.

a sufficiently high melting point so as not to exude from munitions in hot weather, in possessing suitable physical qualities for casting or pouring, and in withstanding prolonged storing at tropical temperatures without deterioration. RDX was at first very expensive to produce and highly sensitive. The U.S. arsenal at Pickatinny had examined it after World War I and had rejected it. The British, however, were still fascinated by the promise it held of producing far superior destructive power than TNT, and at the outbreak of World War II they were still working on it. They had succeeded in making it by the direct nitration of hexamine and they had discovered that a mixture of it and beeswax was stable enough to allow safe handling. What was still badly needed was a new and much cheaper method of production. This was one of the many urgent problems brought across the Atlantic by the Tizard Mission. The rewards for success in this field were glittering, as already stated, for RDX was $1\frac{1}{2}$ times as powerful as TNT by weight and nearly twice as powerful volume for volume. Under water the advantage of RDX over TNT was even greater than elsewhere, and this carried a special appeal to the Admiralty.

The British were particularly keen to develop a more effective weapon against the new, thicker-skinned, faster-diving, speedier U-boats, which even more than in 1917 were threatening to cut British lifelines in the North Atlantic and thus bleed white the British war effort, or even starve out the inhabitants of Britain entirely. A mixture of TNT, RDX, and aluminum (known as Torpex) held out the promise of providing a new lethal punch against the Nazi submarine.

The mobilization of Canada's resources in the field of chemical research had begun before the actual outbreak of war. In July of 1939 the National Research Council had convened a gathering of heads of industrial chemical research organizations to discuss cooperation between industrial research and government laboratories. A steering committee had been set up for further action, and when the National Research Council met on September 15, 1939, it had before it from this committee a resolution calling for the setting up of a War Research Committee. Rather than create a brand new committee with executive powers, however, such as already existed in the Council itself, it was decided at this meeting to enlarge and reorganize the "Assisted Researches" Committee. On October 17, Major-General McNaughton, President of the National Research Council, assumed his new duties as Officer Commanding the First Canadian Division, and on the following day Dean C. J. Mackenzie of Saskatoon came to Ottawa as Acting President of the Research Council. Two weeks later, on October 31, Dean Mackenzie met with a small group of key men in the field of industrial research, all of whom had been present at the July Conference. It was then decided to set up a chemical advisory committee to aid the "Assisted Researches" Committee on war problems in the field of chemistry. Dr. Otto Maass, Chairman of the Department of Chemistry at McGill University, who had been recently appointed to the National Research Council, was chosen as chairman of this new committee, which, formally established on December 14, 1939, took the name of the Advisory Committee of Industrial Chemists. A sub-committee on war researches of the standing committee on Assisted Researches was set up at the same time, that on Chemical Problems consisting of Dr. O. Maass (Chairman), Dr. E. W. R. Steacie, and Dr. R. K. Stratford.

During the late winter and spring of 1939-40, Dr. Maass also called together an advisory sub-committee on explosives. In the spring of 1940 Dr. Maass made the first of several overseas flights to Britain to find out in what fields Canada could most usefully serve. He conferred with Dr. C. Rotter of Woolwich, and came back convinced that one very valuable service would be to tackle the large-scale production of RDX. Under Dr. Maass' direction, and with the advice of the explosives sub-committee, this and other war tasks were promptly begun in various Canadian laboratories, notably at McGill and the University of Toronto.

The RDX job at McGill was entrusted to Dr. J. H. Ross,[2] Lecturer in Chemistry, and associates including Dr. R. W. Schiessler, Dr. H. S. Sutherland, and Dr. Raymond Boyer. After several months of work there, a radically different method of producing RDX was evolved, using formaldehyde and ammonium nitrate in the presence of a dehydrating agent (acetic

[2] Pilot in World War I; later head of the Forest Products Laboratories in Montreal.

anhydride). This process was so different from the traditional British method as to cast some doubt on whether the new product was, in fact, identical with the British explosive known as RDX.

Under the circumstances it was decided to fly a sample of the new product to a British arsenal without delay. The story has frequently been told of how Ross and Sutherland prepared packages of the new explosive compound totalling about twenty pounds, and left Dorval by air for the other side. At the airport in Newfoundland they were warned that because of unfavourable weather it would be necessary to fly the Atlantic at a very high altitude, and that as the cabin was unheated, freezing temperatures were to be expected.

Even such relatively stable explosives as dynamite have to be thawed out with great caution after freezing, and the Canadian scientists, working with an unclassified product of presumably great sensitivity, had to face the threat that their sample of high explosive would freeze at the high altitude and then thaw out again—and explode!—as the aircraft returned to sea level on approaching Britain. The fate of aircraft and crew, the other passengers, and themselves, as well as of the whole Canadian RDX experiment, was thus at stake. After weighing the urgency of proceeding with the new process against the dangers involved, the scientists decided to reduce the hazard by using the warmth of their own bodies to prevent the packages of RDX from freezing at that elevation high over the Atlantic. Far from shrinking away from their packages of super-explosive, the two scientists affectionately shielded them through the icy blasts of the upper atmosphere. It was a nightmare crossing, but the RDX withstood all shocks and temperature changes, and so the sample of Canadian-made explosive was safely carried to the laboratories in Britain for testing.

There, analysis and tests of performance showed that while the new compound was largely RDX, it was not sufficiently pure to pass British War Office specifications. Nor did the method as originally conceived and explored lend itself to large-scale production. Obviously further research was required.

This was promptly undertaken at McGill. Meantime the trail blazed by Ross and his associates had given scientists elsewhere a valuable new lead. The Ross discovery had been promptly shared with British and American scientists, and an RDX Committee was set up of representatives of the three countries. Following the visit of the Tizard Mission to the United States, during which the secret data about RDX had been shared with U.S. scientific authorities, Roger Adams, head of U.S. chemical research, mobilized the outstanding organic chemists in that country, and asked, among others, Werner Bachmann, of the University of Michigan, to aid in tackling the RDX production problem. James Phinney Baxter 3rd has related[3] how Bachmann's heart sank when Adams suggested work on explosives, but how he set to work at once after being briefed (in November 1940), wrestling with the problem in his laboratory daily from 8 a.m. until midnight or after. By January, Bachmann had hit upon a new idea, combining the older British method with the new Canadian discovery. This combined method eliminated the enormous requirements of nitric acid which had been a limiting factor of the British method, and at the same time required much less of the dehydrating agent than the Montreal process. "The high yields possible by this combination method," says Baxter, "were most encouraging." However, the product of the early stages of the Bachmann process was, like that of Ross and associates, unacceptable to the British War Office as not reaching the required proportion of true RDX.

Meanwhile, at Toronto, Dr. G. F. Wright, of the National Research Council and the University of Toronto, had been investigating methods of improving the British (Woolwich) method by the nitration of hexamine using excess nitric acid. By August 1941 Wright had so improved the Woolwich process that yields had risen from about 35 per cent. to about 80 per cent. This process in turn suffered from the fact that tremendous amounts of ammonium nitrate were yielded as a by-product.

Work continued in the fall of 1941, and by December Wright had made another important advance by an adaptation of the Bachmann process, introducing liquid feeds and continuous production, which proved to be speedier and more economical than the batch method.

[3] *Scientists Against Time* (Little, Brown and Co., 1948), p. 256.

LABORATORY AND FIELD TESTS OF A NEW EXPLOSIVE

(*above*) RDX receiving the ballistics mortar test in which ten ounces of RDX sent the arrow twice as far as ten ounces of TNT and (*below*) results of the explosion of one pound of RDX in a tree trunk

THE NEW EXPLOSIVE IN ACTION

With the Royal Canadian Navy

The Canadian representatives on the RDX Committee, which at this stage was meeting at frequent intervals, were Drs. Ross, Wright, Boyer, and Winkler. Of their activity in this critical stage the official American war historians, Connor and Kistia- kowsky, report that it "represents an example of perfect interna- tional cooperation in research, especially in the case of the Canadian and U.S. investigators who could meet personally for discussion. The experimental programmes were thoroughly in- tegrated, sometimes to the point of assigning specific experiments among various laboratories. Ideas presented and considered worth while were investigated in the laboratory which was prepared to do this most promptly or which had special facilities for the experiment. Samples were freely exchanged, and a laboratory having special analytical facilities often used these for the entire group of workers. The complete unselfishness and the devotion to the programme of the various laboratories led to a relationship in which there was no distinction between the nationality of the workers, and did much to make the entire development progress rapidly."[4]

Great Britain was anxious to obtain a large-scale supply of RDX at the earliest possible date, and by the summer of 1941 the U.S. Navy had also become interested in the explosive. Development and proof of one or both of the new methods became an urgent matter. Shawinigan Chemicals Limited in Canada and the Tennessee Eastman Corporation in the United States had been asked to work with government scientists in carrying RDX production through the pilot-plant stage to large- scale output. Shawinigan Chemicals, in the summer of 1941, had developed the Ross process to the point where it was adaptable to mass-production and yielded a product able to meet British War Office specifications. However, as a result of the success achieved in pilot-plant production in Tennessee with the Bachmann-Wright process, Shawinigan finally decided in April 1942 to install that method. Large-scale production actually began in Canada on July 19, 1942. Original plans at Shawinigan called for an output of 50 tons of RDX per month. This was

[4] W. A. Noyes Jr., *Chemistry*, Science in World War II, Office of Scientific Research and Development Series (Little, Brown and Co., Boston, 1948), p. 38.

brought up to 350 tons by the end of hostilities. Shawinigan was first in the world to produce useful quantities of the new explosive acceptable to British War Office standards. Tennessee Eastman, considerably later in coming into useful production (May 1943), subsequently reached the colossal output figure of 340 tons of RDX per day!

The new super-explosive was rapidly introduced into warfare with dramatic effect. Torpedo warheads using Torpex were so much more destructive than earlier types that the limited early issue of it was distributed by the United States Navy to submarine commanders in the Pacific with the highest score of kills. RDX mixtures were used by British Bomber Command in the 12,000 pound block-busters or "earthquake" bombs used against the great concrete submarine pens at Lorient and St. Nazaire, and in the sinking of the *Tirpitz*. That ill-starred Nazi battleship, which had never taken part in any naval engagement, finally succumbed on November 12, 1944, to three direct hits from such super-bombs, delivered while she lay in Tromsoe Fjord.

RDX is a substance which chemists classify as a nitramine. Another nitramine, this time a new explosive produced for the first time in Canada, was DINA. It was the discovery of Dr. G. F. Wright at the University of Toronto. DINA was relatively unstable, was sensitive to impact under certain conditions, and its melting point was low, which might result in its exuding from munitions if used in tropical climates. Accordingly it was no general rival to RDX, but there was one important special use to which it might be put. U.S. chemists had been asked in 1942 to produce a flashless propellant for the increasing number of night actions being fought by the U.S. Navy in the Pacific. The British Admiralty used Cordite N for this purpose, but there was a U.S. Navy tradition against Cordite N, because it contained nitroglycerine, which might cause an explosion in their ventilated magazines. After an examination of many candidate explosives, the U.S. Navy chose DINA as a substance which might be combined with Cordite N as a replacement for nitroglycerine. In due course such a material, called Albanite (because it was a white powder), was produced and a pilot plant was projected in the United States. To speed up the production of enough Albanite for thorough tests, meantime, an order for 65,000 pounds of Albanite was placed and executed in Canada. By the summer of 1945, the U.S. Navy was satisfied with the results, and contracts to procure four million pounds of Albanite a month were let in the United States just before final hostilities ended.

CHAPTER V

ATOMIC ENERGY

THE story of the events which culminated in the most spectacular man-made explosion since time began, when at 5:30 a.m. on July 16, 1945, the first atomic bomb suddenly illuminated the lonely mesa of New Mexico—a moment that was "unprecedented, magnificent, beautiful, stupendous, and terrifying" (to quote Brigadier-General T. F. Farrell, one of the eye-witnesses)—makes up perhaps the most complex and fascinating of the many chronicles of scientific triumph. The bomb itself was essentially an American achievement, resting, of course, on numerous discoveries in fundamental nuclear research by scientists of many lands. Canada took no direct part in the manufacture of the bomb. But in the broader story of the search for methods of utilizing the nuclear energy of the atom for industrial purposes and the arts of peace, Canada was destined to play a varied and important role. The estimate of the Chairman of the Atomic Energy Control Board of Canada, General A. G. L. McNaughton, made before the Engineering Institute of Canada on May 8, 1946, may be quoted in support of this assertion: "As a consequence of our war effort in the field of atomic energy, Canada attained a position in development which, while not of the same order of magnitude as that of the United States, *was nevertheless second only to that country*. Canada has considerable reserves of uranium, she has a staff of scientists—not nearly as many as we would like—who have wide experience in carrying out nuclear research, and at Chalk River we have excellent facilities for further research which are being developed to acquire new knowledge, to train other scientists, and for the carrying forward of the particular investigations required to expedite the peaceful application of atomic energy in our own country."

Canada's first link with research into nuclear energy came through Rutherford's work at McGill, in the very infancy of the science of radio-activity. Ernest Rutherford (later Lord Rutherford), who was later to become one of the greatest names in modern science, had arrived at Montreal in 1898 at the age of twenty-seven. It was only two years previously that the French physicist Becquerel had observed the blackening of photographic plates by uranium and had thus obtained the first evidences of radio-activity. Soon after his arrival at McGill, Rutherford began that series of investigations of newly-found radio-active elements which paved the way for all subsequent research. It is pleasant reading for Canadians to learn that the genius of this youthful investigator was soon recognized in Canada; that John Cox, then Director of the Macdonald Physics Laboratory at McGill, lightened the burdens of teaching and university routine for Rutherford, and thus "greatly accelerated Rutherford's rapid rise to fame."[1]

So swiftly and successfully did Rutherford and the chemist Frederick Soddy (also at McGill) apply themselves to these new phenomena that they were able in 1902 to announce a comprehensive theory of the spontaneous disintegration of atoms. It is interesting to note in passing that among Rutherford's students at McGill was Otto Hahn, whose experiments in Germany on the bombardment of uranium atoms by neutrons in 1938 provided one of the key discoveries which led up to the atomic bomb.

Another Canadian pre-war connection with atomic research concerned the vital supply of uranium. Thanks largely to the intelligence and enterprise of a Canadian prospector, Gilbert La Bine, Canada ranked, in 1939, as one of the two principal sources of this ore in the world. In May 1930 La Bine and his partner, Charles St. Paul, had discovered on the shores of Great Bear Lake in the Northwest Territories what proved to be a large and valuable deposit of pitchblende. By 1939, ores valued at nearly $6,000,000 (chiefly because of the radium in the pitchblende deposits) had been extracted from this field. The whole process of radium production had been carried out in Canada,

[1] A. Norman Shaw, *A History of Science in Canada* (Ryerson Press, Toronto, 1939), p. 133.

from mining to refinement and final testing, using processes developed by Canadian scientists and engineers of the Research Council at Ottawa and the Mines Branch. In addition, some metallic uranium was made in the National Research Laboratories at Ottawa.

The loss of radium markets and other difficulties connected with the outbreak of war led to the Eldorado mine being closed in June 1940, but as soon as the feasibility of making a bomb from uranium had been foreseen by Allied scientists, the mine was reopened in great secrecy in August 1942 as a source of uranium oxide, and was soon operating at capacity. During 1944 the shaft was enlarged and deepened, and the plant expanded to a capacity of 100 tons of ore every twenty-four hours.[2]

When hostilities broke out in 1939, there were comparatively few scientists in Canada engaged in research in nuclear physics. Queen's and Dalhousie Universities were the most active centres in this branch of science;[3] over a period of many years, these and other Canadian universities had done valuable work in spite of limited facilities, and had trained many of the scientists who later on joined the atomic energy project. In the National Research Council at Ottawa there was a very small group, headed by Dr. George C. Laurence, which had been working for a number of years on applications of nuclear physics, such as the measurement of radio-activity, radiology, and related matters. The startling discoveries being made year after year in nuclear physics in Europe, Britain, and the United States were being followed at Ottawa, even though no experiments were under way.

The possibility of tapping the resources of atomic energy for new military explosives and as an energy source of wide application was debated at Ottawa in the early months of the war, just as it was in other military and scientific circles elsewhere in the world. There seemed to be a remote chance indeed that anything could be achieved in time, but it was something which could not be ignored, especially as the Germans were certain

[2] *The Northwest Territories*, published by the Department of Mines and Resources (Ottawa, 1944), pp. 32-3.

[3] Plans were under way before the war for the construction of a cyclotron at McGill; these were temporarily abandoned in 1940 and resumed after hostilities ceased.

to be exploring such possibilities to the hilt. Encouraged by
Dr. C. J. Mackenzie, Acting President at that time, and by
Dr. R. W. Boyle, Chief of the Physics and Electrical Engineering
Division, Dr. Laurence began in the early months of the war
the first experiments in Canada in the building of a crude
atomic energy "pile". These paralleled in purpose, even though
they did not match in scale or go anything like so far as those
conducted in the United States and the United Kingdom. (The
progress made in Germany does not appear to have exceeded
what was accomplished in Canada.) For their intrinsic interest
as scientific beginnings of investigations which at length culminated in the magnificent Chalk River plant, some account
of these early Canadian experiments is given here.

To see what these rather primitive exploratory investigations
at Ottawa between 1939 and 1942 were being aimed at, it is
necessary to recall briefly the progress of atomic research up to
the outbreak of the war in 1939.

The discovery that several natural elements of very high
atomic and mass numbers (uranium, thorium, radium, and
actinium) spontaneously exhibited the property of emitting radiations and thus "disintegrating" into other elements of a different
atomic and mass number had naturally led students of atomic
structure into many experiments to see whether methods could
be devised to bombard atoms of various elements with suitable
projectiles and cause further effects not observable in nature. Up
to 1919 no scientist had succeeded in affecting the behaviour of
other than naturally radio-active elements, but in that year
Lord Rutherford used high-energy alpha particles (the nucleus
of a helium atom is an alpha particle) to bombard nitrogen
atoms, and succeeded in changing a few atoms of nitrogen into
atoms of oxygen by knocking a proton (a particle which is identical with the nucleus of the hydrogen atom) out of the nitrogen
atom.

Rutherford's success led to many similar experiments, and to
a prolonged search for more powerful and penetrating projectiles
than the alpha particle. A particularly promising one was found
in a series of experiments between 1930 and 1932, when J.
Chadwick at Cambridge identified and named the neutron, a
particle of about the same mass as a hydrogen nucleus. The

neutron proved to be an extremely useful agent in initiating nuclear changes, because unlike electrons or alpha particles, the neutron was neither negatively nor positively charged with electricity. The bombardment of atoms with electrically charged particles is handicapped by the fact that they exert electrical forces of repulsion and attraction, ionize atoms of the material through which they are passing, and in so doing lose energy and are slowed down. The neutron exerts no such electrical forces and so maintains its energy and penetration until it collides directly with an atomic nucleus.

The neutron proved to be an especially effective projectile for bombarding elements of the highest atomic number and weight (such as uranium) in which the strong electrical charge of the nucleus had repelled such charged particles as protons and deuterons. When uranium was bombarded with neutrons, some particularly interesting and baffling effects were produced. This was first noted as far back as 1934 by the Italian physicist Enrico Fermi and his colleagues, but it required several years of investigation of the phenomena before a satisfactory explanation was forthcoming. When light did dawn upon the researchers it proved to be of the highest importance, opening up the way, indeed, for the atomic bomb and the practical production of atomic energy.

Hitherto the bombardment of atomic nuclei had resulted at best in particles being chipped off the bombarded element, changing it into another element, and releasing at the same time relatively large amounts of energy. The results were tremendously interesting, but they did not suggest any early practical application since far more energy was used up in the experiment than was released from the atom, and the reaction was not self-propagating, but ceased as soon as the man-made bombardment ended.

The great significance of the bombardment of the uranium nucleus by neutrons, once the phenomena had been understood, after four years of groping, was two-fold: first, the uranium nucleus was proved to split into two roughly equal parts (e.g., into elements such as palladium, barium, etc.) with the release of enormous quantities of energy; secondly (and this was the really breathtaking discovery), the "fission" or splitting of the

ATOMIC ENERGY

The townsite of Deep River built to house employees of the Chalk River Plant

ATOMIC ENERGY

The Chalk River Plant, where materials for the release of atomic energy are produced

uranium nucleus was accompanied by the emission at high velocity of several neutrons. If these neutrons could in turn be employed to cause fission of further uranium atoms, the possibility of a chain reaction immediately suggested itself, with its sensational implications of a possible atomic bomb and the production of enormous quantities of industrial energy from relatively tiny quantities of uranium or similar material.

The discoveries connected with the fission of the uranium atom came to a head late in 1938 and early in 1939. The whole story is fascinating but must be brutally condensed here. During 1939 nearly one hundred scientific papers on the new phenomena were published, and nuclear physicists all over the world (including, of course, Canadians) had begun to examine the problems suggested by the discoveries of Fermi, Bohr, Hahn and Strassman, Frisch, Meitner, Joliot, Nier, Wheeler, and others.

Although Canada had not taken an active part in nuclear research, it was one of the two prime sources of uranium in the world, and in the early months of the war the National Research Council decided to carry on some experiments in bombarding uranium with neutrons. It was known by this time that what stood in the way of the immediate application of the "fission" principle was the existence of uranium in three forms or isotopes, distinguished by their mass numbers as U 234, U 235, and U 238 (natural uranium occurring as a mixture of these three); the fact that, unfortunately for the early success of the experiments in atomic energy, it was only the U 235 isotope of uranium which was split by the bombardment of neutrons; and that the proportion of U 235 in natural uranium was only 1 in 140. Worse still, since the three isotopes were identical in chemical reactions, they could not be sorted out from one another except by incredibly slow and difficult methods which were quite beyond the available resources in Canada in 1939-40. The bombardment of natural uranium with neutrons would, it was known, result in some atoms of U 235 being split with a release of energy, but it was doubted whether a chain reaction was thus possible, since the much more numerous U 238 atoms, far from contributing to the fission effect, tended to absorb most of the neutrons released by the fission of U 235, and thus choke off the reaction at once. (It was not then known in Canada that in absorbing the free neutrons, the U 238 atoms underwent a two-stage transmutation into the new element plutonium with atomic number 94, itself in turn capable of fission when bombarded with neutrons—the raw material, in due course, of the atomic bomb used at Nagasaki on August 9, 1945.)

Thus there was no great point in bombarding a mass of natural uranium with neutrons, for no matter how large a mass was used, the presence of U 238 would damp down any chain reaction by absorbing most of the free neutrons released when the U 235 was split. However, this absorptive effect of the U 238 might be reduced by the use of what was called a "moderator". If the neutrons emitted by the U 235 undergoing fission could be greatly slowed down by the interposition of some suitable substance, they would be much less likely to be absorbed by U 238 atoms, and therefore more likely to cause the fission of further U 235 atoms, thus increasing the probability of a chain reaction. Attempts had been made in France to use ordinary water as a moderator, but it was found that ordinary water was unsuitable for this purpose: although very efficient in slowing the neutrons, it absorbed too many of them. Laurence felt that it was worth while to try some other material which, if not as effective as water in slowing the neutrons, would absorb fewer of them. Of the several moderators which satisfied the theoretical requirements—of low atomic weight and with little tendency to absorb neutrons—helium was difficult to use, heavy water[4] was unobtainable, and beryllium was scarce. Carbon was the substance which seemed most practicable at the time. The secrecy of this work was such that it was not learned until later that similar experiments using carbon as a moderator were being undertaken independently in the United States and the United Kingdom.

For a chain reaction to occur at all, the loss of neutrons (taking place in three ways: through escape from the energy "pile", through absorption or non-fission capture by Uranium 238, and through absorption or non-fission capture by impurities in

[4] Of which the molecule consists of two atoms of Deuterium (heavy hydrogen, Atomic Mass 2) to one of Oxygen: D_2O, or Deuterium oxide.

the uranium or moderator) had obviously to be reduced. Using uranium in its natural state, it was conceivable that after eliminating all possible loss of neutrons in these non-productive ways, there would still not be enough neutrons released by the fission of U 235 (and thus available for further fission) to set up a chain reaction. But the experiment seemed worth trying. The loss through escape could be reduced by building as large a "pile" as possible. The loss through non-fission capture by Uranium 238 could be reduced by the interposition of a suitable moderator to slow down the neutrons, and the loss through non-fission capture by impurities could be reduced by using pure uranium and as pure a moderator as could be procured.

Testing out this line of reasoning, the first experiments at Ottawa began in March 1940. A ton of uranium was borrowed from Eldorado Mining and Refining Limited, without it being necessary to explain to that company (then privately owned) what was intended to be done with the material. Ten tons of quite pure calcined petroleum coke (a form of carbon used in the manufacture of graphite) was purchased. This came in fifty-pound paper bags, most of which arrived at the laboratory in a broken condition. There were amusing aspects to the early experiments. The coke was a fine black powder and incredibly dirty to work with. It blackened everybody who worked with it, and it sifted out through the smallest cracks and down the corridors of the National Research Building. Dr. Laurence carried out his experiments with the utmost secrecy. He obtained a room on the third floor and changed the lock himself. Only Dr. Boyle, his divisional chief, knew anything about the experiment. By September of 1940 a bin had been erected, lined with paraffin wax and filled with the coke, in which were embedded uniformly spaced packages of uranium oxide—the "lattice" structure which seems to have been first suggested by Fermi and Szilard as likely to be more effective than a homogeneous mixture of uranium and moderator. There was no anxiety about an atomic explosion, because even if the experiments were successful, the bulk used was known to be below the critical size needed for a great release of atomic energy. The object of the experiment was to obtain measurements of the number of neutrons released, which might show whether, by building a much larger pile of similar materials, a chain reaction could be produced. As a primary source of neutrons, to initiate the reaction, a mixture of radium and beryllium was employed. The alpha particles from radium and the elements into which it disintegrates penetrate the nuclei of beryllium, which in turn give off neutrons. Such "sources" were introduced at different points within the bin of uranium and moderator, and the production of additional neutrons through fission of U 235 was then calculated by the use of Geiger counters. Early in the summers of 1941 and 1942, Dr. B. W. Sargent, Professor of Physics at Queen's University, worked in the National Research Council's Laboratory on the project. With the effectiveness of the project greatly increased by Dr. Sargent's participation, more rapid progress was made. Though the results were not of a spectacular character, they were sufficiently interesting to justify work on a larger scale.

Meantime, work at Ottawa had been stimulated by the visit of Professor R. H. Fowler, of the Tizard Mission, who reported that experiments with heavy water as a moderator were being conducted at Cambridge, England, and that experiments with carbon and uranium, using different methods than at Ottawa, were also under way in the United States. Though the United States was not yet in the war, Dr. Laurence visited Dr. L. J. Briggs at the Bureau of Standards in Washington and Professor G. B. Pegram's laboratory at Columbia, and this led to an exchange of technical information between the two countries relating to the Ottawa experiment.

The U.S. experiments with natural uranium were pursued with great vigour and on a mammoth scale. Under the deceptive title, "Metallurgical Laboratory", a large energy pile was erected on the floor of a squash court under the West Stands of Stagg Field at Chicago. By the autumn of 1942, about six tons of uranium metal had been accumulated there, a large quantity of highly purified graphite had been procured specially for the experiment, and a pile constructed on the lattice principle. A chain reaction, or self-sustaining pile, first came into operation there on December 2, 1942. Though the Canadian experiments were never carried forward to a self-maintaining basis, the fact that a self-sustaining nuclear chain reaction could be produced in a system using natural uranium showed that the Ottawa experiment begun in 1940 had been on the right trail. As was learned after the war, the Germans were also working on a pile of this kind, using normal uranium and moderators.

Pearl Harbor brought the United States into the war and greatly intensified the search there for an atomic bomb. Two lines were pursued: the separation of U 235 from natural uranium, and the production and separation of plutonium by the bombardment of U 238. This spurred on efforts in the United Kingdom also, but there were sharper limitations to what could be accomplished across the Atlantic. The intensive preoccupation of the British with anti-submarine warfare, radar, and other vital research, the threat of air raids on their own atomic research laboratories, and even the possibility of Nazi commando raids (such as the British ventures against the Norsk Hydro plant making heavy water), suggested the desirability of sponsoring a joint British-Canadian enterprise located in North America rather than concentrating their efforts in Britain. Inquiries along these lines were made in the summer of 1942, and in September the Canadian government agreed to the establishment of a British-Canadian laboratory at Montreal, to be under the administration of the National Research Council. H. H. Halban, an Austrian refugee scientist, who, with Dr. Lew Kowarski, had been in charge of the slow neutron research at Cambridge (where heavy water was employed as a moderator), was chosen as the first Director of the Canadian project. He came to Canada late in 1942 and was followed in January 1943 by the first group of British scientists. Meanwhile the Ottawa group was recruiting staff from various universities of Canada to provide the Canadian nucleus at Montreal.

First quarters for the project consisted of a spacious old residence in Montreal which was soon so crowded that even the bathtubs were stacked high with books and papers. The following month, laboratory space was provided in the new buildings of the University of Montreal. The combined staff grew to 340 within the year.

The early months of the Montreal project were devoted to accumulating the data necessary for the design of a "pile", or, more technically, an "atomic energy reactor". At first there were delays and frustrations. One problem was to decide upon the basic objective so that it would not merely duplicate the massive and pulsating U.S. effort. Another was the extent to which the project should count upon access to the results of fundamental U.S. research—results which could certainly be worked out eventually in Canada but which, if they could be immediately obtained, would save at least a year of preliminary work. A third problem was whether to go in for a reactor using carbon as a moderator or heavy water. There existed at Trail, B.C. a plant capable of making this latter rare substance (a few hundred pounds, most of the world's existing supply at the time, saved from France on the very eve of the invasion, had been brought out from England to Montreal), but it was by then under contract to supply U.S. needs. At the time, also, Canada still depended upon the U.S. for the reduction of Canadian uranium to the metallic form. The issues came to a head during the historic conference of President Roosevelt, Prime Minister Winston Churchill, and Prime Minister Mackenzie King at Quebec City in August 1943. Full coordination of nuclear research with the United States was then confirmed. A technical committee consisting of Sir James Chadwick, General Groves, and Dr. C. J. Mackenzie was formed for the purpose of correlating the policy decisions of the three governments. In January 1944 a joint programme of research was apportioned between Chicago and the Montreal project. Heavy water was decided upon for the moderator. A few weeks later the three governments concerned agreed that the plant should be built in Canada, and a search began for a suitable site. The Canadian government agreed to finance the undertaking through the Department of Munitions and Supply, research and basic design was to be the responsibility of the Montreal Laboratory of the National Research Council, and Defence Industries Limited undertook the detailed engineering design and supervision of the construction. Dr. J. D. Cockcroft was appointed Director in Charge, and additional U.K. and Canadian scientists were added to the staff.

The site chosen had to meet a number of exacting conditions: access to large quantities of pure water for cooling the reactor and to ample hydro-electric power, to begin with. It seemed wise to build it well away from large centres of population for considerations of security, and because the risks of contamination and explosion had not yet been fully evaluated. Reasonably close access to industrial and scientific resources and personnel seemed desirable. Finally, a location fulfilling all these requirements was found on the south bank of the Ottawa River, near Chalk River, Ontario, about 130 miles west of the Canadian capital.

The first "experimental pile" was built for the purpose of checking details of design being worked out for the atomic energy pilot plant. As rapidly as laboratories for this purpose were completed at Chalk River, members of the research staff from Montreal transferred their operations to that site. On September 5, 1945, Dr. Lew Kowarski was able to telephone his colleagues in Montreal that the "ZEEP", the first atomic energy reactor in Canada (in fact, anywhere in the world outside of the U.S.A.) had been put into operation that day. (ZEEP stood for "Zero Energy Experimental Pile", signifying that it could be operated to yield only very low energy.)

It is difficult to single out, without some injustice, names from among the several hundred persons who contributed to the success of the Chalk River project. In the development of theory and calculations necessary for the design, Drs. Placzek, Volkoff, Mark, and Wallace were prominent; on the chemistry of extraction, Drs. Steacie, Paneth, Cook, and Spinks; on the physics side, Drs. Pierre Auger, B. W. Sargent, and D. G. Hurst. In mechanical design and engineering, the work of George J. Klein was important. Dr. Lloyd Pidgeon made valuable contributions in metallurgy. The work of Dr. H. G. Thode at McMaster in mass spectrometry, and of Dr. Beamish, of the University of Toronto, is an indication of the contributions made by Canadian universities to the project.[5]

When the pilot plant, laboratories, and town (named Deep River) approached completion, the administration and management were taken over entirely by the National Research Council.

[5] The universities also made an invaluable contribution to the work by lending members of their teaching staffs. This had to be done on faith, since the super-secret nature of the project made it impossible to spell out what they were wanted for.

Dr. David Keys of McGill was appointed Vice President. W. B. Lewis was appointed Director of Research, succeeding Dr. J. D. Cockcroft, who returned to England to assume charge of British research on atomic energy at Harwell. The Montreal laboratory was finally vacated by June 1946.

CHAPTER VI

LAND

THE scientists of Canada, mobilized through the agency of the National Research Council, performed, in due course, valuable services for each of the three armed services as well as for war industry, supply, agriculture, medicine, and other non-military fields. The unpredictable fortunes of the war determined the fact that the Canadian Army did not get into intensive action until the summer of 1943: its mobilization and training up to that time had perforce to be planned as an integral part of the whole British military effort; also, as in the past, the Canadian Army for the most part used British army equipment. Under these circumstances, and with no imminent threat of an invasion of Canada's shores, the Canadian Army did not turn to the National Research Council for scientific assistance in the same measure as the other two fighting services. The massive contribution to anti-aircraft radar, however, has been described in Chapter II.[1] In the following pages some illustration will be provided of Canadian scientific participation in problems mainly connected with land warfare or the defence of Canada's territory from possible enemy attack.

Among the minor but still highly useful services of scientists and engineers of the National Research Council in the early months of the war was a variety of aids in the strengthening of Canada's Coast Artillery. This included the adaptation and improvement of obsolescent equipment. One obvious improvisation in a time of great scarcity of new equipment was to take over and adapt naval guns or anti-aircraft artillery for coastal defence purposes. Another was to modify or supplement the equipment of coastal anti-aircraft batteries so that they could be employed against surface vessels and thus serve a dual role. The National Research Council, at the request of the Army, provided certain

[1] Anti-aircraft artillery is traditionally an Army responsibility.

anti-aircraft batteries with a standard range finder and a means of converting range into quadrant elevation (i.e., the angle of elevation which the gun must assume to carry shot, aimed at surface vessels, the required distance). The design was such that this converter could be used with any of the range-finding instruments in use, including radar, and be applicable to any of the anti-aircraft or Coast Artillery guns then in service. A pilot model of the converter was built in the instrument shops at Ottawa, approved by the Army, and was succeeded by a number of converters built for actual service on Canada's coasts.

Early in the war the Army installed a battery of 7.5-inch high-angle Naval mountings as Coast Artillery. New fire-control instruments were designed and built by the Mechanical Engineering shops at Ottawa, which proved to be simpler in control, subject to decreased personal errors, and less expensive than standard fire-control instruments earlier obtained from Britain. This equipment was in continual use and gave trouble-free service.

Automatic sights were designed and built for a number of converted guns including a 4.7-inch Canadian pattern and a 4-inch Naval mounting. Cams for these and other automatic sights were designed and cut.

At the request of the Army a new device for measuring the range (distance) of enemy batteries by comparing the time taken for the report of hostile guns to reach a series of sensitive microphones set some distance apart was investigated, and a model of the device built. It was about one-fifth of the weight of the earlier British type and was accurate to 50 metres over a range of 16,000 to 25,000 metres. It was discussed with Sir Lawrence Bragg, U.K. Scientific Liaison Officer, but the great advances then being made in radio ranging (employing electro-magnetic pulses nearly a million times as fast as sound) discouraged further work on this project. Radar also superseded development of a position-finder proposed to the Army by the Metrology Section and authorized up to the experimental model stage. This was an optical device which determined the position of a hostile vessel by the intersection of lines of sight from any pair of a number of observing stations. It was capable of being made fully automatic, tests proved it to be accurate, and it operated successfully when installed at the Coast.

An automatic sight for coastal batteries which overcame many of the difficulties due to differences in height above sea level (caused when guns were moved from one site to another, or even by the variations in relative altitude resulting from the excessively high and low tides found on some of Canada's shores) was suggested in 1938-39 by Major-General A. G. L. McNaughton, then President of the National Research Council, and considerable work was done on it. Details of the design were forwarded to the British War Office. Though it was more accurate and could be more simply set and calibrated than alternative designs under consideration, a simpler and more readily produced sight was finally adopted.

Two models of sights devised for the Bofors 40 millimetre gun were built and tested at Petawawa, at Wicked Point in Prince Edward County, at Camp Davis, North Carolina, and elsewhere. Here again alternative designs were available and the Canadian model was not adopted.

All these adaptations, refinements, and new designs were, of course, dwarfed in 1940-41 by sensational new applications of radar to fire-control and coastal defence, in which Canada actively participated, as already narrated in Chapter II.

The Weasel

The late summer of 1942 saw the military fortunes of the Axis at their peak, with the Nazis at Stalingrad and El Alamein, and the Japanese driving for Port Moresby, New Guinea, preparatory to an invasion of Australia. There was increasing clamour for a "Second Front" in Europe. Britain and the United States were far from ready for a full-scale invasion of the European mainland, but it became imperative to explore every opportunity for large-scale diversionary raids on the fringes of Nazi-occupied Europe. Northern Norway offered some interesting possibilities. Also, the fact that the hydro-electric power plants there were known to be manufacturing "heavy water", obviously for atomic bomb research, made some action there very desirable. With the idea of an airborne invasion in mind, to be staged in the winter of 1942-43 (a project which was tagged "Operation Plough"), Churchill asked North American technicians to develop a vehicle capable of negotiating snowfields and yet small enough to be carried in gliders. The Weasel was the outcome. It never saw action on Norwegian snowfields, since "Operation Plough" was finally cancelled, but in its several versions, including an amphibious one, it proved to be one of the most versatile and generally useful small crafts in the final stages of the war. Canadian scientists and laboratories played a useful part in the development of the Weasel, drawing on their long experience in battling snow problems and in working out the mechanics of traction in snow.

Actual research began in May 1942 when General Marshall asked Dr. Vannevar Bush to develop a snow vehicle for the proposed Norwegian adventure. A combined Canadian-American-British-Norwegian committee was set up, on which G. J. Klein of the Mechanical Engineering Division (National Research Council) was the senior Canadian representative. What was wanted was a light vehicle with exceptional speed and climbing ability in deep soft snow. Fortunately, Canada had done a good deal of research on snow before the war, largely in connection with aircraft skis. In order to test different designs of skis in and on snow it had been necessary to obtain a snowmobile of some kind which could negotiate snow in all the conditions and varieties in which it might be encountered, as well as icecrusts and other obstacles. The Ottawa scientists employed a "half-track" with skis in front, and in the course of their extensive experiments, learned a good deal about what would keep moving in snow and what wouldn't.

Klein's recommendation, based on this Canadian experience, was the development of an all-track vehicle with the lowest possible unit pressure between the track and the snow. Wet snow, when compressed by the vehicle, would form solid ice on tracks, wheels, and sprockets, Klein insisted; and the only answer (judged by Canadian tests, and based on Canadian experience from 1934 to 1939) was an all-rubber track, rubber-tired wheels, and sprockets which were either faced with rubber or self-clearing. The Canadian laboratory also gave the military authorities its findings on such matters as track-tread form, size and spacing of wheels, belly clearance, the desirability of a

smooth flat belly, and the importance of the correct location of
the vehicle's centre of gravity (which should be central and
as low as possible).

U.S. engineers connected with the Goodrich Rubber Company were at first of the opinion that an all-rubber track strong
enough for the purpose would be too heavy. The National
Research Council at Ottawa then designed a light all-rubber
track and made a half-scale model in the Rubber Laboratory.
With the cooperation of Goodrich engineers, the track was
redesigned several times, and a final model proved satisfactory
in all respects.

Meantime, the first experimental models using metal tracks
had been hastily assembled and sent to the Columbia Ice Field
north of Lake Louise for trials, where, among other conditions,
wet snow was encountered. As forecast by Klein, tracks and
sprockets rapidly iced up on the model so as to make operation
impossible. These tests went a long way toward ensuring the
acceptance of Canadian ideas on the construction of the Weasel.
Icing difficulties were overcome by making the sprocket of the
next model self-clearing, and, as time did not permit all-rubber
tracks to be manufactured, the next best alternative was chosen:
track plates coated with rubber. Weasels built under the new
specifications operated in wet snow (as well as in all other kinds)
without further difficulty.

The Studebaker Corporation in the United States continued
its development of the Weasel and came up later with the
model M29, which used all-rubber tracks differing from Klein's
design only in details included to facilitate mass production.
The load distribution on the track and the location of the
centre of gravity were altered in model M29 closer to the
original recommendations made by Ottawa.

Planned as a light, speedy snowmobile, the Weasel actually
saw service in a wide variety of operations. With its exceptionally light pressure on the ground, less than a third of that
exerted by the feet of a fully equipped soldier, less than one-
sixth of an army truck, it was, in fact, the only vehicle available
during the war capable of making its way through very soft
mud and marshland. The M29C, a self-propelled amphibious
model, went ashore at the Anzio beachhead, was used at Mount

Cassino, landed at Utah Beach in Normandy, and saw extensive use in winter campaigns in Italy, France, and Germany. It was especially favoured by medical units for getting over snow-drifts and in negotiating mine-fields, where its light unit pressure saved it from destruction by mine detonation. It was given extensive use also on Walcheren Island, in the Scheldt Estuary, and in the jungles of the Pacific War. Its development was a joint effort in which U.S. industry played a very large part. Canadian knowledge of snow conditions assisted greatly in the whole process of design and development.

Chemical Warfare

The poison-gas used by the Germans in the First World War left an emotional scar in the public memory quite out of proportion to its military effectiveness. As the show-down with the Axis neared, civilian gas-masks became more and more prominent. When World War II finally broke out, there was wide-spread apprehension that Hitler would shortly exploit his air superiority by drenching the crowded urban areas of Britain and France with deadly gases, including, perhaps, some "secret weapon" of a gaseous nature, more deadly and more appalling than anything ever met with before. Possessing the most advanced chemical industry in the world, Germany was known to be prepared, or preparing, for chemical warfare on a vast scale. Allied strategy from 1939 until the end of hostilities was compelled, therefore, to take account of the likelihood that at the most advantageous moment for him, Hitler would begin the wholesale use of poison-gas. Both defensive and offensive plans for the Canadian armed services had to assume the probability of chemical warfare on a vaster scale than anything seen in World War I; and steps were taken in Canadian scientific and industrial mobilization to meet such a threat. The fact that hostilities finally ended without the unleashing of a single poison-gas attack as such anywhere has tended to obscure the magnitude of the effort put forth in this preparation.

There has been considerable speculation as to why Germany did not finally resort to poison-gas. In view of the crimes of Rotterdam and Buchenwald, moral or humane considerations do not seem to have entered into the decision. Military men, however, differ widely in their estimates of the relative effectiveness of chemical warfare. Most would agree that there are local and temporary circumstances under which poison-gas would be more effective than any other weapon. But there is also a wide-spread conviction that, taking into account all the additional defensive complications involved in the resort to poison-gas— the inconvenience, the uncertainty of weather, the additional logistics, the certainty of reprisals, the probability that any new or secret gas could be quickly neutralized or countered—chemical warfare would be less effective offensively than other techniques developed in World War II, and the game not worth the candle. These general considerations are mentioned only as a prelude to the observation that so long as it was possible that the enemy might resort to chemical or bacteriological warfare, it was imperative for the Allies to maintain a strong position— a superiority, if possible—in both departments. The official view in Canadian military quarters was that what deterred Germany from unleashing chemical warfare was the speed and magnitude with which the Allies undertook the preparation of counter-offensive measures. When Dr. Otto Maass was recommended on January 1947 for the Gold Medal of the Professional Institute of the Civil Service of Canada, a letter signed by Lieut.-Gen. Charles Foulkes, Chief of the General Staff, and Brigadier G. P. Morrison, Deputy Master General of the Ordnance, contained these words: " . . . although the enemy powers had, for many years, studied, developed, and produced the means for waging chemical warfare on a scale which dwarfed the pre-war Allied resources, its use was never attempted. In a surprisingly short space of time, the Allied defensive technique and subsequent counter-offensive resources had developed into an effective threat which the enemy dared not risk to invoke. In this achievement, the name of Dr. Maass ranks second to none among the Allied scientists whose joint efforts rendered impotent a weapon which otherwise the enemy might well have used decisively."

Canada had been one of the signatories of the 1925 Geneva protocol outlawing gas warfare, and up to the mid-1930's no research on either the defensive or counter-offensive aspects of chemical warfare had been carried out in Canada. After the

Manchurian incident and the change of government in Germany, however, the Department of National Defence began to give serious thought to the matter. A member of the Chemistry Division of the National Research Council was authorized to review the technical literature, and to keep informed about new developments. In 1936, the Department of National Defence commenced the production of a gas-mask, haversack, and other accessories, exclusive of the container, which at that time was to be imported from the United Kingdom. The following year the Department asked the National Research Council to send a staff man to Britain to obtain data. Dr. E. A. Flood of the Division of Chemistry was selected for this mission, and while overseas he attended a course at the British Experimental Station at Porton. (All the production of chemical warfare equipment in Canada owed a good deal to the research conducted at this station.) Dr. Flood returned with sufficient information to enable the Canadian manufacture of gas respirators to begin, using Canadian materials for the most part, but importing a few of the components from the United Kingdom.

A small laboratory was set up at Ottawa to test the containers and the active charcoal which was the main filler-substance. An Associate Committee of the National Research Council on Container Proofing and Research was created. The outbreak of war in September 1939 found the production programme for masks well advanced. During the previous year, also, the National Research Council had produced small amounts of mustard gas, and two other toxic gases for use in the summer training of troops at military camps.

Activity in the Chemical Warfare Section of the Division of Chemistry was sharply accelerated after Dunkirk. The Associate Committee was strengthened by adding additional representatives from the forces, and staff members were sent to the United Kingdom to become familiar with British projects and to keep the British informed about Canadian research. In the chemical warfare investigations of the first two years of the war between fifty and sixty projects were begun.

Early in 1941 the Associate Committee was dissolved, and the Council's staff engaged in this work joined the Chemical Warfare establishment set up under the Army's Directorate of

SMOKE ON MANOEUVRES

In Western Canada

SMOKE IN ACTION

With Canadian Engineers near a German frontier town

Technical Research. This marked a separation of the chemical warfare group from the Division of Chemistry, but the divorce was never final or clear-cut. The cooperation between the Division of Chemistry and the Chemical Warfare Laboratories maintained by the Army remained so close that for many of the subsequent projects it was difficult to say who should receive primary credit for them. The National Research Council had provided the scientific nucleus, had supplied laboratory space and equipment, and continued throughout the war to provide some scientific direction.

The fall of France suddenly deprived Britain of the use of the Experimental Station for Chemical Warfare in French Algeria. Since it was impossible to find in Britain a substitute area which would meet all requirements, other sites in the British Commonwealth were hurriedly investigated, and early in 1941 the Experimental Station at Suffield, Alberta, was established as a joint United Kingdom-Canadian project. This grew into one of the most important war experimental stations maintained anywhere during the war. There were not many places in the world where there could be found 1000 square miles of territory almost completely uninhabited, yet adjacent to necessary facilities and easy of access. The Suffield station was in the semi-arid short-grass country of south-eastern Alberta, level, or very slightly undulating, which had once been home-steaded but was by then largely abandoned as unsuitable for cereal production. By transferring a few score of families, a very large area could be quickly set aside and made secure against espionage, while its distance from all the active theatres of war protected it from any threat of such an assault as fell, for example, upon the Nazi rocket research centre at Peenemünde, or from such raids as did some damage to a British radar research station at Portsmouth in 1940 and 1941.

A small team of British scientists came over to form the core of the Suffield Establishment. By May of 1941 the staff there had risen to twenty. All subsequent staff was recruited from Canada, and at the peak as many as 60 scientists and 100 key technicians were stationed there. Teams and groups of scientists and Army personnel visiting from Britain, and, after Pearl Harbor, from the United States, continuously added to the activity. It was primarily a Canadian Army show, with R.C.A.F. assistance and with close collaboration from National Research Council scientists and staff members of Canadian universities. U.S. scientists and Army staff engaged in setting up experimental stations on Chemical Warfare found, in 1942, an establishment already operating in Canada, which, to quote the U.S. official history, "was known to be doing high-grade work on these matters and which possessed an excellent staff and adequate facilities."[2]

No attempt will be made here to report or appraise the whole Canadian chemical warfare programme which was centred at Suffield.[3] Much of the research there was conducted exclusively by Canadian Army staffs in cooperation with Britain and the United States. Some of the discoveries made by the National Research Council are still secret. Bacteriological research was conducted both at Suffield and at Grosse Ile, Quebec, of which few details have been made public. But the nature of the problem can be illustrated and some account given of the work of Canadian scientists in this field.

The counter-offensive side of gas warfare required a continuous search for new toxic gases and smokes. Nothing really revolutionary was found on either side, as it later transpired, and if gas warfare had actually broken out between 1939 and 1945, it would have been waged essentially with the same toxic materials as were used in 1914-18. Improved methods were found, however, of manufacturing certain deadly gases which had gone out of favour in World War I owing to their instability and other defects. But Allied chemists, not knowing what the enemy might be discovering, could not afford to pause in their persistent investigation for more toxic compounds than anything yet listed in the pharmacopoeia of poisons. Chemists of the National Research Council synthesized, or attempted to synthesize, a number of promising compounds related to the mustard gases, and also a group of deadly alkaloids. Some work was done on

[2] W. A. Noyes Jr., *Chemistry*, Science in World War II, Office of Scientific Research Development Series (Little, Brown and Co., Boston, 1948), p. 318.

[3] In a letter (1944) to Dr. Otto Maass, General G. Brunskill, Director of Special Weapons and Vehicles, The War Office, wrote: "For various reasons, the contribution which Canada has made to Chemical Warfare in all its facets has been out of all proportion to the contribution that could rightly have been expected from the Dominion. Suffield has played a large part in this."

cadmium compounds. Following a report that the Germans were manufacturing large quantities of a nitrogen mustard, chemists at Ottawa as well as in Britain and the United States immediately turned their attention to the suspected compound. Several kilos of it were prepared in the National Research Laboratories to supply workers at the Council and others in Canadian universities who had volunteered to study its rate of hydrolosis in water, its rate of reaction with itself and its chemical properties. An extremely toxic gas was discovered at the University of Chicago by Dr. M. S. Kharasch, but since it decomposed very readily on standing, it could not be safely stored. A number of studies on this gas were made at Ottawa to ascertain whether the last stage in the means of synthesis could not be carried out in the projectile, just before detonation, thus overcoming the problem of the instability of the final product.

Another aspect of the offensive side of gas warfare was to increase our practical and theoretical knowledge of the behaviour of various airborne agents, vapours, and smokes—there being a technical distinction between true gases and aerosols or particulates, which are particles of liquids or solids suspended in air. In carbon monoxide, for example, the molecule CO is the fundamental particle, and the gas has a specific gravity slightly lighter than air. But smokes are chemically more complicated. They may be broadly classified as crystalline and liquid: the former consist of tiny particles, aggregates of very small crystals, which often have featherlike or jagged edges; the latter, being liquid, are spherical. In order to use toxic aerosols to advantage in offensive warfare, such data needed to be known as the most effective size of particle for penetrating the enemy's respirators, the effect of temperature (of the environment and of modifications caused by the explosion of the gas-bomb) upon their behaviour, the manner of the penetration of gases into buildings, and what happens to gases in dense woods and jungles as well as on treeless prairies and mountain sides. The amount of the dosage which would be needed to be lethal or at any rate sufficient to cause casualties, and the technique for laying down such an effective dosage had to be ascertained by repeated experiments in actual field trials, using live animals as well as mechanical measuring devices. This was the sort of thing which could be done—and was done on a vast scale—at such proving grounds and experimental stations as Suffield. To illustrate the kind of research which was necessary to measure the concentration of lethal gases in field tests, a project of the Physics Department of the University of Manitoba may be cited. Under Dr. G. O. Langstroth, a group there developed a special lamp and photocell for the instantaneous measurement of phosgene concentrations. Phosgene, passing between the lamp and the cell, reduced the effective radiation reaching the latter. A continuous record of the phosgene concentration at any given point could be obtained by photographing with a motion picture camera the dial of a meter.

The defensive side of gas warfare had to keep pace with the discovery and development of new toxic agents. Since it was impossible to guess which of hundreds of possible poisonous compounds the enemy might suddenly introduce, the respirators taken into battle by Allied service personnel had to be capable of screening out or destroying all the really lethal ones. In practice there were six or eight chemically diverse gases which the enemy might be likely to employ, and a gas-mask effective against this entire group would very probably protect our forces against any other non-persistent agent. One of the earliest and most vital tasks assumed by Chemical Warfare establishments was the design and improvement of the absorbents used in gas-masks so as to guarantee the protection of service personnel under all the conditions of concentration, humidity, etc. they were likely to encounter. Charcoal and merino wool were the two stand-bys used to fill the canisters of gas-masks, but it was learned in the earliest investigations that charcoal exists in many different forms and conditions of widely differing effectiveness, and that against certain types of gases it was necessary to impregnate the charcoal with such substances as silver nitrate and copper before it would prevent lethal penetration.

When war broke out in 1939, it had been planned to import from Britain the charcoal and asbestos fillings for Canadian-made masks, but developments overseas soon suggested the imperative need of finding a Canadian source for the fillings.

In the late autumn of 1939, preliminary inquiries began in the Research Council at Ottawa, and contacts were made with industrial firms in Canada able to turn out such materials. Production began early in 1940. By the spring of 1940 a second company had begun producing experimental batches. Early tests of these pads showed that the penetrometer in use, which measured the degree of penetration of the mask by toxic agents, was not satisfactory, and the Physics Division immediately designed a more sensitive type.

Late in 1939, while in the United Kingdom, Sir Frederick Banting had learned that there was reason to fear that the Germans were planning to use arsene in a gas offensive. The standard respirators offered inadequate protection against this gas, and the British were busy producing an emergency canister attachment, in which the charcoal was impregnated with silver nitrate. Scientists at Ottawa obtained a supply of copper-impregnated charcoal from the United States, which proved to give somewhat better results than the silver-treated charcoal.

A good deal of work was done in anticipation of the enemy's using mustard gas, which had been the most effective agent used in World War I. Mustard gas in either its liquid or vaporous form produces destructive blisters when it comes into contact with human skin, and a great deal of effort was employed in 1939-45 in devising service suits which were impermeable to mustard or which were impregnated with chemicals that would alter the mustard gas into a harmless chemical compound. The objection to impermeable suits—not porous to air—was that they would be physically intolerable if worn for long, especially in hot, humid climates. Substances which would destroy mustard gas could be readily incorporated into service clothing, but all the early compounds proposed rotted the service uniforms so fast as to be impracticable.

Work on this problem began in September 1939. Facilities were available in the Textile Laboratory of the Division of Chemistry at Ottawa, and a small pilot plant for processing fabrics and garments was later set up. The investigations and tests covered many types of equipment, battle dress serge, capes, gloves, decontamination mitts, eyeshields, detector gas sleeves, and helmet curtains. Among the fabrics tested were butyl-coated, neoprene, rayon, cellophane, oilskin, and pliofilm.

The manufacture of anti-gas fabrics began in Canada in 1940. The Council cooperated with four industrial firms in an effort to step up production in a field in which there was no earlier experience. Only one of the four firms appeared to possess the necessary knowledge and technical control to produce a satisfactory range of anti-gas fabrics. A second firm produced a fair amount of A-type fabric, but its lack of proper technical control caused great difficulty. Among the problems was the tendency for oil-dressed fabrics to start fires by spontaneous combustion. Hundreds of tests on experimental production runs were necessary, as well as numerous consultations and plant visits. The Inspection Board requested the Textile Laboratory to undertake all the necessary testing of the fabrics produced. This resulted in 2500 routine inspection reports covering the manufacture of sixteen million yards of anti-gas fabrics.

The production of impregnated garments—made of fabrics treated to react chemically with the vapours of mustard gas or Lewisite—was also carried out on a large scale in Canada, with the technical aid of the Council. A British and an American Impregnite compound were extensively tested. Among the problems was the fact that the active chemical (chlorine) employed in destroying poisonous liquids and vapours also destroyed the tensile strength of the cloth. Tests with different kinds of cloth to discover the effects of different types of dyes and cloth finishes and the extent to which washing or dry cleaning impaired the anti-gas qualities of the cloth, and the development of the safest types of laundering for such fabrics, were among the activities of the Textile Laboratory.

Work in impregnation began in 1941 and was extended to pilot-plant scale the following year. In 1942 a thousand suits of Army battle dress and a thousand pair of socks were treated and found satisfactory. Full commercial production was then begun, using the techniques developed at Ottawa, in the dry cleaning plants of Langley's Limited, Toronto, and Vail's Limited, Ottawa. Some 400,000 suits of battle dress were processed by these firms.

The poisonous gases and vapours to be feared were not all of enemy origin. Troops in armoured tanks and in tank-landing craft were exposed to poisoning from carbon monoxide, ammonia and nitrous fumes. Gas-mask containers were developed using hopcalite (a mixture of manganese dioxide and copper oxide). This was widely used for the purpose and proved to be an efficient oxidation catalyst for carbon monoxide. However, it had many disadvantages. It was rapidly poisoned by water vapour, which was strongly absorbed. Also, it liberated a great deal of heat in the presence of relatively high concentrations of carbon monoxide—so great, indeed, as to require a cooling device for the protection of the wearer breathing the heated air passing through the respirator. Other compounds were accordingly investigated by scientists of the National Research Council. Silver permanganate and zinc oxide proved to be the most effective of these, giving a better performance than equivalent hopcalite containers. Research on this problem was still continuing when hostilities ended.

The need of improved ventilation in various types and models of armoured tanks was explored at Camp Borden. Under battle conditions, carbon monoxide, nitrous and ammonia fumes were found in significant amounts, the concentration of carbon monoxide under some circumstances being over double the danger limit. At Suffield, clinical and physiological tests were conducted to determine the effect of gases on tank personnel. These showed that dangerously high concentrations of both carbon monoxide and ammonia were released during the firing of the armament of the Ram II tank.

Complete protection could be provided against both the gun fumes and non-persistent gas attacks of the enemy by use of an "anti-gas protective unit", which supplied four cubic feet of filtered air per minute to each crew member. Better ventilation systems were installed in both the Ram I and Ram II tanks as a result of these investigations.

Screening Smokes

Screening smokes were used widely in World War II. It was behind a smoke screen that the *Graf Spee* made its escape to a neutral port in the battle of the River Plate on December

13, 1939. In March 1945 Field Marshal Montgomery laid
down the greatest concentration of smoke—a cloud fifty miles
long—to hide his massed forces for the crossing of the Rhine.
General Simonds employed smoke screens laid down by artillery
along the front and flanks of the advancing Canadian columns
during one of the critical thrusts down the Falaise Road. The
surprise landing of the Allies on the Anzio beach, the screening
of the German battleships *Gneisenau* and *Scharnhorst* at Brest,
and the British defence of Malta all used this device.

The smokes used in World War II were more effective
than in 1914-18 because scientific research had been applied to
their improvement. Canadian scientists at Ottawa and in various
Canadian universities cooperated with the Directorate of Chemical Warfare and Smokes in certain aspects of this research. For
example, a group at the University of Manitoba under the
direction of Dr. G. O. Langstroth, Associate Professor of Physics,
undertook a study of the mechanism of obscuration. Using a
smoke chamber, they investigated the phenomena of screening.
The determination of the limits of visual ability was explored
by means of experiments in physiological optics. The brightness
of smoke screens was studied in the field, and a theory of screens
was developed over an extensive range of conditions both by
day and night. Military commanders were thus supplied with
data as to the optical density of smoke required under those
various conditions. O. J. Walker and F. H. Foxlee of the
University of Alberta carried on for three years a project
which had as its objective the development of a smoke which
on dispersal from aircraft would be stable and tend to settle
rather than rise. Several successful methods for thickening
such smokes were developed by them.

In the earliest use of smokes, especially by the Navy, the colour
had usually been black, and the aim had been to create enough
density to block off completely the target to be protected. It
was discovered, however, that more diffuse clouds of white smoke,
using much less raw material to produce, possessed equally
effective qualities of confusing the observer by reflecting light
strongly back into his eye. White smokes came to be favoured
in certain circumstances. However, white smoke tends to stand
out and draw attention to the target being shielded, whereas

suitably coloured smokes may at times serve as a camouflage. The production of screening smokes thus involved not only the chemistry of production, the physics of the behaviour of aerosols, and the meteorology of air currents under different weather conditions, but also the physiology and psychology of observation.

Flame Throwers

Flame throwers in World War I had a range of only about 20 yards. They used liquid fuels, of which not more than 10 per cent. could be counted upon to reach the target. They were, if limited in application, still a terrifying weapon when used on appropriate occasions, though their chief value even so was believed to be psychological. A great advance was made in World War II when thickened fuels were introduced; the Canadian Army used flame throwers in several thousand operations.[4]

By adding a substance which would cause gasoline to gel, ranges up to 110 yards could be obtained, and the weapon could be aimed with much greater exactness. Moreover, as much as 90 per cent. of the fuel could be delivered at the target. Results such as these were obtained by the Gasoline and Oil Laboratory of the National Research Council, which undertook, at the request of the Directorate of Chemical Warfare, some work aimed at securing the maximum range and target effects of such fuels.

Many different fuel mixtures were prepared at the Ottawa laboratory, and tested in Ronson and Kincaid flame throwers. The greatest increase in range was obtained by the use of gels, rather than by simply thickening the fuel to increase its viscosity. The internal strength of the gel resulted in the fuel being shot in the form of a "rod", which might break into large pieces toward the end of its flight. A liquid, on the other hand, tended to break up much earlier in flight into droplets which lost velocity rapidly. Moreover, the gel type of fuels were found to cling tenaciously to the target, and as much as 90 per cent.

---

[4] Some account of the Canadian-designed flame-throwing vehicle, the WASP2C, which was employed with great effect against the Nazis in Holland, can be found in *Flame Over Britain* by Sir Donald Banks (Sampson Low, London, 1946).

arrived at the target to burn there. The most effective composition was determined, to meet various conditions including low temperatures.

Dr. Langstroth's group at Winnipeg began, late in the war, the determination of the thermal conductivity and specific heat of thickened gasoline over a wide range of temperatures, in connection with the problem of ensuring the ignition of the fuel on ejection from the weapon, particularly in cold weather.

Tropical Deterioration

The outbreak of war in the Pacific in 1941, and later the likelihood that the main theatre of operations would eventually shift to that part of the world, led to increased concern about the protection not only of foods but of war equipment, textiles, and medical supplies, and not solely against water and water-vapour but also against the moulds and bacteria which flourish in high temperatures and humidities. The Division of Applied Biology and the Division of Chemistry (of the National Research Council) teamed up in these investigations with the Departments of Agriculture and National Defence.

It comes as a shock to a person reared in one of the temperate zones, especially if he has lived in one of the sub-humid or semi-arid areas, to read about, and still more to experience, the devastation which tropical insects, moulds, fungi, and corrosion can speedily cause to equipment and fabrics in the jungles and on tropical beaches. One reads with amazement of moulds that grow up and hide your boots overnight, of uniforms rotted to the point of uselessness in a week, of cork plugs rapidly falling apart, of organisms that can find a foothold on the glass lenses of a camera or telescope, of broadcasting sets which in one month lose 80 per cent. of transmitter output from mould development, of corrosion which quickly destroys delicate metal components, of the need of packing a desiccant with certain assemblies, of fungi which readily attack the varnishes, lacquers, and other coatings applied to equipment to protect it against moisture corrosion.

Among the materials examined to be used for packaging stores for Pacific jungles and beaches the most effective barriers against moisture were laminations of kraft to foil and cellophane, or scrim to kraft and foil with a Butvar coating. Laminations with kraft or metal foil were less likely to fracture when subjected to rough handling. Laminating the stocks produced a barrier which was more effective against water-vapour than was typical of either of the base sheets when used alone. Wax coatings reduced the passage of water-vapour but offered little additional protection when the packages were subjected to rough handling. The growth of moulds had little effect on increasing the passage of water-vapour. Moulds seriously affected some materials, especially glassine and some samples of kraft paper. These discoveries were used in designing packages for tropical use and in drawing up codes or standards for tropical packing.

Canadian radio equipment was tested for use in tropical conditions by comparing the performance of treated and untreated wireless sets after exposure to artificial jungle conditions for one month. For the untreated sets, reduction in transmitter output was 80 per cent. before cleaning the tubes and 40 per cent. after cleaning. Audio-amplifier output was reduced 35 per cent., and many other aspects of the performance were adversely affected. A similar set sprayed with a fungicidal lacquer obtained from Research Enterprises showed much less mould growth after one month of exposure to 95°F. and 98 to 100 per cent. relative humidity, but even so, certain susceptible or untreated parts were covered with a medium to heavy growth, glue failure was evident in places, and corrosion of the microphone capsules was extensive. A battery charger exposed for five weeks exhibited heavy moulding and corrosion of certain parts. Tubing and cable coatings of various materials were tested, and practically all of them supported mould growth.

Tests of mould growth on batteries and battery packaging materials were undertaken for the Department of National Defence. The first set of batteries submitted deteriorated rapidly under high-humidity conditions. A number of different materials for battery construction were tested for mould resistance. Changes in design and the impregnation of the battery composition with suitable chemicals improved the performance.

Expectation of an early Canadian participation in the Pacific war zone led to a great expansion in the mould testing of textiles. Fungicides which have proved effective on other equipment may have to be ruled out in application to fabrics which are likely to be worn or handled by army personnel, because of their toxic nature. If fabrics are to be impregnated with chemicals, it is important that they retain their original physical qualities as far as possible: for example, they must not become unduly stiff or brittle. The colour imparted by the chemical to the cloth may be important. Extensive investigations were made on fungicides suitable for army textiles, and many commercial preparations were tested.

The most drastic method of testing fabrics was soil burial, in which half of a strip of cloth was left underground and deterioration could be compared with the upper half, exposed to air-infection only. Stretching and wearing machines were applied to the damaged cloths after exposure.

When the Canadian tests began, copper compounds were in favour for protecting fabrics against fungi. Copper naphthenate had been widely used. Impregnation with it protected canvas for several weeks, but it had the disadvantage that it made canvas stiff and dyed it a light baby blue. Also, after a few weeks the copper leached out and the protection against mould was lost.

Among the specialists working on the problem was a young chemist who did not pretend to know much about moulds but who remembered his chemistry. While he was considering the various possible organic copper salts, he suddenly recalled the simple qualitative test for nickel, known to all chemistry students. You simply add an organic chemical known as dimethylglyoxime, and the solution turns pink, because the nickel forms a pink salt with the dimethylglyoxime. A similar complex is obtained with the copper salts. Could copper be fixed in fabrics with this compound?

The young scientist tried it, dipping a piece of canvas first into a solution of dimethylglyoxime, then into one of copper acetate. It worked. Right inside the fibres of the canvas a complex copper salt was formed. The canvas was still flexible, as it had not been when treated with copper naphthenate, and instead of a baby blue, this sample came out, of all colours, an acceptable shade of khaki!

So far so good. But would it resist fungi? Under jungle conditions, untreated canvas rots in a week, but lasts for several weeks with the naphthenate treatment. Canvas treated with the new chemical came through the same test for much longer periods, and after it had been washed could not be distinguished from unburied canvas.

The tests continued, and some fungicides were discovered which were even more satisfactory than the copper-dimethyl-glyoxime treatment. The investigation was still in progress when hostilities came to an end in August 1945.

CHAPTER VII

SEA

THE true dimensions of Canada's aid toward winning the war at sea cannot be measured without some reference to the critical fortunes of the *Battle of the Atlantic*—the grim fateful see-saw between the Nazi U-boats and Allied sea power, with the whole outcome of the war in mortal hazard. When a scale is so evenly balanced that the weight of even a hair may be decisive, the factors on each side take on a special significance. So nearly did the enemy win the Battle of the Atlantic—and with it, possibly, the whole war—that the value of Canada's aid in this campaign cannot readily be exaggerated.

How close Germany came to winning the First World War by unrestricted submarine warfare needs no labouring at this date. How much more the conditions favoured the Nazis in their plan to bleed Britain white by the same means in 1939-45 is less well understood. It is debatable how effective Allied naval press censorship was in hiding from the German Naval Staff the enormous inroads they were making into Allied shipping; but it did serve to cloak from the people of Britain, the United States, and Canada at the time the perturbing fact that this was the most anxious and critical of all the desperately fought contests of World War II.

The background and timing of the Nazi submarine offensive will be readily recalled. The "Seventy Fearful Days" of 1940, which began with the invasion of Norway in April 1940 and ended with Hitler's armies overrunning virtually all of western Europe, failed to cow the British into surrender. The aerial Battle of Britain, then conceived as a preliminary to actual invasion, opened on August 8, 1940, and came to a crisis on September 15, with the R.A.F. barely stemming the tide. This ended the second phase. As a German invasion was doomed by lack of air mastery, Hitler then set out to starve Britain into

subjection by surface and submarine thrusts against the ocean
life-lines linking her with the foods and war potential of North
America and other parts of the world, meantime seeking in
the East (by conquest of the Ukraine and annexation of the
Caucasus) the enlargement of his economic resources necessary
for a possible long war of naval and aerial attrition.

Hitler's naval staff had much reason to be hopeful about the
results of their sealane strangulation of Britain. The naval odds
had turned heavily against Britain in the spring and summer
months of 1940. After June 1940, the Nazis solidly occupied a
2500 mile European coast-line from North Cape to the Bay of
Biscay, outflanking Britain both by air and sea. The Royal
Navy was gravely handicapped even in comparison with the
dark days of 1917, moreover, by denial to them of naval bases
in Eire. The Nazi submarine of 1940 was a much more formidable weapon than the U-boat of 1918: it had a tougher skin,
could submerge to greater depths, and could safely withstand
much more powerful depth-charges. Offensively it possessed new
aiming devices, and it launched a much more destructive torpedo. In numbers, as well as in striking power, Britain's anti-
submarine fleet was inferior and even woefully inadequate for
a time. At the close of the First World War, Britain and her
naval allies together had been able to deploy nearly 900 destroyers, but she went to war in 1939 with only 180; and
France (whose aid in any event substantially collapsed nine
months later) possessed only 59.

In the sea warfare on all fronts Nazi scientists and war
technicians introduced from the beginning a steady stream of
ingenious and even diabolically clever new weapons and other
gadgets, of which the most widely publicized were the magnetic
mine, the acoustic mine, the "homing" torpedo, and the "schnörkel"—a breathing tube which allowed the U-boat to cruise at
top power—and not far below top speed—on its Diesel engines,
without fully surfacing. The U-boats of the Second World
War, moreover, were employed in radically new tactical action.
In 1914-18 they had operated as true submarines, "diving by
day and attacking submerged, surfacing at night, individualists
with a free hand, working in the limited areas of coastal waters
and in the comparatively close approaches to the British Isles."

But now, as an Admiralty Anti-Submarine Report phrased it in April 1942, "We are dealing with U-boats which prefer to operate as 'submersibles' and will not dive until forced to do so, which attack for preference at night on the surface as torpedo-boats, which cooperate in numbers in reconnaissance and attack, and which will move anywhere over the Atlantic at the dictates of the U-boat Admiral, who rigidly controls all their activities from the moment they sail until they return to harbour." These were the savagely vaunted "Wolf Packs" of the North Atlantic sealanes.

When to such adverse factors were added the ravages of Germany's few but powerful surface-raiders, and the serious destruction of British coastal shipping by the *Luftwaffe,* it is not surprising that the loss of Allied tonnage soon reached crippling totals. By the time security considerations had dictated a complete "black-out" on monthly shipping losses, over seven million tons of British, Allied, and neutral shipping had admittedly gone to the bottom. In subsequent months the Allied public was left vaguely apprehensive that the situation was serious, but, because of tight censorship, was unaware of just how critical the Battle of the Oceans had become. The precise figures would have been even more distressing.

The highest published monthly loss up to the time when the censorship curtain went down was 589,000 tons sunk in April 1941. Over a year later, largely owing to the operations of U-boats in the coastal waters of the United States and in the Caribbean (June 1942), a new peak of 671,000 tons was reached. In November 1942 the tonnage lost soared to 690,-000 tons to set another black record. This appalling figure was never exceeded, but the blackest hour of all was reached the following March (1943) when three-quarters of the total loss of 627,000 tons for the month *consisted of ships shot out of guarded convoys.* Indeed, a Canadian naval historian calls the first half of March 1943 "U-boats' field day", when "the Atlantic was to all purposes their ocean." It was even feared that the convoy system, which had saved Britain from starvation in 1917 and was still regarded as the best answer to the U-boat, would have to be abandoned, though no one seemed to know what naval tactic could be substituted.

THE ARMY AND THE WATER

A "weasel" crossing the Beveland Canal in Holland during the Beveland operations

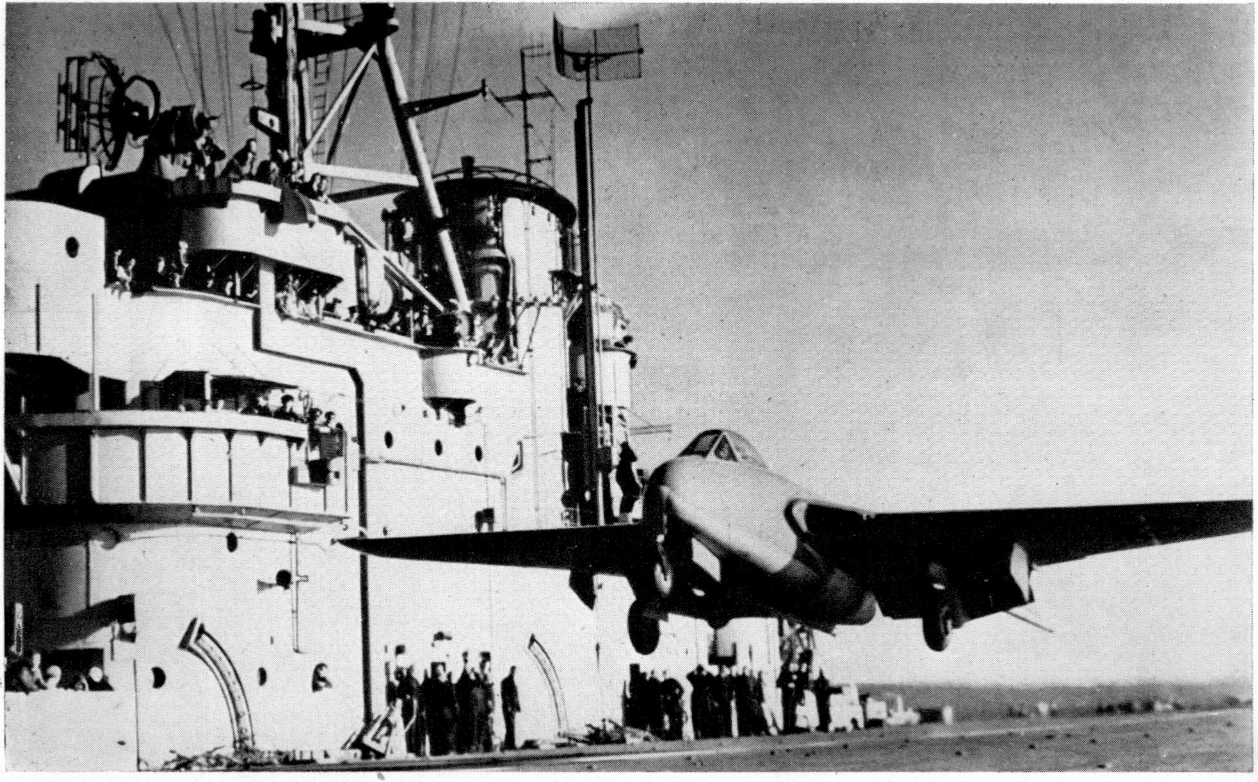

THE NAVY AND THE AIR

Meantime it had proved utterly beyond the ship-building resources of the British Isles to replace more than a small fraction of the steadily mounting losses. Each month Hitler seemed to be drawing closer to his grim objective of starving out Britain, and at the least he was grievously delaying the building up of war potential adequate for a landing on the coast of Europe. Until the tide on Atlantic sealanes turned in the spring of 1943, it grew clearer every month that "although the war could not be won by defeating the U-boats, it would assuredly be lost if they were not defeated."

Even after the crisis had passed, there was no easy victory. In his Mansion House Speech on November 9, 1943, Winston Churchill announced: "We have broken the back of the U-boat war which at one time had seemed our greatest peril." But the scientists, the naval technicians, the naval staff, could never rest on their oars. In June 1944, for example, as was pointed out by the anonymous Canadian naval historian quoted above, "the introduction of *schnörkel* rendered obsolete the tactics which had given the Allies their victory, and initiated the Second Battle of the Atlantic. The U-boat war was by no means over when the Army achieved victory. New types of U-boats, Types 21 and 23, which acted as true submersibles and would have presented Allied scientists with a new set of problems, had begun to operate off the east coast of the United Kingdom and were poised for a new campaign in the Atlantic. On May 7-8 (1945), the very eve of victory, two merchant ships were sunk near the entrance to the Firth of Forth, and a mine-sweeper of the Royal Norwegian Navy was sunk in Lyme Bay. The longer the U-boat war lasted, the more awkward it would have become for the Allies."[1] Among the ingenious counter-measures introduced by the Nazis was a new outer skin for their U-boats which absorbed the sound beam employed by the searching Asdic of the Allied anti-submarine fleet, and thus rendered practically useless one of the most effective weapons of earlier under-water detection.

Though there was never a conclusive victory in this sense, the Nazi submarine offensive was at least severely blunted long

[1] From a manuscript account of the North Atlantic Convoy Operations by the Historical Records Office, Canadian Naval Mission Overseas, London, November 1945.

enough to make the land victories of 1944 and 1945 possible. The details of how it was done—the story of the rapid expansion of the anti-submarine navies of Britain, the United States, Canada, and other United Nations, the prodigious programme of merchant ship-building in North America, the development of air cover for convoys, the offensive operations of airships equipped with radar—all fall outside the scope of this narrative. Canada, of course, contributed materially, if not massively, to the general naval offensive and to the building programme. Here our attention must be focussed almost exclusively on the aid given by the scientists of Canada to this critical battle of the Second World War.

Neither in degree of preparedness nor in the scale of available personnel had Canada been ready to play an important role in the science of sea warfare when hostilities broke out in September 1939. The Royal Canadian Navy possessed no research organization nor facilities at all. Such scientific devices as the small Canadian Navy was using had been obtained fully developed from the Admiralty. Fortunately there were other potential and incipient resources at hand in Canada.

The nucleus of a radar research programme which existed at the National Research Council's Laboratories at Ottawa has already been described (see p. 29). There were physicists in Canadian universities competent to cope with Nazi secret weapons. In Dr. R. W. Boyle, Director of the Physics and Electrical Engineering Division at Ottawa, the National Research Council had a notable pioneer in ultra-sonics and the acoustic detection of submarines. In 1917 Dr. Boyle had been entrusted with Admiralty's secret Asdic research, based on theories originally propounded by Lord Rutherford and Professor Paul Langevin of France, and had successfully carried it through to the installation and demonstration of the apparatus on ships of the Royal Navy. From 1920 to 1928 Dr. Boyle had continued fundamental studies of the theory of ultra-sonics at the University of Alberta, and one of his students and associates at Edmonton, Dr. G. S. Field, had come to Ottawa in 1930 to open the Acoustics Laboratories of the National Research Council.

Canada's early role in the naval conflict, on the scientific front as elsewhere, was determined by the grand strategy of the war and by the limited nature of Canada's immediately available resources. It was inevitable that in the early stages the defensive side should be stressed almost exclusively. The early *offensive* operations of the Royal Navy (1939-41) did not call in any way upon Canada's scientific potential. Canada's own small pre-war navy had been conceived of in a strictly defensive light. But from the outset, Halifax was a key naval base in Britain's defence of the North Atlantic and a logical convoy-gathering base. Canada thus occupied from the very beginning a front seat in the naval warfare and this fact soon began to affect the shape of Canada's scientific activities. Ports like Halifax, Sydney, and Esquimalt offered suitable havens in which Allied shipping could be equipped with counter-devices against such German inventions as the magnetic mine. Halifax, indeed, was always in the front line of the naval war. Canadian supplies and engineering skills could be drawn upon there to supplement Britain's overstrained resources.

Subsequently, as Canada assumed a heavier load in the battle against the submarine, the emphasis in Canadian research shifted from passive defence to more dynamic detection and offensive strikes against the enemy. On the scientific side, accordingly, the story begins with the consideration of such problems as harbour protection, the detection of poisonous gases on ships, counter-measures to the magnetic mine (and later the acoustic mine and the acoustic torpedo), radar for coastal warning, and minor scientific and engineering aids to keep Canada's small but growing defensive navy in efficient operation. As months went by, the emphasis shifted to improved means of hunting out and attacking the enemy submarine, employing optical, sonic, and electronic devices, culminating in microwave radar, RDF (radio-direction-finding) pin-pointing of enemy warships, and the location of signals emitted whenever the enemy broke radio silence. Finally, before the war was over, Canada contributed usefully to the naval offensive by her work on such explosives as RDX and her valuable early work on the theory of the proximity fuse already described. The story as it is unfolded in the following pages follows in a broad way this chronological shift from early defensive phases to aggressive detection and finally to active offensive measures.

The Magnetic Mine: De-gaussing and Deperming

On November 18, 1939, six cargo vessels were sunk off the south-east coast of England by mines. Two more merchant vessels were sunk within the next forty-eight hours. The Admiralty noted at the time that some of the mine explosions occurred further aft on the hulls than had been usual when vessels had been sunk by the old-style contact mines of World War I. Moreover, it was recalled that during September and October a number of merchant ships had been sunk at the entrances to British harbours, though these had been properly swept for mines. On the night of November 21, three German sea-planes were seen over the North Sea, and light patrol forces fired at them, without, however, obtaining a hit. A few minutes later the British destroyer *Gipsy* was almost cut to pieces by a terrific explosion while passing through the area where the sea-planes had been detected. There were unusual features about the disaster: the casualty list was abnormally high, and it was noted that immediately after the explosion which wrecked the *Gipsy* another explosion had occurred about fifty yards away. When the hull of the *Gipsy* was later examined, it was discovered that the first explosion had taken place directly under the ship's bottom, amidships, and not at the bow, as was usual with a contact mine.[2]

This was the first taste of a new Nazi "secret weapon" which, it is said, had been confidently counted upon by such Nazi naval authorities as Hans Langsdorf, Captain of the German pocket battleship *Graf Spee*, as providing the decisive weapon to starve out Britain and win the Second World War.

Though the magnetic mine received a good deal of publicity, and an answer was soon found by the scientists of Britain, the nature of the new menace was not widely grasped. There was even a general impression that it was a mine containing large magnets which served to attract it to the steel hull of a vessel,

[2] Gilbert Cant, *The War at Sea* (John Day Co., New York, 1942), pp. 123-4; *see also* Winston S. Churchill, *The Gathering Storm* (Houghton, Mifflin, New York 1948), pp. 505-8, 706-11.

where it would explode by contact. But it was more subtle and ingenious than that; it possessed some notable advantages over the contact mine, and threatened to be far more destructive to shipping. The contact mine, it will be recalled, floated near the surface, moored there by a cable attached to an anchor which rested on the sea bottom. To be detonated, it had to be actually struck by a ship's hull. It could readily be cut loose from its moorings by a mine-sweeper, causing it to float on the surface, where it could be seen and destroyed by gunfire.

The new magnetic mine, however, could be laid upon the seabed in shallow water: it could not be found, detached, or brought to the surface like the contact mine. And not only was it not necessary for the victim-vessel to strike the mine: it sufficed if the ship passed *nearby* overhead; the path of danger for a ship was, indeed, as much as ten times as wide as for the contact mine. And when the mine did explode, it tended to be far more effective for two separate reasons: first, unlike the old contact mine, which had wasted a large part of its energy in the air, the new mine transmitted its destructive effect through water to the hull of the vessel; and secondly, it tended to open up the plates along the bottom of the ship instead of blasting a hole near the water-line, well up on the hull where it would be less destructive. All in all, the magnetic mine confronted Admiralty scientists with a novel and very formidable menace to merchant and naval shipping alike.

The story of how, on November 23, 1939, the first German magnetic mine was recovered by the British on the shore at Shoeburyness, after the tide had gone out, how British scientists risked their lives to uncover its mechanical secrets, and how quickly they did so, has been often told. So has the nature of the mine's working principles. It is only necessary to recall here that it contained a magnetic needle which was deflected when the magnetic field in its vicinity was distorted by the passage overhead or nearby of the steel hull of a warship or a merchant vessel. This deflection of the needle closed an electrical circuit from a battery to a relay, which actuated the main firing mechanism, and thus detonated a third of a ton or more of high explosives.

That any such structure as a ship coated with iron or steel plates, and fitted with engines and other equipment made of iron and steel, acquires the properties of a huge magnet is well known to all students of magnetism. There are two quite separate effects. The ship acquires some permanent (and more or less invariable) magnetism while it is being built, the amount it will acquire depending on a number of factors, including the direction it is pointing while being hammered and rivetted into shape, and the strength of the earth's magnetic field in the area where it was constructed. In addition, it acquires magnetism (fluctuating as it moves and turns) solely by virtue of the fact that it is a large mass of iron intersecting lines of magnetic force passing through and around the earth. This acquired magnetism will vary with different latitudes and with the bearing of the course currently being followed. There is both a vertical and a horizontal polarity about the magnetism of such a vessel, that is, a pole at bow and stern, and another at the keel and topside. A ship built in the northern hemisphere acquires the characteristics of a magnet with a north (Red) pole along the keel and a south (Blue) pole topside. (A ship built on a north heading will also have a north (Red) pole at the bow and a south (Blue) pole at the stern—a longitudinal effect. It was, however, only the first of these two characteristics (the vertical one) which was exploited by the Germans in their early magnetic mine.)

As such a ship approaches a magnetic mine lying on a shallow seabed, or harbour bed, the north (Red) pole along the ship's keel begins to act upon the suspended needle in the mine below, and when the magnetic intensity is increased by such an approach to the point where the needle swings over to close the circuit, the mine explodes, and the ship's hull is ripped apart.

The reaction of the British scientists, once they had unbared the secrets of the mechanism, was a solution simple in theory but increasingly complicated and costly in practice as the Nazi mines grew in ingenuity. The first answer was merely to devise an apparatus to *reverse* the magnetic polarity of all ships compelled to navigate in dangerous waters. Fortunately it was found possible to do this by fitting girdles of wire or cable about the vessel through which currents of electricity of appropriate intensity could be passed. By over-compensation this would give the keel of a ship so fitted (*de-gaussed* was the technical term, derived from the unit of magnetism) a Blue (or south) rather than a Red (or north) pole along its keel. It could then safely pass over a magnetic mine of the earlier type, which responded only to a Red excitation. (Later models of Nazi mines were devised to detonate on the approach of a ship with either a Blue or Red magnetic pole along its keel.)

First steps were taken, naturally, by the Admiralty to de-gauss and thus safeguard vessels lying in British ports and plying coastal waters within easy reach of Nazi mine-layers, surface and aerial. Before an adequate programme of protection could be undertaken, losses from mines became serious: more than half the total loss of 200,000 tons in January 1940 fell victim to Nazi magnetic mines. On January 10, 1940, with losses rising sharply, the emergency de-gaussing of all merchant ships navigating in British waters was ordered by the Admiralty. For a time as much as 1500 miles of cable a week was being used for this purpose in British ports. Steps were also necessary to safeguard ships in far-distant waters planning to proceed to British ports. Halifax was a logical haven in which to de-gauss not only Canadian vessels but ships of British and foreign registry bound for Britain.

In February 1940 Captain (later Vice Admiral) H. E. Reid, Commanding Officer, Atlantic Coast, called upon Dr. J. H. L. Johnstone and Dr. G. H. Henderson, physicists on the staff of Dalhousie University, for help in setting up a de-gaussing station in Halifax Harbour. The first ship so coiled or *de-gaussed* in Canada was H.M.C.S. *Fleur de Lys* (on March 21, 1940).

Even in the earlier cruder protection of ships against the magnetic mine, consisting of merely *reversing* the polarity of the ship—a less delicate operation than complete neutralization of a ship's magnetism—it was necessary to measure with some precision the actual magnetic field beneath the ship being safeguarded. The scientific pioneers at Halifax possessed no detailed information about the apparatus being used in Britain for the purpose, but they quickly devised from their own knowledge of the principles of magnetism a satisfactory magnetometer for the

purpose. The early device consisted of an instrument built
into a water-tight box which could be dragged from stem to
stern beneath the keel (a procedure called keel-hauling), thus
providing the scientists with necessary data about the variation
in magnetic strength along the ship's keel—the ship's *magnetic
signature,* in other words. With this data it was then feasible to
build coils about the ship and energize them sufficiently to
offset or reverse the original magnetism of the vessel. Keel-
hauling by use of this early device continued during most of
1940, and among the many ships so protected were the fifty
"over age" destroyers turned over to Britain by the United
States.

The growing seriousness of the struggle in the spring of 1940
placed an excessive strain upon the resources of the British Admiralty and imparted new urgency to the operations at Halifax.
This led to a number of expansions and developments: several
additional magnetometers were made and further scientific
staff was enlisted. The facilities of Dalhousie University were
soon overtaxed, and the National Research Council at Ottawa
took over and supplemented the team of Halifax physicists and
technicians headed by Drs. Henderson and Johnstone. Dr.
Henderson sailed to Britain to visit the naval laboratories there,
returning in July 1940 with valuable information. The de-
gaussing programme was speeded up. By working a stretch of
forty-eight hours of continuous activity, the ships *Antonia, La-
conia,* and *Silver Elm,* for example, were calibrated in a single
effort. The tedious task of calibrating such large vessels as the
Pasteur and *Niew Amsterdam* (an operation which required
four tugs holding the ships on a magnetic heading) led to the
decision to abandon keel-hauling and to set up an "open range"
as rapidly as possible. This consisted of establishing a number
of coils laid in a line on the harbour bottom and connected to
recording instruments ashore, over which the ships under test
could be navigated a number of times for calibration and later
for checking as the girdles of de-gaussing cable were adjusted
and energized. This first "open range" in existence outside of
the British Isles was constructed on the eastern shore of Bedford
Basin, and declared ready for operation of November 13, 1940,
after several satisfactory runs had been taken over it by

H.M.C.S. *Arras.* It was in continuous use from that date onward, and by V-J Day over thirty-eight hundred ships, ranging in size from battle-ships to mine-sweepers, had been calibrated and tested there. Subsequently, other open ranges were laid and staffed by the National Research Council at Sydney, N.S., in the Halifax Channel, at Quebec City, and on the West Coast.

Professor H. J. McLeod of the University of British Columbia, after spending part of the summer of 1940 at Halifax, took charge of the de-gaussing station in English Bay near Ferguson Point, which was officially opened on March 21, 1942. As on the East Coast, the Vancouver Group was organized by the National Research Council, and later served as part of the Scientific Research Arm of the Royal Canadian Navy in that area. By the time the R.C.N. took over complete responsibility for the de-gaussing and deperming ranges on the West Coast (in December 1944) a total of 732 ships had been "ranged" and 150 "depermed", including many Canadian war and merchant vessels constructed in West Coast shipyards during the period of operation, and nineteen small aircraft carriers built at U.S. West Coast ports in 1943-44.

Naval scientists were ingeniously active on both sides of the struggle. The early German magnetic mines, which had responded only to a Red or north polarity along the keel of a vessel, were supplemented, in April 1940, by "Blue" mines. These would detonate even under a so-called de-gaussed ship, if the earlier cruder method of over-compensation had been employed. It became increasingly necessary to measure all aspects of a ship's magnetism precisely, and to fit "tailor-made" girdles or coils, some longitudinal, some vertical, and to adjust the currents flowing through those coils with great exactness, so as to nullify both vertical and horizontal magnetism. When it is remembered that the magnetic characteristics of every vessel varied with its geographical location, and with its compass bearing from moment to moment, some idea of the complexity of the task can be surmised.

The job of de-gaussing, it was decided, could be simplified if the ship's *permanent* magnetism could first be nullified or at least reduced. This was the process known as *deperming,* or *wiping.*[3] Suitable coils were installed about the ship and then energized by passing through them an extremely heavy current (several thousand amperes), applied alternately in reverse directions, with a gradually reduced intensity. (The original magnetism tended to return and the operation might have to be repeated at intervals.)

The Electrical Engineering Laboratories of the National Research Council at Ottawa designed and purchased the equipment, and directed the installation of a deperming station for the West Coast. It consisted of H.M.C.S. *Gryme,* converted into a mobile deperming unit. They also assisted the Royal Canadian Navy in equipping a second deperming unit for the East Coast.

This may be the most convenient point at which to summarize the growing measure of correlation between the Navy and the Research Council as the war progressed. In 1941 the Acting President (Dr. C. J. Mackenzie) of the National Research Council discussed with the Deputy Minister of National Defence (Navy) a closer administrative liaison. This led to the appointment of the National Research Council as the "Scientific Research and Development Establishment" of the Royal Canadian Navy, with Dr. Mackenzie as Director, and Dr. D. C. Rose (head of the General Physics Section) as Liaison Officer for Naval Research, and later, Deputy Director of Scientific Research. As the war grew in intensity, groups of scientists were set up under this new dispensation to deal with specific naval problems. There were, for example, the Halifax Group under Drs. Johnstone and Henderson, the Vancouver Group under Dr. McLeod, the Acoustics Group, and a Naval Radar Group. A branch of the Halifax Group was lodged at Sydney, Nova Scotia, a group on magnetic equipment was set up within the General Physics Section of the N.R.C., while in the Electrical Engineering Laboratory at Ottawa a group was formed to grapple with electrical power problems. The personnel, resources, and financial means of the National Research Council were thus placed squarely behind the scientific work of the Royal Canadian Navy, and an intimate liaison with the Directorate of Scientific Research of the Admiralty and with parallel bodies

---

[3] Wiping removes the permanent *vertical* magnetism in the ship's structure; deperming the permanent *horizontal* field.

in the United States was provided. This arrangement lasted until the Royal Canadian Navy found it more expedient to create its own Research Division in 1943. By this time the staff of the National Research Council at Halifax had grown to about thirty physicists and engineers, most of whom were recent graduates of Canadian universities. They were of military age and subject to National Selective Service. The simplest method of retaining the invaluable services of these young scientists was to take them on to the naval staff and put them into uniform. This brought them under the direct administrative control of the Royal Canadian Navy, but the close and fruitful liaison with the National Research Council continued.

Counter-measures Against the Magnetic Mine

While early priority had been given to protecting ships against the magnetic mine by nullifying their magnetic field, attention soon had to be directed also to the destruction of the mines in infested waters. It was not overlooked that the Nazis might find it feasible to sow mines even as far away as Canadian and Newfoundland coastal waters by the use of long-range mine-laying submarines. Early steps were taken by the Royal Canadian Navy, with the scientific and technical aid of the National Research Council, to sweep Canadian harbour entrances and other logical or probable areas of enemy mine-laying.

The first apparatus supplied for this purpose consisted of actual magnets, 27 inches long, of which 200 were sent to Halifax by the Admiralty in the summer of 1940. The early "coil skid" type of magnetic sweeper consisted of a flat barge with a platform on which was mounted a large coil of electric cable, through which a suitable current could be passed. This provided a maximum magnetic "front" of about 56 feet. But both of these early expedients were rendered virtually obsolete by the development of the so-called LL, or "Longitudinal Sweep". This device employed the conducting characteristics of salt water, using the sea as part of the electrical circuit. Two well-de-gaussed ships, stationed abeam of each other, trailed long floating cables, which were insulated from the water, except at the ends where copper-wire electrodes provided contact with the sea-water. The ships were equipped with generators which sent short powerful pulses of current into the electrodes, and by synchronizing the pulses, current flowed between the cables, and a magnetic field was created sufficient to trip the magnetic needle and thus detonate any mine well aft of the area over which the sweepers were passing. This device had the advantage of creating a magnetic field which would excite and detonate a Red-sensitive mine if the current was flowing in one direction, and would also excite and explode a Blue-sensitive mine when the current was reversed.

When the menace of mines in Canadian waters was first actively faced, a building programme was already under way which called for the construction of special wooden mine-sweeping ships (which would be easier to protect against the magnetic mine than would steel construction). But the urgency of the problem made it imperative to improvise some sweeping equipment immediately. Small whaling vessels were requisitioned by the Navy, and the Electrical Engineering Laboratories of the N.R.C. were asked to install the necessary mine-sweeping equipment on these. Six such units were installed, the last two on specially built wooden ships.

The creation of this magnetic mine-sweeping gear confronted the Research Council scientists and engineers with some interesting problems. It was necessary to design and construct, for example, a switching system capable of handling thousands of amperes, and synchronized precisely to a fraction of a second, so that the pulses of the two ships worked in harmony. No equipment could be obtained from Britain, and the switching system and the power supply were developed from Canadian components. Another difficulty was the design and production of a satisfactory floating cable. The magnitude of the currents demanded heavy conductors, and these in turn necessitated sizable floating units. Moreover, the cable had to be completely water-tight, for the smallest leak would cause the copper of the cable to disappear by the electrolytic action of the sea-water.

Another delicate matter was the protection of the mine-sweepers themselves against the magnetic mine. The powerful current-circuits with which they were of necessity equipped created powerful additional magnetic fields around the ships,

all of which had to be suitably neutralized or offset. And as
the enemy mines became more and more sensitive, the precision
of such de-gaussing had to be correspondingly increased. Nor
was it enough merely to attempt to counter new enemy gadgets
as they were met. Thought had to be given to what the enemy
might very well be "cooking up" in that line. The Electrical
Engineering Laboratories explored the likelihood that as the
war progressed the enemy would devise magnetic mines which
would respond to some predetermined sequence or combination
of Red and Blue excitations. Had the Nazis done so, the
ordinary sweeps would have failed to detonate them, but they
might well have responded to the next approach of an inadequately de-gaussed cargo ship or war ship. These refinements,
as it proved, were never introduced by the Germans in Canadian waters (they were operating off the Normandy Coast on
D-Day), but the scientists were ready for them if they showed up.

Though for many months a systematic sweeping of East
Coast waters against enemy mines may have seemed a rather
remote and profitless precaution, it paid big dividends when
the Nazis sent special mine-laying submarines against the Halifax coastal area late in May 1943. On June 1 of that year,
three surface mines were sighted by H.M.C.S. *Dundas* and
Kamsack, 67 miles south-west of Sambro Light Vessel. That
night, the port of Halifax was closed, and mine-sweepers went
into organized action. Sweeps over the next forty-eight hours
disclosed that a ring of mines had been laid on a six- to seven-
mile radius around Sambro Light Vessel. A total of fifty mines
were swept, three others were recovered, and two more are
believed to have been self-sunk. There was one casualty on June
3, the S.S. *Halma,* a vessel of 2,000 tons, which thus paid the
price of being off course at the time.

In October 1943, moored magnetic mines were laid in the
approaches to St. John's, Newfoundland. Twenty-two of them
were destroyed by sweeping, but two ships were lost on the 19th.
These incidents underscore the value of the preventive measures
taken by the Canadian Navy and the contribution made by
Canadian scientists to the critical sea war.

Harbour Protection

If the magnetic field which surrounds a ship will trip a mine, it can also be made to trip a warning signal when it crosses the entrance to a harbour. It was not enough to clear enemy mines from approaches to Canadian ports. Protection had also to be provided against the undetected entrance of an enemy submarine or other craft into Canadian harbours, by day or night, in clear weather or heavy fog. As the war progressed, Canadian scientists were called in to assist in the design and operation of such harbour protection. There were several ways in which this could be done, using the new principles of radar among others. The use made of radar in this field has been dealt with earlier (see p. 50).

Harbour loops had been employed since World War I. They used a system of conductor cable laid on the bottom of the harbour, from one to two miles long and about four hundred yards apart. Whenever a surface vessel or a submarine crossed the loop, it created a slight change of voltage in the loop, which was recorded by a delicate instrument called a galvanometer integrator, thus alerting the harbour defences.

In June 1941, the Canadian Navy came to the General Physics Section of the National Research Laboratories with a harbour protection problem. The device mentioned above was no longer being manufactured, and could not be replaced. The General Physics Section at Ottawa then designed and built a galvanometer and electrical integrating unit for use at Camperdown, Nova Scotia. This served the immediate purpose, but its sensitivity was not equal to earlier gear in use, and so a fresh attack was made on the problem. Scale-model tests were made, and a new equipment (called the C-100 gear) was devised. This proved so satisfactory that the Navy asked the National Research Council to make twenty-six of them, of which twenty-three were placed in operation in Canada, two were sent abroad, and one remained in the Laboratory. In some respects C-100 was superior to the loop-recording mechanism earlier devised by Admiralty scientists. For example, earlier types had to be closed down when magnetic mine-sweepers passed over the loop, because the pulses emitted by them were too powerful for the delicate recording apparatus. The C-100 gear ingeniously eliminated this effect and enabled the loop detector to operate without a break.

Friendly ships were required to identify themselves when passing over a harbour loop by using a special device operating at fifty cycles, which made a signal that could be picked up and amplified by the naval station guarding the entrance. While the C-100 gear was being tested at Camperdown, it so happened that the identification gear was giving trouble because of sixty-cycle interference from nearby industrial activities. The National Research Council staff undertook to redesign the equipment, and soon eliminated this industrial interference.

About the time Canadian scientists were working on the Camperdown loop, an interesting report was received from the British Admiralty which suggested a possible new principle of detecting enemy craft, including submarines. The British had noted that when ships crossed harbour loops there was, in addition to the identifying signal sent out by the friendly vessel, a beating sound not unlike the noise of ships' engines or propellers. It was not, however, an acoustical effect, and the popular explanation was that if a ship's hull was coated with a metal different from that of the propeller (and this was almost invariably the case, since even different kinds of steel created the effect) the two metals acted as separate poles of a battery, with the sea-water acting as an electrolyte in between. Thus a tiny current always flowed between them. This could be detected, and as the voltage varied with the turning of the propeller, the effect varied in time with the beat of the propeller.

The General Physics Laboratory undertook to redesign the Identification gear (L.I.S.A.—Loop's Identification Signal Apparatus) to study and test this new effect. The first trials at Camperdown were not very promising, though a few freighters, tankers, and destroyers registered these *Variable Field Effect* signals. The redesigned gear was then tested on a temporary loop at Sleepy Cove, 1200 feet long and 200 feet wide, just outside the harbour gates, and practically all vessels (except, of course, sailing vessels and outboard-motor boats) could be heard on the apparatus. The results were sufficiently encouraging to induce the Canadian Navy to order seven L.I.S.A. gear, to be built at the laboratories of the National Research Council.

When, in January 1944, the Canadian Navy was contemplating laying a small warning loop in the harbour entrance at Prince Rupert, B.C., the General Physics Section undertook to find the most satisfactory location for it. A model of the harbour was made from sheet lead, while variations in the earth's magnetic field were simulated by placing the model harbour inside a large coil through which a suitable current could be passed. Based on these tests several sites were chosen, and having in mind the site offering a minimum of laying difficulties, the loop at Prince Rupert was set up: after some suppression of industrial interference, it operated satisfactorily. A high percentage of yachts, fish-packers, tugs, and Fairmiles registered audible signals on the new equipment, as well as all larger vessels.

Arising out of these successes, the Royal Canadian Navy asked the scientists of the N.R.C. to investigate the possibility of using the new *Variable Field Effect* principle in very deep water to detect miniature submarines, against which existing indicator loops would probably not give any warning.

The problem was tackled by suspending coils at appropriate depths so as to provide adequate sensitivity for all possible paths of such a submarine. A trial installation was laid by the R.C.N. at Whitecliffe Point, B.C. in a depth of a hundred fathoms. The results were not encouraging, as all but those coils very close to the bottom gave false signals owing to vibration. Further work was projected using parmalloy-core coils mounted on the bottom, but as the difficulties of laying this type of coil were known to be very great, the project was dropped when the end of the war was in sight.

The Acoustic Mine

The magnetic mine was far from being the last word in this theatre of war from the Nazi secret-weapon arsenal. In September 1940, Germany began to lay acoustic mines, that is, mines detonated by sound. In the late summer of 1941, she introduced an ingenious combination: the Acoustic-Magnetic

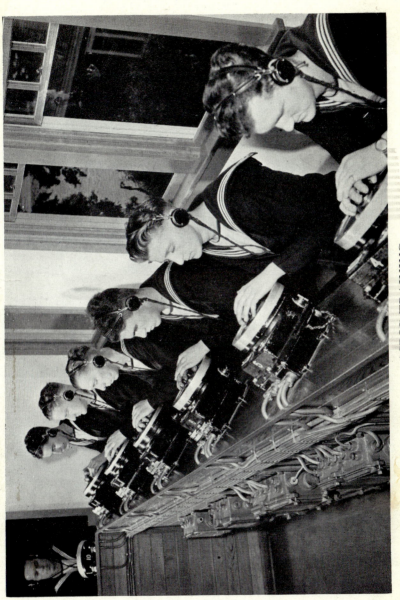

ASDIC TRAINING

Men being trained in Asdic at Esquimalt, British Columbia

ASDIC IN ACTION

Anti-submarine control officer and A/S operator at the Asdic set on the bridge of a Canadian corvette

(or "Sammy") Mine. In September 1943, Nazi submarines launched their first acoustic torpedoes, or Gnats. All of these weapons posed new problems for the Admiralty, the Royal Canadian Navy, and Allied scientists; all of them led to new activity in Canadian scientific laboratories.

The German acoustic mine was designed to fire when noise picked up by a microphone attachment in it reached a certain level of intensity, such as that made by a freighter or warship passing directly overhead. The microphone, in the early models, responded best to an audible sound of about 250 cycles per second (middle C on the piano is 256 cycles per second) but to a lesser extent they were sensitive to other notes. Some of them contained an anti-sweeping device, which caused the mine to be inactive for about thirty seconds if suddenly subjected to an especially loud noise, such as that produced by an acoustic mine-sweeper. The microphone in the mine was connected with a battery, and, as the battery ran down from continuous use, the sensitivity of the mine declined accordingly, but after falling to about one-half its original sensitivity, deterioration thereafter was slow, and the mine might retain some life almost indefinitely.

At the request of the Admiralty, Dr. G. S. Field, head of the Acoustics Laboratory, visited Britain early in 1941 to gather data on counter-measures being devised there to meet the acoustic mine. Allied knowledge of the sound-output of ships was limited, and an extensive programme of measurement had already begun in the United Kingdom and in the United States. When Dr. Field returned to Canada a programme of research was got under way here also, the field being divided to some extent between the three countries. To determine the output of a ship's noises at various speeds (and thus the likelihood that the ship would detonate the acoustic mine if it passed overhead) acoustic ranges were set up at Halifax in conjunction with the de-gaussing range. Others were established at Sydney, Esquimalt, and Vancouver using equipment provided by the Acoustics Laboratory at Ottawa. Hydrophones and microphones were planted on the harbour floor at suitable points, connected with amplifiers, loud speakers, and recorders on shore. Detailed noise records of many ships were thus obtained. The acoustic ranges served also for measuring the output of the noise-makers, which were developed to use on mine-sweepers so as to detonate the acoustic mines. They provided a constant check upon the noise output of the acoustic mine-sweepers, as these proceeded from day to day on their routine sweeps.

Since ships could not readily be protected by masking or silencing their noise output (the principle employed in protecting ships against the magnetic mine by de-gaussing), the counter-measures adopted to deal with the new German menace consisted essentially of some means of producing on a mine-sweeper a sound sufficiently powerful (and within the sensitive sound-range of the mine) to detonate it well ahead of the course on which the sweeper was navigating. A number of possible noise-making devices for sweeping were examined. A pipe noise-maker conceived in the United States and developed into a practical device by the Halifax Laboratory was thoroughly tested. It had great advantages, but some serious flaws as well. It consisted simply of two pipes or rods mounted close together and towed behind a vessel so that the fluctuating pressure between them caused them constantly to collide and then sharply rebound. Properly mounted and towed, their noise output was very large; they were cheap; they required no auxiliary power; and they merely had to be thrown overboard to begin operating. They were used extensively by the Royal Canadian Navy. But the Admiralty considered them as essentially a "stop-gap" pending the evolution of another apparatus. They failed to work at all at slow speeds, the volume varied directly with the speed, and they had to be towed astern, whereas the mine to be exploded lay ahead. Moreover, unless they carried a hydrophone or a similar device (and they usually did not), it was impossible to be sure whether the required volume of sound was, in fact, being produced. These pipe noise-makers, however, as finally designed and developed by the Halifax Group, became the chief acoustic sweeping device off the Atlantic coast, and were adopted as standard by both American and Canadian Navies.

The Admiralty preferred a "hammer-box" device, developed in England. This was a noise-maker consisting of a vibrating hammer contained in a water-tight steel box, one end of which provided a diaphragm which could be struck continuously by the hammer. A Canadian model was made and tested by the Acoustics Laboratory on the Ottawa River, the box being suspended from a raft. The design was such as to produce the maximum theoretical output of sound. The Electrical Engineering Section tested the box for conformity to electrical and mechanical specifications, and the final Canadian product compared favourably with those produced in Britain and the United States.

The fundamental investigation of the nature and characteristics of ships' noises went a long way in Canada, and subsequently served as a useful theoretical foundation for the counter-measures employed against the German acoustic torpedo. The inquiry was important, too, as a precautionary measure against other refinements. While the threat of the early Nazi acoustic mine was quickly countered, the possibility that a much more perplexing and deadly acoustic weapon, using sensitivity to ultra-sonic noises, might be well advanced in German laboratories had to be borne in mind. As such high-frequency noises could be "beamed", the new German mine might be triggered so that it would only respond to a high-frequency sound directly overhead. This would add materially to the problem of sweeping. At the other end of the sound spectrum, Nazi mines might well be built to respond only to sub-sonic or very low-frequency noises from ships. This would raise the new problem that the energy involved in the low-frequency region produced by ships would be so great that it would be difficult to simulate by any synthetic or decoy device which a mine-sweeper could carry or tow.

It was decided that the United States would concentrate its research on the sub-sonic and sonic end, and Canada on the high-frequency or ultra-sonic end of the noise spectrum.

Thorough investigation of the output of ship-noise in the higher frequencies was subsequently made over a period of several years by the Acoustics Laboratory at Ottawa and elsewhere. Specially made noise-makers and propellers were operated in the Ottawa River and at Vancouver, and their outputs over a wide range of high frequencies were measured. It was discovered that ships' noises of 250,000 cycles per second and higher could be measured, and that the energy output was considerable even at that level. A study was made of the absorption of high-frequency sound in sea-water, at frequencies ranging from 300,000 to 2,500,000 cycles per second. The programme being pushed by the Acoustics Laboratory in Canada was given new zest and incentive by telegrams from Britain stressing the urgency and importance of the research. For example, on March 11, 1942, the Acting President of the National Research Council received a message from London announcing, among other things, that "intelligence reports . . . say Germany working hard to produce mines for upper range."

It was reassuring to the Canadian scientists to discover that the noise-makers already being used had a very substantial output of energy even at the much higher frequencies now being investigated. They would thus serve, if necessary, to detonate even a directional high-frequency mine if they were passed directly overhead. Each time a noise-maker exploded a mine, that particular sweep-device would presumably be destroyed, but as they were cheap and easy to manufacture, this did not unduly concern the naval authorities.

The electrical circuits of the ultra-sonic measuring devices presented no great problem, but no hydrophone suitable for such high frequencies existed in any British or American laboratory, and so it was necessary for the Acoustics Section to pioneer in a new field. This took some time, but a satisfactory hydrophone was finally built and measurements were begun with it in the Ottawa River.

Warm praise and appreciation was expressed by the Director of Scientific Research, Admiralty, for this pioneer work in ultra-sonic theory and application. The knowledge acquired in Canadian laboratories, supplemented by some work in Britain, guaranteed that if the Germans did introduce an ultra-sonic mine, the knowledge of theory already acquired would enable suitable counter-measures to be quickly developed and put into operation.

The Acoustic-Magnetic Mine

Counter-measures against Nazi mines had to be constantly revised and improved to keep pace with the new German devices. Magnetic mines soon appeared which did not respond to the first excitation, but which required two or more impulses (the combination was adjustable and could be pre-set) before they would explode. Several sweepings of the same area were then required to make it safe. Then, in the late summer of 1941 the Combined Acoustic-Magnetic Mine appeared. This was designed so that the magnetic field of a ship first cocked the firing mechanism, and then the sound output of the ship detonated it. The gain lay in the fact that the magnetic cocking device could thus be set to a far greater sensitivity than if it were the actual firing device, since there was no longer any danger that a minor distortion of the magnetic field would cause it to destroy itself automatically and fruitlessly. With this super-sensitive cocking device, the relatively crudely de-gaussed ships of the earlier period were no longer safe. Even when de-gaussed they might still possess sufficient active or unneutralized magnetism to trip the delicate magnetic device of the new mine and then detonate the acoustic apparatus with the sound of their propellers. It became necessary for Canadian scientists working in conjunction with the Navy to devise sweepers equipped for simultaneous acoustic and magnetic sweeping. Moreover, the protection of the mine-sweepers themselves became a more precise and troublesome problem. It was no longer possible to detonate these combined acoustic-magnetic mines some distance ahead, but only astern, under the tails of the Longitudinal Sweeps described above.

The Admiralty developed a type of hammer-box that could be towed from the tail of a magnetic mine-sweeper. The Royal Canadian Navy sought the same effect by towing pipe noise-makers in the same way. Experiments showed that the means devised were a satisfactory answer to the new Nazi menace.

The Acoustic Torpedo

In April 1943, the Admiralty warned Naval Service headquarters at Ottawa that the Germans were using, or were about to use, a new secret weapon, the acoustic torpedo or "Gnat". It was actually brought into play in September 1943, and it claimed several victims before the end of the month. The sinking, on September 20, 1943, of the Canadian destroyer H.M.C.S. *St. Croix,* with a loss of 145 lives, brought the matter vividly home, and heightened the sense of urgency with which the new problem was tackled in this country.

The acoustic torpedo's most ingenious and disturbing novelty was its capacity to leave its original course and head for a source of noise lying anywhere within a fairly wide angle ahead. In the nose of the torpedo were two hydrophones with an automatic steering device which kept the torpedo aimed at the source of the noise. If this happened to be a ship, the torpedo was usually drawn toward the propeller, and the resulting explosion by contact would usually disable, and often sink, the vessel thus tracked down by the mechanical ears of the new weapon. Since a torpedo equipped with the acoustic head might be discharged merely in the general direction of a warship or other vessel, and still stand a very good chance of finding the propeller or hull of the intended victim, the factor of accuracy was automatically multiplied several times.

Fortunately, the secret weapon did not catch Allied scientists entirely by surprise. It had already been guessed that such a torpedo would be sensitive to sound frequencies high enough in the noise spectrum to possess directional characteristics, but low enough to be within the high-energy band. This suggested a sound range from 5,000 to 50,000 cycles per second. (The average ear can hear up to 14,000 c.p.s.) It had been further deduced that "decoys" capable of producing sounds in these ranges and at energy levels considerably higher than those made by a ship would be able to attract such torpedoes away from the target and detonate them harmlessly.

Laboratories of the National Research Council immediately attacked the problem from a number of angles. One proposal, examined by the Mechanical Engineering and Electrical Engineering Division, was a rocket-launched noise-maker. Two types of these were developed, one driven by a storage battery, the other by compressed air. Trials showed that the electrical noise-maker produced the greater noise. The Explosives Laboratory of the Chemistry Division experimented with detonators, and the Chemistry Division itself tested underwater gas explosions. The Acoustics Laboratory began work on several towed devices, one a rochelle salt-crystal unit driven by an electronic noise-generator. It worked on a number of other designs also.

At Halifax a quantity of pipe noise-makers were made and run over the Acoustic Ranges to determine their sound output in the high-frequency range to which the acoustic torpedo was most sensitive. In the end it was decided that the best answer was the towing of pipe noise-makers behind all vessels operating in areas where Nazi submarines were known to be active. The Admiralty's similar counter-device (highly successful) was called the Twin-Foxer.

It cannot be said that these counter-measures were popular with the officers of escort vessels. The Twin-Foxer gear slowed them down, hampered manoeuvres, and interfered seriously with the operation of Asdic. But the gear was improved, and new tactics were adopted. Up to June 1944, of the twenty-seven ships known to have been attacked by the acoustic torpedo, Admiralty reports show that with two possible exceptions there was no loss when either the recommended tactical procedure had been adopted, or the Twin-Foxers or similar noise-makers had been in use. Indeed, looking back, the Nazi secret weapon was seen to have had serious limitations. To reduce the sound output of the torpedo itself, its speed had to be cut down sharply, its homing radius was limited, and it was unable to distinguish between actual ships' noises and other natural and synthetic sounds. But for all that it would have been one more serious source of naval loss and attrition, at a time of critical margins and unparalleled anxiety on the high seas, had scientists of the various Allied countries not prepared, partly in advance, adequate counter-measures to deal with it.

Camouflage by Diffused Flood-lighting

An ingenious scheme for the diffused flood-lighting of Allied cargo vessels and warships at night so that when searched for from the deck of a submarine the brightness of their illumination would exactly match the skyline against which they would be seen, rendering them practically invisible, was proposed early in the war by Professor E. Godfrey Burr of McGill University. Normally, a ship is seen by a submarine Commander as a black object against a lighter background, and the idea was to raise the illumination of the hull and superstructure to exactly that of the patch of sky against which it would otherwise be seen.

Using photocells directed toward the illuminated ship and its background, and employing the current from them to operate rheostats controlling the flood-lighting, the control could be made automatic to match changes in the brightness of the night sky. The Royal Canadian Navy became interested in the idea, and illumination units were installed experimentally on the corvette H.M.C.S. *Cobalt*. The first experiment, held off Halifax on January 22, 1941, proved so successful that the Navy asked Professor Burr to follow it up. During the next three months, many experiments were conducted aboard the corvette H.M.C.S. *Chambly*.

The Optics Section and the Electrical Engineering Laboratories of the National Research Council began work on the problem early in 1941. By the middle of August a prototype illumination control had been built and installed on H.M.C.S. *Kamloops*. The automatic control proved feasible, but in early trials the operation of such a sensitive circuit under severe weather conditions raised some practical difficulties. These were overcome after further experimentation on trial runs. The apparatus was sent to England for further sea trials there. When the feasibility of automatic control had been fully demonstrated, the actual manufacture of the apparatus was arranged with the General Electrical Company at Schenectady, New York, from data supplied by Canadian scientists and engineers. Final sea trials were given the equipment late in 1944 and early in 1945 off the East Coast, at Bermuda, and in Britain. But for the fact that radar was rapidly replacing the optical detection of ships at sea, this ingenious project[4] would almost certainly

[4] In *McGill University at War* (pp. 340-41), published by McGill University, 1947, R. C. Fetherstonhaugh describes a number of startling demonstrations of the effectiveness of the Burr apparatus when it had been perfected. During one of the exercises on a dark night with intermittent rain, "an 'attacking' submarine sighted a control corvette accompanying *Edmundston* [a corvette equipped with the Burr installation] at 700 yards, despite the fact that the corvette was camouflaged with the latest design approved for use in the British 'Western Approaches'. Seeking *Edmundston*, the submarine crept closer, but failed completely in the search. Then, fearing an accident, the submarine stopped and sent out the order 'Lights Off', whereupon *Edmundston* leaped into view off the submarine's bow at a range of only 300 yards. When 'Lights On' was again ordered, *Edmundston* dramatically disappeared. Knowing her precise position, the submarine eventually saw her with night-glasses, but could be sure that what was seen was indeed the corvette only after long and careful scrutiny. From *Edmundston*, meanwhile, the wake of the submarine had been clearly visible."

have been heralded as one of the most useful Canadian contributions to sea warfare. And even so, the counter-measures which were later developed against radar tended to restore the device to something of its earlier significance before hostilities were over.

Miscellaneous Aids

Canadian scientific ingenuity made many minor contributions toward winning the Battle of the Atlantic, of which only passing mention is possible here. They ranged from a year's continuous effort to improve the plastic armour in use by the Navy (as a substitute for steel armour plate) to the development of a method of collecting samples of oil slicks from the surface of the sea. They included an automatic life-jacket inflator which would save from drowning those seamen thrown into the water in an unconscious condition, and a sea-rescue lamp which would give forth a strong signal for a long time. There was help in the manufacture of plywood naval dinghies relatively immune to machine-gun fire, gas-detector paints, mariners' sextants and naval telescopes, the testing of gear-cutting machines for the Tribal Class destroyers built in Canada, and the inspection by radium rays of castings and forgings used in the same naval vessels. Methods were devised for producing potable water from sea-water, and a chemical discovered and produced for maintaining the oxygen supply in a submerged submarine or for providing oxygen in gas-masks independent of the oxygen of the outside air. In these and other related fields, aid of one kind or another was almost continuously forthcoming.

Detection of Submerged Submarines by Sound Echoes

One of the most jealously guarded secrets of the British Admiralty at the outbreak of the war in 1939 was *Asdic,* a device which enabled destroyers and other anti-submarine vessels to locate submerged U-boats by bouncing back off their hulls a short burst of high-pitched sound and listening for the echo. (A lapse of one second between burst and echo would indicate a "sub" nearly half a mile away, since sound travels about 5000 feet per second in water.) Knowledge of the principle dated back at least as far as 1912, when, after the sinking of the *Titanic,* a British engineer named Richardson had suggested the detection of icebergs by echoes of sound waves emitted by an approaching ship. Important progress was made during the war of 1914-18 by the Allied Submarine Detection Investigation Committee[5] (which apparently provided the name of the secret device).

Though Asdic did not see action against enemy underwater craft in the First World War, by the spring of 1918 Admiralty scientists were obtaining echoes from a British submarine at a range of a few hundred yards; and so much additional work was done between 1919 and 1939 to overcome the really formidable practical difficulties of operating the device from a rapidly moving destroyer, and obtaining accurate range and direction data under variable temperatures and salinities of sea water, that by 1939 Britain's anti-submarine detection equipment (A/S) was a highly efficient piece of apparatus, in some respects in advance of that of any other nation. The British device beamed a short burst of sound-waves (at a frequency of about 20,000 cycles per second, just above the audible range for the average ear), produced by subjecting a disc of a special kind of quartz to an alternating current—the "piezo-electric" effect discovered by Jacques and Pierre Curie. The transmitter was mounted in a dome forward on the centre line of the bottom of the warship, in such a way that it could maintain acoustic "vision" the full 360 degrees around the ship. The transmitter was slowly rotated so as to *scan* the nearby waters at a steady speed, independent of any turning of the ship. Under ideal conditions, the range and bearing of a submerged U-boat could be obtained up to several thousand yards. The United States Navy had developed independently a super-sonic echo-ranging gear based, however, on a different principle (a magneto-restriction effect, using the capacity of certain metals to change dimensions under the influence of magnetism, producing high-pitched notes in the process) and lacking the recording device employed on the British equipment.

The Royal Canadian Navy was using Asdic from the outbreak of war in September 1939, but at first the Admiralty preferred

[5] The Committee included Lord Rutherford, Professor Paul Langevin of France, Professor W. H. (later Sir William) Bragg, and Dr. R. W. Boyle of Canada.

to supply the secret equipment all ready for Canadian installation rather than procure the Asdic equipment on this side of the Atlantic. However, after the fall of France, and with an invasion of Britain seemingly imminent, it was decided to undertake the manufacture of Asdic equipment in Canada. Under the initial guidance of specialists from the Admiralty, the Canadian Navy procured the various components by negotiation with Canadian manufacturers. One of the most secret parts of the device was made at Renfrew, Ontario, by a special section of the Department of Mines and Resources. The National Research Council was called upon, however, to supply technical assistance in the making of the most critical component, the quartz crystal, which converted the electrical energy into sound. The Optics Section worked out a method of processing the special quartz (of which Brazil was the only known source) in October 1940, and early in 1941 production was begun. By May, 107 satisfactory quartz discs had been produced, and further manufacture was then turned over to the Department of Mines and Resources. The Acoustics Laboratory built ten testing instruments for measuring the electrical-acoustical properties of the crystals; these proved to be rugged, fast, and simple enough to be operated by a comparatively untrained person.

Canadian scientists made two useful contributions to the efficiency of Asdic as a submarine detector. One of these was in connection with an improvement (called the Bearing Deviation Indicator) which supplied the attacking ship with much more precise information than earlier models as to the exact location of the submarine and the direction in which it was travelling. The other was the help given in developing the McGregor Recorder.

The McGregor Recorder was proposed by Sub-Lieutenant D. E. McGregor as a means of supplying to the ship's conning officer a much more complete picture of the ship's movements relative to the movements of the submarine, as disclosed by the Asdic. By presenting both of these movements graphically and synchronously on a single recorder, the offensive tactics of the corvettes or other anti-submarine vessels could, it was hoped, be made substantially more effective.

There was already in existence the Chemical Recorder (introduced in 1930), which automatically made a series of dots on a chart, corresponding to the range of the detected submarine from the attacking vessel. McGregor suggested that this range-recording mechanism might be further linked up with the training gear of the Asdic. This would result in each point on the plot indicating not only the range of the submarine from the attacking vessel but also its bearing. The succession of dots would then represent the track of the submarine relative to the surface vessel, and if the ship maintained a steady course, the plot would be geographic. To represent the submarine's course accurately, the paper had to be moved at a rate proportional to the speed of the ship. The ship's conning officer would thus be presented with a complete picture of the submarine's movements, and it would no longer be necessary to try to integrate the piecemeal information supplied by the earlier system.

In the spring of 1943 (with the aid of Sub-Lieutenant Mc-Gregor and another mechanical engineer, Sub-Lieutenant N. Campbell), the Acoustics Laboratory designed such an instrument and blueprints were sent to the Ford Motor Company, which undertook construction. First trials were at the Navy Training Base, H.M.C.S. *Cornwallis*. For trials in deeper water, the Recorder was installed on a corvette and sent to Bermuda. The United States Navy showed an interest in it, so that it was sent to their research station at Quonset, Rhode Island, where comparative trials on a number of similar aids were under way. The results were very favourable, and the Recorder was then taken to Fort Lauderdale, Florida, for further tests. The Royal Canadian Navy also sent it to the British establishment at Fairlie, on the Clyde Estuary, for demonstration. Like the B.D.I., it had the tough luck (from the inventor's viewpoint) to reach a promising stage only after the main bout against the Nazi submarine had been fought and won, and so it did not see active service during the war.

Studies of the Refraction of Sound-waves

Asdic was an efficient detection device under the right conditions, but it was as important to know its limitations as its capacity. Sound-waves, like light-waves, can be bent by passing them from a medium of one density into another. For example, a layer of cold water lying above a layer of warmer water—a condition not unusual on the ocean in the wintertime—causes the Asdic sound-beam to be refracted upward, so that it may never strike the hull of a submarine at all, or, if it does, the returning "echo" may be bent still further upward so that no signal will be heard on the attacking ship. Under these circumstances, as happened at least once off Halifax, the vessels on patrol might be operating on the blithe assumption that their Asdic devices were scanning the nearby waters for a distance up to three miles, when in reality the temperature "gradients" were so adverse that detection beyond a few hundred yards was quite impossible. German submarine commanders were fully aware of the queer behaviour of Asdic sound-beams under such sea-water conditions, and their defensive tactics included taking shelter under such "positive" layers which deflected the Asdic beam harmlessly upward. It became necessary for the Royal Canadian Navy to acquire much additional knowledge about the exact behaviour of Asdic beams in the waters off the East Coast, and in the summer of 1942 the Navy asked the National Research Council to conduct such a study. As a first step, the Acoustics Section sent a member of their staff to the Woods Hole Oceanographic Institution in the United States to examine results obtained by their new invention, the Bathythermograph. This was an instrument which quickly and automatically obtained a graph of the variation of water temperature with depth, and provided for a quick interpretation of this graph in terms of Asdic ranges. Six of these instruments were ordered by the Acoustics Section, and trial runs conducted in the Ottawa River.

The following year the Royal Canadian Navy appointed a Naval Officer to Bathythermograph duty under technical direction from the National Research Council. Numerous readings of temperature gradients were taken off the coast of eastern Canada, and the findings applied to detection patrols. Toward the end of that year the West Coast naval authorities became interested and called upon the Acoustics Laboratory for help in technical direction. Observations taken there soon established the fact that for certain of the coastal waters, where fresh and salt water were found in mixture, it was also necessary to study the salinity gradients as well as the temperature. New devices aimed at obtaining greater Asdic penetration in waters where the gradients were "positive" (i.e., where cold water was super-imposed over warmer water) were tested thoroughly on the West Coast. The development of a device for automatically registering salinity gradients occupied a good deal of the time and energy of the Acoustics Section at this stage. Help given by American naval and scientific sources in these projects was generous and proved invaluable.

Submarine Detection by Magnetic Means

The fact that a large body of iron or steel like a submarine slightly distorts the earth's magnetic field as it moves through the ocean (whether submerged or not) comes as no surprise to anyone who recalls that this principle underlay the detona-tion of the German magnetic mine. It occurred to scientists on the Allied side that it might be possible to detect the presence of submerged Nazi submarines by extremely delicate magneto-meters, instruments which detect and disclose very delicate changes in the magnetic field of the area where they are used.

Such a device, if feasible, would be a most valuable auxiliary for Asdics, both to detect submarines too near for the effective range of Asdic (which lost contact as the pursuing ship closed in), and under adverse conditions when the Asdic, for one reason or another, was not providing dependable or adequate data.

A formal request from the Royal Canadian Navy to the National Research Council to pursue this possibility was made in the latter part of 1941. In the United States, a similar inquiry was going forward, using, however, coils instead of magneto-meters. The work being done in the two countries was co-ordinated by sending a member of the General Physics Section at Ottawa to work with a United States group in the Naval Ordnance Laboratory at Washington. A division of work was agreed upon under which the Canadian research would examine the possibilities of using an electronic fluxmeter with large area coils of very few turns. Since the United States Navy was making tests on destroyers, it was decided to test the latest findings on a Canadian corvette. Trials were accordingly carried out on H.M.C.S. *Kamloops* at Pictou.

Research on both sides of the border ran into formidable obstacles. Success in detecting the very delicate magnetic manifestations of a nearby submarine was linked up with the ability to distinguish such tiny changes in the magnetic field from those which were constantly occurring around the corvette when it pitched, rolled, or altered its course bearing. It was found in the trials aboard the *Kamloops* that even in fairly rough weather (20 degree roll) the changes due to these movements of the attacking ship could not be well enough isolated to permit the balancing of the coils, and thus to detect any outside magnetic change such as might be expected from proximity to a nearby submarine. Further study of methods to achieve this necessary balancing of the coils was made on a training course on the *Kamloops*, but the results were disappointing. No unique balance of the four-coil system could be made, and it was noted that on some headings, false signals showed up every time the corvette changed course. These were evidently caused by added magnetic currents induced in the hull of the *Kamloops*—which, it should be remembered, was itself, like the submarine being hunted, a floating maze of varying magnetic fields—and while in theory these could eventually be corrected by a suitable apparatus, the task would be arduous and involved. The scientists were driven to conclude that this particular means of detecting enemy submarines did not offer very promising results for use on corvettes, and American scientists, meantime, had come to a similar conclusion based on destroyer tests there.

It should not be inferred that these studies bore no fruit. The increased knowledge of magnetism and magnetometers in Canada during the war aided the development of the airborne magnetometer, which is being employed to prospect vast reaches of the Pre-Cambrian Shield in Canada where the overburden is such as to thwart the geologist, and where surface indications may fail to reveal important bodies of ore a few feet out of sight.

In the United States, the Magnetic Airborne Detector was perfected in time to play a useful role in the inexorable battle against the U-boat. Late in 1941, trials in a PBY-1 plane, using an automatically stabilized magnetometer, were so successful in detecting submerged submarines that production was pushed, first at Quonset Point Naval Air Station, and later at Mineola, Long Island. Submerged submarines were repeatedly detected from altitudes of more than 300 feet. Such a detector located the submerged submarine *S-20* four times in nine tries in deep water south of New London. Installed in "blimps", it was effectively used against Nazi U-boats along the American coast, and in 1943 it was a large factor in "corking" the Straits of Gibraltar against Nazi submarines during the critical landings in North Africa.

Studies of the Ionosphere

In connection with the warfare at sea, the Radio Branch of the National Research Council carried out, at the request of the Royal Canadian Navy, a thorough study of the conditions affecting the transmission of radio waves. This in turn required an exhaustive inquiry into the ionosphere—that group of layers of ionized gases far above the earth which act as a reflector of radio waves and permit communication around the curved surface of the earth as the waves bounce or reflect back and forth between the earth's surface and the several ionized "ceilings" or layers. The more our scientists knew about the ionosphere, the more efficient would be our own communications, while at the same time greater advantage could be taken of enemy transmissions.

So important did the British and American authorities regard this study that a network of ionosphere observing stations was set up early in the war in the British Empire and the U.S.A., controlled by laboratories at London and Washington. In October 1941 the Royal Canadian Navy asked the National Research Council to construct immediately an apparatus to measure vertical ionosphere heights. This was completed and the equipment installed in the Naval Station at Chelsea, Quebec, at the end of December 1941. In March 1943 the programme was extended. Three more units were made. The first was completed and tested in June 1943 and shipped to Churchill, Manitoba. The second was completed in July and sent to Clyde River, Baffin Island, N.W.T., where it was installed

RESEARCH SUCCEEDS

De-gaussing cables (here shown installed around the forepeak of H.M.C.S. *St. Stephen*, a River Class frigate) which defeated the magnetic mine

RESEARCH FAILS

(*below*) constructing an experimental model of Habakkuk; (*above*) a roofed-in experimental Habakkuk. The plan was to develop a refrigerated flat-top of ice to be used as a mid-ocean "island" landing-field for aircraft

and operated for one year by personnel from the Carnegie Institute. Operation was later taken over by the Department of Transport. The third was completed in August 1943 and shipped to Prince Rupert.

In January 1945 the National Research Council was asked to design an automatic ionosphere recorder for Canadian stations, and this was completed in time to be set up as a mobile unit at Victoria Beach, Manitoba, for observations connected with the solar eclipse of July 9, 1945. About 3000 records were made by a National Research Council group of five observers during the month. This provided material for a later analysis of the effect of the sun's radiation on the ionization of the upper layers of the atmosphere.[6]

Training Devices for Naval Warfare

The ingenuity of Allied scientists in placing in the hands of the Navy new devices for detection and new instruments of attack would have been largely wasted unless skilled and highly trained personnel had been promptly forthcoming to man these devices. In the early stages of the war, the quality of the existing gear tended to forge ahead of the training of those who were to operate it. It became necessary to devise new teaching apparatuses so that adequate staff could be trained to read and interpret Asdic echoes and radar cathode ray displays, for example, and so to use effectively the new weapons available for attack. Actual battle experience was best of all, but it was highly desirable that preliminary training should take place under conditions resembling as closely as possible those of real combat. In connection with at least two of the training devices used by the Royal Canadian Navy, the scientists and engineers of the National Research Council played a useful if not invaluable part.

[6] It is probably unnecessary to add that the height of the several layers can be measured with great precision by directing a radar pulse vertically and timing the "echo"—the fundamental principle of most acoustic and electro-magnetic detection devices—and that radar waves of different frequencies behave differently, some reflecting back from the lowest layer, others reflecting from higher layers, while a point is reached in very high-frequency radar waves when even the loftiest ionized layer is pierced by the "pulse" of energy, and consequently no reflection or echo is obtained.

There was, for example, the *Radar Trainer*. This consisted of a ship's bridge, a radar, and silhouettes of ships projected on the wall of a circular room in which the apparatus was set up. In a second room a grid system showed the position of each ship. The speed and course of the vessels being detected were under the control of an instructor.

The *Torpedo Attack Teacher* was another useful project. Indeed, the Canadian version of this training device was actually one of the most ingenious machines developed during the war. It was very largely the achievement of the Metrology Section of the National Research Council.

Late in 1941, Dr. G. H. Henderson of Halifax placed before the National Research Council the nature of the Navy's problem; and work was begun early in the following year. The purpose of the "Teacher" was to simulate as closely as possible the conditions of an actual torpedo attack as directed from the bridge of a Canadian escort vessel. An officer stationed on a *facsimile* ship's bridge would be presented with the image of a ship at a distance, and his problem was to get within firing range of it, and then discharge torpedoes in such a way as to strike it if possible. Meantime, in an adjacent classroom, the manoeuvres of the attacking ship and the intended victim were to be visible on a screen which represented, in scale, an area of ocean some 40,000 yards square.

To be effective, the problems of an actual attack, involving range, bearing, and both relative and real speeds of the two vessels and of the discharged torpedo, had to be reproduced in miniature with great accuracy. Anyone who thinks that aiming a torpedo from a moving ship at another moving ship thousands of yards away is as simple as shooting at a tin can on a post with a .22 rifle should consider some of the factors involved: the speed and course of the corvette or destroyer at the moment the torpedo is discharged; the speed and course of the torpedo; the probable evasive action of the attacked ship; the precise estimation of range; the curvature of the earth, and so on. Something of the mathematics and the engineering required to evolve a satisfactory trainer of this type can be perceived even by the non-technical reader.

The attacker's bridge included a steering wheel and a speed indicator close at hand, and a compass repeater allowed orders for speed and helm to be given, just as on an actual ship at sea. If the mechanism for computing and transmitting the presumed resultant motions of attacker and attacked were properly designed, the two men on bridges in adjacent compartments would be able to fight one another exactly as in a real sea battle.[7] The ship's bridges of the "Teacher" were wooden structures about five feet square, roomy enough to hold two men, and equipped with repeater compass, torpedo sight, firing pistol, telephone, etc., while the wheelhouse units and helmsman were accommodated on the floor alongside the bridges. Regular instruction-type model ships were used for targets. A curved foreground made of plaster was painted to represent the sea and a curved background simulated the sky. With proper lighting the appearance of ships in the distance was highly realistic.[8]

In the classroom itself, separated from the training portion of the Attack Teacher, a horizontal glass table top, five feet square, rested on a welded frame and was illuminated by three projectors suspended above by a travelling crane type of gantry. The centre projector gave the position and course of the attacking ship, and the carriage moved under the control of the mechanism, reflecting the ship's course. When the firing button was pressed on the attacker's bridge, projector spots representing the course of the torpedoes moved from the ship's side. Beneath the glass screen there was a second projector, focussing a spot which represented the course of the target ship. The results of the simulated attack and defence could thus be readily followed in the instruction room.

Habakkuk—Fabulous Floating Islands of Ice

The story of Canada's wartime research was not denied its moments of drama, even of melodrama. Few of those who

[7] In this respect, the Canadian Attack Teacher broke new ground, as earlier models elsewhere had provided control of the target vessel by an operator viewing the relative position of the two ships on the screen, rather than by a man who was, to all intents and purposes, stationed on the target ship itself.

[8] A well-known Canadian artist, who was also a member of the Gauge Laboratory, the late Wilfrid J. Flood, painted the sea and sky scenery.

were connected in any way with the fantastic project then known under the code name of *Habakkuk*[9] are likely ever to forget it. When the President of the National Research Council, Dr. C. J. Mackenzie, was reminiscing before the Royal Canadian Institute in January 1946, he said:

"One can vividly recall moments of intense excitement and enthusiasm over a strikingly novel proposal, and the memory remains long after the promising infant has passed away. One such project, conceived in the boldest manner and on a grand scale in every way, occupied my personal attention most of my waking hours for four feverish months. Feverish is perhaps not the proper word, as the conditions of our experiment called for weather temperatures of 40 degrees below zero, and experimenting on a large scale with ice as a structural material. There was drama in that story as we built engineering research stations in the middle of winter, high up in the Rockies near Lake Louise and Jasper, and on a mountain glacier. We made northern trips, flew the Atlantic, had private audiences with high officials who were personally sponsoring the project which, if feasible, would have been a most spectacular and effective contribution."

The project appears to have had its birth in the fertile mind of an eccentric and original Englishman named Geoffrey Pyke, whose life story reads like an extravagant romance. By a commentator on the BBC, shortly after his death, Pyke was ranked with Einstein and Sir Frank Whittle (of jet-propulsion fame) as one of the outstanding innovators of our time. Pyke went to Lord Mountbatten with a plan to build scores of aircraft carriers cheaply out of floating ice. This was in 1942, when the desperate need of the moment was some way to beat the U-boat. Aircraft equipped with radar seemed to offer an answer, but the limited reach of land-based planes left hundreds of miles in mid-Atlantic unpatrolled, and therefore fat hunting-ground for the U-boat packs. Pyke thoroughly convinced Lord Mountbatten of the value of the plan. A journalist has circumstantially told how they first met—how there came to the Chief of Combined Operations "an inventor

[9] From Habakkuk i.5: "For I will work a work in your days, which ye will not believe, though it be told you."

in glasses and a goatee beard who gave his name as Geoffrey Pyke" and who "produced a hundred-page report on a scheme named Habakkuk." That, says the journalist, was the first morning since the formation of Combined Operations that Mountbatten did not go to work. Instead, he sat up in bed until noon reading Pyke's report.

Mountbatten in turn appears to have convinced Churchill that the plan of constructing vast floating platforms of ice was worth an earnest try, and in characteristic language the British Prime Minister dictated a memo to the Chiefs of Staff Committee for urgent action:

"I do not, of course, know anything about the physical properties of a lozenge of ice 5,000 feet by 2,000 feet by 100 feet," he observed, "or how it resists particular stresses, or what would happen to an iceberg of this size in rough Atlantic weather, or how soon it would melt in different waters at different periods of the year. The advantages of a floating island or islands, even if only used as refuelling depots for aircraft, are so dazzling that they do not at the moment need to be discussed. There would be no difficulty in finding a place to put such a 'stepping stone' in any of the plans of war now under consideration."

With his dynamic imagination, Churchill could already see in some detail a possible way of attacking the construction of such floating islands of ice, and he added a possible plan of attack which he had thought out:

"Go to an ice-field in the far north which is six or seven feet thick but capable of being approached by ice breakers; cut out the pattern of the ice-ship on the surface; bring the right number of pumping appliances to the different sides of the ice-deck; spray salt water on continually so as to increase the thickness and smooth the surface. As this process goes on the berg will sink lower in the water. There is no reason why, at the intermediate stages, a trellis-work of steel cable should not be laid to increase the rate of sinking and giving stability. The increasing weight and depth of the berg will help to detach the structure from the surrounding ice-deck. It would seem that at least 100 feet in depth should be secured. The necessary passages for oil fuel storage and motive power can be left at the proper stages. At the same time, somewhere on land the outfits of huts, workshops, and so forth will be made. When the berg begins to move southward so that it is clear of the icefloes, vessels can come alongside and put all the equipment, including ample flak, on board."

Engineers with some knowledge of the mechanical characteristics of ice may have been inclined to smile at the naive ingenuity of such a project. But it was conceived in the same spirit of audacious unorthodoxy as brushed aside all protestations of impracticability, and created in short order the floating harbour "Mulberry", which was taken across the English Channel in June 1944 to secure the beaches of the Normandy bridge-head against all the desperate and concentrated fury of the Nazi war machine.

In his original memorandum, Winston Churchill had pointed out that the scheme would succeed only if Nature could be made to do nearly all the work. Sea-water and arctic temperatures were to be the prime ingredients. Northern Canada, notorious for its sub-zero temperatures and washed on the north and east by frigid oceans, immediately occurred to the Chiefs of Staff as the logical place in which to fashion these floating platforms of ice. The actual task of making these synthetic aircraft carriers, or at least of pushing an inquiry vigorously and imaginatively right up to the point where its practicability could be determined, accordingly fell to the National Research Council at Ottawa. The order stemmed from the highest authority, its temper was mandatory, and as a result a tremendous flurry of activity got under way in Canada in the autumn of 1942. It extended, indeed, from Newfoundland to Jasper Park in the Rockies, and soon mobilized refrigeration experts, the Civil Engineering faculties of several western Universities, a camp of conscientious objectors, the director of the Applied Biology Division at Ottawa, an engineering firm at Montreal, and pulp and paper engineers and executives right across the country.

The "most secret" nature of the project added considerably to the magnitude of the task, because all but a privileged few at the top found themselves conscripted into an urgent enterprise without being given any idea of what all the excitement was about.

As the proposal began to take form, it resolved itself into a plan to build a floating airfield with dimensions of something like 2000 feet by 300 feet wide (as compared with the largest aircraft carrier deck then in existence of nearly 1000 feet by 113 feet). It would need a freeboard of 50 feet so that its surface would not be swept by at least any normal waves. This in turn meant a minimum depth of 200 feet, and a bulk of at least two million tons.

All sorts of problems immediately presented themselves. Was ice a suitable structural material for such a floating island? Ice being a plastic, not a true solid, how would it flow under stress? Could a stronger product be made using a composition of ice and shavings, or of ice and wood-pulp or straw or some other ingredient? (This was another of Pyke's novel contributions.) What were the structural characteristics or properties of such compositions? What were the coefficients of expansion of such materials, as compared with steel or concrete? What kind of a bond could be obtained between ice and steel or ice and concrete? Could such a floating island be insulated on the outside so that even in the relatively warm waters of the Atlantic it could be prevented from melting by a refrigerating apparatus of reasonable size and modest fuel consumption?

Some theoretical studies were desirable, indeed, almost indispensable. But a vast and speedy programme of a practical or empirical nature had to be undertaken at once. The task was "farmed out" across the Dominion. For example, the University of Manitoba investigated the bond between pure ice or various ice-woodpulp compositions on the one hand, and steel and concrete on the other. The University of Saskatchewan directed much of the experimental work carried on in the winter of 1942-43 at Patricia Lake near Jasper, and at Lake Louise. The University of Alberta tested the strength of beams of pure ice and beams reinforced by wood and straw, carrying on their work both at the Civil Engineering Laboratories at Edmonton and on remote Alberta lakes. The refrigeration problems were examined at Ottawa. Among the sites considered for the actual construction were bays along the northern shores of Newfoundland, where convenient access could be had to the wood products needed and whence the completed carrier could be readily towed to the expected theatre of naval action.

In the end, defeated by the economic, not the scientific obstacles, Habakkuk had to be abandoned before any of the fabulous floating-ice airfields saw service—before, indeed, a single full-scale prototype was ever constructed. But not before many interesting discoveries had been made. New data were acquired concerning the nature and behaviour of ice. Much novel information was gathered about mixtures of ice with other substances—for example, *Pykerete* (named after the inventor), a mixture of from 4 per cent. to 14 per cent. woodpulp and ice, a tough, somewhat plastic solid which could be worked like wood, and which was so impervious that revolver bullets bounced off its surface. Nails could be driven into it. Weight for weight it was as strong as concrete, and it melted slowly even in warm water.

Early in the inquiry it had been realized that the floating airfield would have to be hollow in structure and be divided by bulkheads surrounded by an "insulating skin", which could be kept permanently cold by artificial means. It would have to be capable of resisting waves a thousand feet long and fifty feet high. There would have to be spaces inside for machinery and stores. It could be driven by Diesel engines mounted in the floating ice-island or pulled by tugs; but in the former event, the problem of disposing of the water warmed by the Diesels had to be solved. A more serious aspect was its obvious vulnerability to torpedoing. Even if such an explosion created no more than a three-foot crater in its side below water-level, that would be enough to pierce the insulating skin and almost certainly doom it to ultimate sinking, since the breach once made could not be restored.

As the programme advanced far enough to permit reasonably accurate estimates of the cost ($70 millions per platform was one of the early guesses) it began to be realized that to construct a serviceable ice-island would be as big and slow and costly an undertaking as to build an orthodox aircraft carrier of steel. Once this conclusion came to be fully accepted, the original idea that it offered a cheap and speedy possibility of supplementing or anticipating the large aircraft-carrier building programme then in full blast had to be reluctantly abandoned. The problem of providing "stepping stones" for land aircraft was solved, or the need obviated in other ways, and Habakkuk became a fantastic but fascinating memory.

CHAPTER VIII

AIR

CANADA'S scientific contribution to the early air battles of World War II was governed by political and military factors connected with Canada's international relations. Canada had no aggressive intentions towards any of her neighbours: no potential enemy could be effectively reached at that time by air from Canadian air bases; our geographical isolation still appeared to protect us against anything more than the most sporadic and suicidal aerial raids. There was no justification in the 1930's for building up a large bomber force, even if the Canadian people could have been persuaded to vote the necessary large sums. A few interceptor squadrons for warding off possible raiders seemed a wise provision, but not much more was indicated in the defensive sphere. The far more vulnerable British position was generally recognized, as was Canada's dependence upon the survival of Britain in the event of war. Canada went into World War II with no more than the nucleus of a military aircraft industry, and that was engaged in 1939 solely in the manufacture of training craft. The fortunes of the global conflict after September 1939 rapidly modified Canadian Air Force policies in a variety of important ways, with manifold results, some of which, in the scientific field, are looked at in the following pages.

This of course is not the place to repeat the story of what the official R.C.A.F. history calls "that series of miracles now known as the British Commonwealth Air Training Plan."[1] However, it is interesting to note that one of the minor contributions of the National Research Council to that plan was to help "keep 'em flying". Nor is it inappropriate here to refer to the giant strides in industrial production from the token

[1] *The R.C.A.F. Overseas: The First Four Years* (Oxford University Press, Toronto, 1944), p. 5.

order of training craft of 1939 to the stage reached by 1945, when, according to *The Industrial Front*,[2] we had "sold Britain and the United States on the idea that Canada could mass-produce virtually any type of aircraft in the air."

A factor which tended somewhat to compensate for Canada's aerial unpreparedness in 1939 was the extent to which Canadians had become "air-minded" in the years since the first heavier-than-air flight in the British Empire had taken place at Baddeck, Cape Breton, in 1909. There were many Canadians in the R.F.C. and R.A.F. in World War I. The commercial exploitation of Canada's vast northern resources between the two wars had subsequently stimulated the extensive use of aircraft for exploration and transportation. Canadian experience in aerial photography and in overcoming cold-weather hazards provided a useful background for several of the developments of World War II. And before hostilities ceased, Canadians had made valuable additions to many aspects of the Battle of the Skies.

Assistance to the B.C.A.T.P.

The British Commonwealth Air Training Plan, under which more than 130,000 air crew were trained and graduated before V-E Day, meanwhile converting Canada into what President Roosevelt called—in his address at Ottawa in 1942—"the aerodrome of democracy", was one of the vital ingredients in the success of the United Nations. The National Research Council shared in this Canadian triumph by a variety of minor scientific and engineering services which helped to keep training craft in the air through the critical months.

One of the most practical of these aids was an inexpensive answer to the numerous and costly accidents known as "ground looping", suffered by Harvard trainer craft and other types when landed by student pilots. When an aircraft turns upon landing, the force on the front wheels tends to make it turn at a greater angle, and if this tendency is not immediately counteracted by the pilot, the turn will increase until the aircraft is out of control, so that it finally rolls over on a wing and up on its nose. Some types of aircraft are more prone

[2] Prepared by the Department of Munitions and Supply (The King's Printer, Ottawa, 1943), p. 29.

to ground-looping than others and the accident is more likely on dry runways when wheel friction is high. The swing is usually initiated by a poor landing, but mechanical defects may be responsible. These accidents were usually not dangerous to the pilot, but they caused major damage to the aircraft (average damage to Harvard advanced trainers: $5,000 per accident), and interfered with training.

The Aerodynamics Section of the National Research Council made a theoretical study and then constructed and installed a number of modifications on service aircraft for tests. A statistical study was made of the number of accidents per 1,000 hours flying time, with and without the modifications. The final answer was a small change in the tail-wheel steering-cable system, which was installed on all Harvards. It was calculated that following such an installation, in one month of April (the worst month of the year in previous experience) the sum of $500,000 was saved through this simple device.

Another illustration concerns aircraft engines. When main engine bearings and cylinder linings could not be procured for the Rolls Royce Merlin II, the components of Packard Merlins were adapted and substituted, and a large number of otherwise useless engines released again for flight. No less than 2,000 aircraft engines were similarly returned to use for training purposes when National Research Council engineers succeeded in adapting steel cylinders, centrifugally cast, obtained from the Ford Motor Company, to replace Cheetah engines which could no longer be obtained from Britain.

A series of accidents of unexplained origin to one of the twin-engine aircraft used in the British Commonwealth Air Training Plan was submitted to the National Research Council for investigation. Tests showed that structural failures due to "tail flutter" were probably responsible. A parallel inquiry in the United States confirmed this view. Suitable recommendations were forwarded to the Department of National Defence. Tests of the wings of Tiger Moth aircraft and of Harvard trainer planes which had been taken out of active use because deterioration was feared, showed that there was still a satisfactory margin of strength, and they were kept in active service for an additional period.

To anticipate and prevent any slowing down of air training in Canada due to a threatened shortage of aluminum, the Mechanical Engineering Division designed plywood versions of Anson wings and the Fleet "Fort" aircraft, and later built a moulded-plywood version of the rear fuselage and tail surfaces of the Harvard advanced trainer. Because of an outstanding production job in aluminum, it never became necessary to introduce the plywood programme into the training plan, but a great deal of the necessary work on design and testing had meantime been completed and would have been available if required.

Throttle-sticking, which had already resulted in the loss of about twenty Harvards, was investigated, and corrective measures recommended. A failure of aircraft magnetos at low temperatures was diagnosed and a simple remedy prescribed. The Instrument Section repaired, tested, and calibrated many thousands of aircraft instruments.

A number of investigations, several highly productive, were concerned with relieving the chronic shortage of aviation gasoline. For example, thermally cracked gasoline, considered unsuitable in other countries, was successfully substituted in Canada to keep aircraft flying throughout the most acute period of shortage: provided the fuel was not kept too long in storage and the correct octane rating was used, it proved quite satisfactory. Water injection was tested: it permitted 80 octane gasoline to be used in place of 87 octane. Tetraethyl lead content was increased, and the effect on maintenance examined; substitute fuels such as producer gas were studied. A large saving was made when used aircraft lubricating oil was re-refined: the product was found to be completely satisfactory for use in motor transport engines.

Hydraulic fluids suitable for use over a very wide range of temperatures from tropical to sub-zero were developed and standardized. These are the fluids used in aircraft in a similar way as in the hydraulic brakes on automobiles: they transmit power to operate retractable undercarriages, wing flaps, and gun turrets. Castor oil types of fluids were developed for use with natural rubber, and mineral oil types for synthetic. The task of finding a suitable fluid has been made more difficult in recent years because aircraft now frequently fly from Arctic to tropical conditions in a single flight and it is not practicable to change fluids en route.

The shortage of silks and linens for parachutes led early in the war to the formation of a committee under the auspices of the National Research Council. As a result, the first official adoption anywhere of nylon and cotton for this purpose took place in Canada. Nylon proved to be both lighter and stronger than silk for this use.

Early in the war, before Germany had overrun adjacent agricultural territories like Denmark, Holland, Belgium, and France, the Chemistry Division explored the possibility of crop destruction in Germany by dusting grain and potato crops with some such substance as a-naphthyl acetic acid, or sodium dinitrocresol. With the cooperation of the Division of Applied Biology a series of greenhouse experiments was begun, and the method seemed likely to be effective, using quantities of fifteen or twenty pounds to the acre. The findings were passed along to the British authorities, but the changing character of the war made the proposal no longer realistic.

A proposal submitted to the Inventions Board for the production of small incendiary bombs which would ignite by gentle percussion or shock when sensitized was explored by the Chemistry Division. Pellets consisting of small rods, spheres, and cubes made of nitrocellulose plastic, and coated with a red phosphorus emulsion in acetone were developed, being sensitized by an immersion method in a mixture of sodium chlorate, acetone, and water. In the final method adopted, the pellets were safe to handle while wet, but became sensitive within one minute when falling through the air. When dry they would ignite even when tossed on a bed of soil from a height of five feet. Many millions of them could be carried by a single aircraft, and they could be produced very cheaply.

Aerial Photography in Wartime

Plans and photographs of enemy fortifications and other military works and dispositions may be invaluable in time of war, but security measures make it extremely unhealthy for alien intelligence agents armed with cameras or sketching pads to attempt to obtain data of that nature on the spot. The invention of aircraft greatly extended the scope of photographic wartime reconnaissance. In World War I, relatively slow, heavy kites had sneaked in and out of hostile territory making aerial maps of enemy-held territory from heights of 10,000 feet or less. Tactical circumstances in World War II were less comfortable. Slow unarmed reconnaissance aircraft operating at such altitudes could now be intercepted by high-performance fighter aircraft and shot down on arrival like sitting ducks. It became necessary to strip the armament out of speedy top-line fighters like the Spitfire, to rely upon quick forays deep into enemy territory, and even then to fly these sorties at altitudes of 20,000 feet and higher.

This tactical change imposed heavy new demands upon the art and science of aerial photography. Reconnaissance, of course, seeks the maximum of information, and existing photographic equipment had not evolved in keeping with the new tactical circumstances. These tended to bring the aerial photographer increasingly nearer the limits of photographic definition and resolution, and a radical re-appraisal of the problem was necessary. The principal difficulty in 1939 was that no systematic scientific investigation had previously been made to determine the factors affecting maximum resolution. Some of these factors were lens-film resolving, vibration of aircraft, processing, filters, veiling of glare, camera designs, exposure, and printmaking. The existence of an additional two or three miles of atmosphere interposed between target and camera also raised new problems, of which the most serious was the reflection of light, from suspended particles of dust and vapour, back into the lens, which in turn reduced the contrast of the image fixed on the photographic emulsion, and thus impaired the quality of detail disclosed. However, the reduction in scale and the effect of camera motion were still the major problems.

This situation called for a thorough re-examination of the whole problem of extending the limits of the detail which could be resolved in aerial photographs. Promising approaches were through the use of better lenses, finer emulsions, new techniques in focussing, and research methods based on new ways of averaging the resolving power over the whole area of the photographs.[3]

In this branch of war research, and in the problems of night photography, the Optics Branch of the National Research Council made valuable contributions, partly on its own, and partly in close cooperation with British research, the R.C.A.F. in Canada, and the Office of Scientific Research and Development in the U.S.A. These investigations began on an important scale about the summer of 1942. The major achievement of the Optics Branch during the earlier months of the war had been in the aid given in creating a new optics industry in Canada for the production of optical glass, and the manufacture in vast numbers of such military instruments and equipment as predictors, range-finders and other optical fire-control devices, tank periscopes, sighting telescopes, and binoculars. Of this story, to preserve the chronological order, some account will first be given in the following paragraphs.

In August 1939 the President of the National Research Council, knowing that war was now inescapable, asked the head of the Optics Section, Dr. L. E. Howlett, for a memorandum outlining what steps would be needed to establish an optical industry in Canada. This was supplied to him on September 11. As a first move, Dr. Howlett recommended an on-the-spot examination of such information as could be acquired in the United States, especially at the National Bureau of Standards at Washington, which had been intimately associated with the development of the American optical industry in World War I. Action was approved at once, Dr. Howlett leaving for the United States on September 13. The National Bureau of Standards duly promised to provide complete blueprints of their own optical glass-making plant and any other available written data required. Private corporations such as Bausch & Lomb Optical Company Limited and the American Optical Company were also most cooperative. In a report dated October 1939, Dr. Howlett set forward a summary of the information

[3] The tendency in aerial photographs is for the attainable resolving power in the centre of the target to exceed by far what is possible toward the margin of the field of vision, whereas it may happen that the information most urgently sought concerns some object on the edge of the field. The compromise of a focal position to give all equal areas equal weight was proposed.

obtained. The President of the Council at once addressed Wallace R. Campbell, Chairman of the War Supply Board, outlining the situation and urging the early provision of a Canadian source for optical glass and instruments.

Pending the establishment of a private or crown company in Canada for this purpose, the National Research Council decided to provide at once in its own laboratories facilities similar to those at Washington, for the working of precise optical parts. On November 16, 1939, at the request of Dean C. J. Mackenzie, who had recently assumed the post of Acting President of the Council, the steps required to create such a shop were put down on paper; on November 20 the necessary funds were approved, and during the month of December considerable progress was made in establishing the shop in the National Research Laboratories at Ottawa. In January 1940 the Optics Section began to acquire technical help. By this time most of the types of machinery needed for optical grinding, polishing, and centring had been built, and orders placed for all basic testing equipment. By the end of April a sample of each one of the optical parts likely to be encountered in military optical instruments had been made. Meantime a group of scientific workers had been formed to study the design of optical systems, a pioneer field in Canada up to that time.

These, it will be recalled, were the months of what Chamberlain called the "twilight war", and little progress had been made by the government in providing a source in Canada for optical glass or instruments, though the National Research Council had persisted in reminding them about its necessity. However, by April 1940, Lieutenant-Colonel W. A. Harrison, a member of the Executive Committee of the Department of Munitions and Supply, had become thoroughly convinced of the need for immediate action, largely as a result of conversations he had held in Britain with General McNaughton; and on April 26, 1940, he summoned a meeting to review the situation. There was evidently still some doubt about the best course to pursue, and talks were begun with the American Optical Company to see whether its subsidiary, Spencer Lens Company, would agree to come across the border and set up a Canadian branch plant. Without financial assistance from the Canadian government

and guarantees of large military orders, however, the Spencer
Lens Company was not disposed to take this step.

The ugly turn taken meantime by war developments in Europe speeded up decisions in this field as elsewhere. On June
11, 1940, a floor plan for an optical instrument factory was
drawn up in the Optics Section at the request of Colonel Harrison; and a few days later financial estimates and other data
were supplied him. On June 21 a meeting was held in the
office of Major-General W. H. P. Elkins, Master General of
the Ordnance, to discuss the establishment of a fire-control
instrument factory in Canada. The first disposition was to
locate it in Ottawa; and, indeed, a site of adequate size opposite
the gas works on Lees Avenue had already been discovered.
On June 24, General Elkins was able to tell Dr. Howlett that
the Minister of Defence had given provisional approval to the
whole project. Meantime the Department of Munitions and
Supply had been giving thought to the best corporate arrangement, and the approval of Hon. C. D. Howe had been obtained
for the creation of a new crown company, to be called Research
Enterprises Limited. As such it was incorporated on July 16,
1940: the manufacture of radar equipment and optical glass
and instruments was to be its chief objective.

By this time the whole enterprise was going forward rapidly
on several fronts. During early July, George W. Sweny, Managing Director of Western Neon Products of Western Canada,
was appointed General Manager of R.E.L. After a careful
survey, Mr. Sweny recommended that, having in mind the
supply of labour and raw materials and the transportation
problem, Toronto would be the best site of the several cities
considered. The heads of the Optics and Radio Sections (Drs.
Howlett and Henderson) accompanied Mr. Sweny in early
August on a tour of possible sites in the Toronto area, and
after an extensive search a decision was made to locate at
Leaside.

Meantime the enterprise had been fortunate to obtain the
services of Professor R. J. Montgomery, of the staff of the
University of Toronto, who had had considerable experience
in the optical glass-making division of Bausch & Lomb Optical
Company, and who had been recommended to Ottawa by the

National Bureau of Standards as probably the best available man in North America for the new project. On June 30, 1940, Dr. Mackenzie endorsed the appointment of Dr. Montgomery to the National Research Council staff, with the understanding that he would be transferred to Research Enterprises Limited as soon as it was in active operation.

Professor Montgomery's first task was to go to Washington, in company with the draftsman of the Optics Section, and bring back blueprints, sketches, and other essential information for the new plant. The optical shop at Ottawa had all this time been expanding rapidly, and a number of optical mechanics were being trained. During July and August 1940, extensive orders were placed for pots, casting machinery for pots, furnaces, stirrers, gears, and other equipment, the designs for which were conceived and drawn in the Optics Section. The tight situation pending in machine tools in the United States (due to the vast acceleration in defence measures) led Research Enterprises Limited to order $600,000 of equipment at once, on the recommendations of Drs. Howlett and Henderson. As it turned out, this was a provision that saved many months in getting into production.

At the end of August 1940, Colonel W. E. Phillips became President of Research Enterprises Limited. The first sod was turned at Leaside on September 16, 1940. Less than nine months later, on June 5, 1941, the first pour of optical glass was made. The National Research Council attended the birth of this lusty giant and provided invaluable help and advice during its early months. The remainder of this inspiring story belongs largely to the history of war industry in Canada.

Now to return to the narrative of the optical research pursued by the National Research Council at Ottawa. Attention was focused upon a means of improving the rendering of detail in aerial photographs, as has been stated on an earlier page. A study of fundamentals uncovered a number of fruitful answers which pointed the way toward considerably better results from aerial photography, and toward simpler and more accurate methods of measuring the performance of lenses and emulsions actually employed in wartime photography.

Early telescopic lenses were of course designed for the eye, since they were made before the invention of photography. When telephoto lenses were developed for aerial photography, the assumption was apparently made that a lens-system of a very high resolving quality, as measured by the average eye, would give good results when a photographic emulsion was substituted for the human eye. This turned out to be not necessarily true. It by no means followed that such a lens-system would necessarily or automatically give as satisfactory results with a photographic emulsion as it did with the eye, or that because it had the highest possible resolution for visual use it was therefore the best possible lens-system for photographic use. Yet this fundamental assumption was apparently made by all earlier makers of photographic lenses. That it contained a fallacy was proved by the Optics Section at Ottawa and other scientists in Britain and the United States; by exposing this error, the way was opened for a very substantial improvement in the detail of aerial photographs.

The source of the error is interesting. In order that a good lens may produce a sharp image of a point source of light, the designer must take account of the fact that white light is composed of energy waves of different frequencies, which the eye sees as different colours when presented separately to the retina, making up, in fact, the familiar colour spectrum, from red to violet. Each of the different colours or frequencies has a different angle of refraction, and one problem of the lens-maker is to make lens combinations so that this tendency of the different colours to bend at different angles is completely overcome, and the rays come together again at the eye-piece in (as nearly as possible) a perfect focus or point.

It so happens that the average human eye is not equally sensitive to all the colours of the visible spectrum, but tends to be considerably more sensitive to the energies or colours grouped around the centre of it. When an observer is looking at a point-source of light with a telescope, it is most important—and the telescope-maker must see to it—that these rays grouped around the centre of the spectrum—the yellow-green segment—do come to an exact focus; but it is not such a critical matter if there is somewhat greater diffusion or scattering of the extreme red or blue light, because the average eye tends to disregard these scatterings or chromatic aberrations[4] and to see the point-source as a true point rather than as a blur.

Lens-systems for *visual* (rather than photographic) use are designed and tested to meet these facts. A photographic emulsion, like the eye, is sensitive to light, but is not necessarily sensitive in exactly the same way or equally to the same colours in the spectrum. In fact there is normally a great difference in this respect. Photographic emulsions differ in their sensitivity to the different colours, and a generalization might be misleading. However, contrasted with the average eye, many photographic emulsions have *a reasonably uniform sensitivity to colour right through the spectrum.* Thus a lens-system which focuses the yellow-green light of the point-source to a very sharp convergence, but which scatters the reds and blues a bit, may be thoroughly satisfactory for use by a visual observer, yet when used to make a photograph may cause some physical spread of the image, and thus some loss of desirable definition in the picture. For aerial photographs taken at a great altitude, this loss may deprive reconnaissance of valuable information.

One way to improve the resolving power of lens-film combinations was thus suggested to war scientists: instead of using the same criteria for photographic lenses as for visual use, makers could improve definition materially by taking into account the unique sensitivity characteristics of photographic emulsions when designing telephoto lenses, rather than continuing, as formerly, their preoccupation with the traditional *visual* tests of performance.

Having exposed the unsatisfactory consequences of failing to reconsider testing methods when the purpose of the lens-systems had become photographic rather than visual, the Optics Section then went on to investigate more correct methods of measuring lens-systems designed for photographic use. Following up a number of important contributions made during the war in the Kodak Research Laboratories at Harrow, England, Canadian scientists proposed a new type of target for measuring lens performance. The British had put forward the logical proposal

---

[4] Because of the shape of its "sensitivity to wave-length" curve, which reaches a peak in the yellow-green portion of the light spectrum.

that the particular photographic emulsion to be used in practice should also be used in laboratory tests for assessing the performance of a photographic lens. They had also challenged the traditional technique of testing lenses against a very *high* contrast target when, as a matter of fact, most aerial photographic subjects were *low* in contrast. The Canadian investigators then proposed that the most suitable test target would be in the form of an annulus or ring. To explain the superiority of this test target over the lines (tangential and radial) formerly used would require a more detailed exposition than can be justified here, but it represented a valuable contribution to the assessment of lens-systems for aerial photography.

"The results of the work have been extensively discussed with lens designers of commercial companies," the official history of the Section notes. "Slowly these are becoming convinced of the inadequacies of the criteria so far accepted for photographic lens design. The results of the work carried out by the section have also served to break down reliance which has been placed for so long on the utility of visual tests to assess photographic quality."

The research is believed to have made possible the design of lenses for photographic use which will eventually be from 50 to 100 per cent. superior to any available at the beginning of the war. Nor is the usefulness confined to war purposes. Increasing even by 25 to 50 per cent. the amount of information which can be obtained from aerial photography for such purposes as making aerial maps, studying forest and waterpower resources, aerial prospecting and so on, would obviously be an important contribution to our knowledge of Canada.

Night Photography

The difficulty of maintaining experimental work in night photography in Britain under blackout restrictions and the constant menace of enemy raids, led the British to suggest that Canada stress research in this field. After the visit of the Tizard Mission there was collaboration with U.S. scientists. At first the requirements of night photography had been directed only toward identification of the target, which meant that great detail was not demanded. So long as a few prominent landmarks were

lighted up and photographed, skilled interpreters could subsequently ascertain whether the bomber crew had selected the
right target. Later on, night reconnaissance was undertaken,
and it then became vital to make every effort to improve the
rendering of detail in night photographs.

The general method of night photography is to release a
flash-bomb actuated by a fuse at the same time as the bomb
load. The trail angle or "lag" of the flash-bomb is large compared with that of high-explosive bombs, and so at the time
of burst it is outside the field of view of the camera. For the
rough orientation required in identifying enemy targets over
which bombs were dropped, it was customary to employ a
focal plane shutter in the camera, opening it a few seconds before
the expected time of the flash and closing it a few seconds
afterwards. During this period, the effect of searchlights and
of anti-aircraft shell bursting in the vicinity was registered on
the film, causing considerable deterioration of quality in the
photograph (which did not matter much for checking bomb
targets, but rendered it quite inadequate for good reconnaissance). This was the position when the Optics Section began
working on the problem in October 1940.

The gain to be expected from the exact synchronization of
the flash and the exposure was of course recognized at once,
and a device to achieve this was undertaken. It consisted of
a photo-electric cell and amplifier, which operated thyratrons
so that the shutter of a standard Fairchild K3 camera could be
tripped by the light of the flash-bomb. The equipment was given
air trials: though it was shown to possess certain deficiencies,
the method was obviously feasible and could be employed in
designing satisfactory service equipment. Following the trials,
a company in the United States began the production of an
aerial camera operating on similar principles.

From the middle of the war onward there was a continuous
and growing demand for improvements in night photography
which would make night reconnaissance more valuable. One
possibility was a better flash-bomb. In the autumn of 1942
tests were made with twenty-four experimental nine-pound
flash-bombs exploded statically at Rockcliffe Air Station. Further
tests were made using a wide range of American and Canadian

magnesium mixtures. Canadian magnesium, made by a fuming or vaporizing process (which meant that it consisted of spherical particles with a minimum relationship of surface to weight or volume), was less effective in early tests than American-milled magnesium, which was well adapted for flash-bomb use. A number of special new instruments were built for the photometric study of flash-bombs, and recording instruments gave for the first time a measure of the colour-time characteristics of the flash as well as the intensity-time characteristics. Later in the war these static bursts of flash-bombs on the ground were amplified by observations under actual operating conditions.

These tests, conducted at Rockcliffe Air Station, were the first made anywhere of flash-bombs bursting in the air. Steps were taken to establish not only the position of the aircraft at the time of release but also the position of both aircraft and flash-bomb at the instant of firing. Theodolite cameras were set up on the ground near Ottawa, about seven miles apart, for this purpose. The tests showed that the M46 bomb, standard with the U.S. Army Air Forces, had very uncertain ballistic qualities. Another discovery was that the Mark III clock-work fuse of this bomb was unreliable at low temperatures, and modifications of the fuse were recommended which were incorporated in later production.

The report of these trials provided the most complete data on flash-bomb performance available anywhere, and led the British Ministry of Aircraft Production to select the Canadian experimental station for assessing the value of new experimental flash-bombs. At their request, further and more elaborate tests were arranged in the summer of 1945. Since they were to involve many more "drops" than any previous experiment, it was decided it would be safer to take them away from the built-up areas adjacent to Rockcliffe Air Station and move the equipment out to Carp Air Field, which had been inactive since the contraction of the British Commonwealth Air Training Scheme. A B25 was provided on loan by the Ministry of Aircraft Production. High-speed motion picture cameras were employed in the tests. A problem arose in the aiming of these cameras, which have a narrow field of view, so that they would

EXPERIMENTS

Icing on propeller hub and blades

AND MEN

(*above*) Crew members of the R.C.A.F. before a mission and (*below*) members of a R.C.A.F. squadron in the Middle East after an operation

be trained at the point where the flash-bomb was about to burst. The exact position of this point was very difficult to guess in advance, and it was necessary to devise some technique by which the motion picture cameras could follow the bomb continuously from its departure from the aircraft. Radar seemed to be the obvious solution, and the Army provided two G.L. Mark III C radar sets for the purpose, the motion picture cameras being attached to the antenna. This arrangement worked fairly well, and during August 1945 a series of tests, yielding valuable information both through high-speed motion picture cameras and by other apparatuses, were carried out.

Attention was turned toward the processing of films and prints, since it seemed illogical to pursue gains in lens-film performance if the gains were to be afterwards cancelled out by careless or inefficient processing. The design of a British continuous processing machine was copied with a number of improvements, which permitted a more precise control over the speed with which the negative passed through the developing solution, and over the temperature of the solutions and the agitation of the developer.

Propeller De-icing

When an aircraft flies through cloud in temperatures between 0° and −40°C., clear ice is likely to form on the structure. Once in the air, such icing is the greatest natural hazard to the flier, unless his aircraft has been specially equipped to overcome it. To the motorist, a sleet storm is a temporary inconvenience; at worst he can abandon his automobile beside the curb. To the pilot, such icing may prove fatal. It strikes at his safety from many directions. It may ice up or break off his antenna, preventing him from sending out a distress call, from getting a radio "fix", or vital meteorological information. Ice coats the windscreen and blinds the pilot. Ice chokes up the air intake and reduces the power of the motors, if they do not stall entirely. Ice makes the elevator and other controls stiff, if not unworkable. Ice coats the surfaces of wings and fuselage, quickly destroying the aerodynamic characteristics and capacities of the craft, so that its surfaces no longer lift or guide the plane. Over the Atlantic, complete loss of control has resulted in as little as *twenty seconds* of flight through "clear" icing conditions. Ice adds hundreds of pounds, sometimes tons, to the aircraft's weight, and this, combined with the deterioration in aerodynamic "lift", may prevent it from ascending to find ice-free conditions. Layers of clear ice build up on the propellers, converting them from efficient airscrews into shapeless oval clubs of ice no longer able to cut through the air, so that the aircraft rapidly becomes sluggish, loses airspeed, and may finally stall and crash. Such are the perils lurking in northern skies or at lofty altitudes anywhere.

Arctic weather conditions are enemies of flying in other ways. Ice forming on grounded aircraft may render them incapable of taking off again; excessive cold may prevent the engines from starting, or may "freeze up" oils and greases so that they no longer lubricate. In Canada, with its severe climatic conditions in winter, cold-weather research was always important. During the war, with the necessity of keeping the British Commonwealth Air Training Plan operating all year round, of patrolling the North Atlantic for enemy submarines and surface vessels, of keeping open the northern staging routes to Asia and Europe, such research became a "must"—a high-priority field of war investigation.

Many contributions toward safer and easier cold-weather flying were made by Canadian scientists and engineers during World War II. The most important, perhaps, was the method devised by scientists of the National Research Council for de-icing aeroplane propellers in flight, a method that worked without fail even after the propeller became actually coated. It operated on the principle of heating by electricity the leading edge of the propeller. For metal airscrews this involved employing an edge or shoe or sheath of rubber capable of conducting electricity. Rubber being in its natural state a non-conductor, it was necessary to impregnate it with something which would conduct electricity and yet offer sufficient resistance to the current to heat up when electricity was passed through it. Such a substance was found by incorporating acetylene black into neoprene. The electricity was generated by mounting a small dynamo on the hub of the propeller. The device proved much superior to earlier methods of applying pastes, alcohols, etc., on to the propellers—methods which may have been of some value in preventing new ice from forming, but were incapable of removing a layer of ice already formed. The electro-thermal method melted a layer of ice next to the heating element, and centrifugal force then ripped the loose ice entirely free.

The National Research Council had begun preliminary ground tests on the de-icing of aircraft wings and propellers by means of engine exhaust gas as far back as 1935, and further tests were conducted in 1937-38. In 1939, Trans-Canada Air Lines reported difficulty with the fluid de-icing of propellers. The Associate Committee on Aeronautical Research accordingly recommended an investigation of propeller de-icing by electrical heating. Preliminary investigation by the Physics Division showed that it was a practical means, and that the power required was well within the limits of the electrical system of an aircraft. Britain and the United States were keenly interested. Active work began in 1940 in the Mechanical Engineering Laboratories at Ottawa on several de-icing projects: electro-thermal propeller de-icing as described above, exhaust heat de-icing of wings, and electrical heat de-icing of windscreens. J. L. Orr was in charge of this research.

Severe enemy action over Britain in 1940 led Sir Henry Tizard to ask Canada to take over the entire load of de-icing research, some of which had been earlier undertaken on the other side of the Atlantic. E. Taylor, in charge of aircraft de-icing research at the Royal Aircraft Establishment in the United Kingdom, was transferred to Canada in 1940, and for some months was attached to the staff of the National Research Council at Ottawa. The Test and Development Establishment of the R.C.A.F. operated the two experimental aircraft placed at the disposal of the Council, a twin-engine Lockheed Hudson and a Bristol Blenheim. Crew and observers, which included Orr, Taylor, and R. H. Guthrie, engaged in considerable flying of a hazardous nature in order to test theories and to watch the performance of de-icing equipment. At times when foul weather grounded all other aircraft, test pilots and observers such as these went aloft to find severe icing conditions and to study meteorological conditions. The very first experimental flight from Rockcliffe Airport in January 1941 was prophetic of others to come: one engine of the Hudson aircraft failed because of icing in the air intake system, and the second de-livered reduced power, so that the plane was only with difficulty brought safely back to base.

A test flight from Sydney, N.S. on July 8, 1941, nearly proved fatal to the three observers listed above and an R.C.A.F. crew of four. Static conditions on the wireless transmitter were so severe that, while less than twenty minutes out, the operator was unable to raise stations on the ground. After flying for about ninety minutes, an attempt was made to let out the trailing aerial. This was accomplished with some difficulty. Static sparks as much as two inches long were drawn from the ap-paratus every time the operator's hands came near the units, and wireless operation proved impossible. When some anxiety began to be felt about returning, the pilot twice let down into fog from 2,000 feet and pulled up only about fifty feet off the water when whitecaps were visible. A second attempt to orient themselves brought the aircraft so close to the water that on a climbing turn the starboard wing tip came within ten feet of the sea. Fortunately, after anxiously flying five hours and twenty minutes without any clue as to their whereabouts, it became possible to use the radio again. Weather reports then obtained by radio indicated that all airports in the Maritimes were closed by fog and rain. However, the radio signal of the Dartmouth beam gave some clue to location and a course was set for Sydney. By this time the fuel was running low and a message was sent to Sydney asking for aircraft to be sent out to fly along the beam and find them, and also that rockets be fired from the station in an attempt to mark its position above the fog bank. Ten miles from Sydney the aircraft emerged from the fog bank. While the fuel tanks now showed empty, the pilot elected to try for the airport rather than come down in the sea. Wheels touched down after six hours and forty minutes of flight. The starboard engine stopped from lack of fuel just as the aircraft was taxiing off the runway to the hangars!

A test flight from Rockcliffe on December 13, 1941, with R. H. Guthrie as observer, ended in a crash landing near Mountain Grove two hours and forty minutes later. The air-craft was the same Hudson as was nearly lost with all hands off Sydney, but which had since been equipped with con-

siderable new de-icing equipment. After passing Stirling, Ontario, the craft was turned on the beam toward Toronto.
Static again became so intense that the radio was useless. The
trailing aerial was run out, and one-inch discharge sparks were
observed from the aerial wire. After flying about fifteen minutes
without radio, the aircraft was let down through snow, and
flew contact until its position was established. In attempting
to regain altitude the port engine began to fail and, finally,
conked out. Shortly afterwards the starboard engine also began
failing to deliver full power, owing to icing conditions, and
crew and observer started checking their parachutes. The aircraft was turned back in the direction of Ottawa.

" . . . the aircraft sank lower," Guthrie said in his official
report, "and appeared very sluggish on the controls due to
the slow speed. Sufficient power was obtained from the starboard engine to just maintain flight. The aircraft was flying
with a high angle of attack. Five times before landing, the
aircraft crashed through tree tops and gas spilled in through
the lower rear turret. The aircraft finally scraped over a railway embankment, was nosed down a little by the pilot, took
out a set of telegraph wires and slithered 200 yards across a
hayfield, made a half spin or loop, and came to rest against
a tree. The tree crushed the door and the crew dove out the
emergency exit on the starboard side. There was gas six inches
deep on the snow and the starboard engine had broken free
and was on fire. The fire was extinguished and no one was
hurt."

In the four years of tests, a total of fifty-six flights (aggregat-
ing 150 hours of flying) were taken into and through icing
conditions, two aircraft were completely destroyed, and a third
seriously damaged when the pilot's vision was obscured on
landing. Fortunately there were no serious casualties, though
minor injuries were suffered by the crew in a crash-landing at
Rockcliffe due to loss of elevator control.

Pilots' reports contain many illustrations of the hazards of
ice. From the log of a Catalina aircraft on patrol north of
the Shetland Islands, quoted in the official history of the
R.C.A.F.,[5] this eloquent passage may be cited:

[5] *The R.C.A.F. Overseas: The First Four Years* (Oxford University Press,
Toronto, 1944), pp. 244-5.

"The aircraft climbed to 13,000 feet, but even running at full throttle and the maximum permissible revolutions, the A.S.I. [air speed indicator] was 70 m.p.h. and the aircraft was failing to climb. . . . At this point the elevators froze up and it was only by the concentrated effort of both pilots that the correct 'attitude' of the aircraft was maintained. At the same time the windscreen iced up and it was only by putting his head out of the window and peering ahead that the pilot was able to avoid further cloud. . . . Bearings were requested repeatedly, but after failing to obtain any, on investigation the operational frequency crystals were found to be unserviceable. Attempts were made to get astral fixes, but these could not be obtained because the navigator's breath condensed and froze on the lens of the sextant, whenever it was brought to the sighting position."

Such reports could be multiplied if space served, and would reinforce the significance of finding an answer to aircraft icing.

In June and July of 1941, the two experimental aircraft placed at the disposal of the scientists were based at Sydney, and subsequently, from October on, at Rockcliffe. Taylor, who had returned to Britain, was killed there in a crash landing near Prestwick. J. L. Orr went to England to re-establish liaison with the Ministry of Aircraft Production and the Royal Aircraft Establishment, and to report on Canadian test flights.

In the spring of 1942, a set of conducting-rubber heater elements was installed on a full-scale Blenheim propeller blade by the Rubber Laboratory at Ottawa and subsequently ground-tested at Rockcliffe and Kapuskasing. In June, another set for a Hudson was fabricated by the Laboratory and installed on an experimental aircraft. In July, another Hudson aircraft was equipped and based at the Trans-Canada Air Lines Headquarters at Winnipeg. Tests continued with this aircraft during August and September, the first test flights conducted anywhere in the world with the electro-thermal method of propeller de-icing under actual icing conditions. Reports of those tests formed the basis for all subsequent designs of such equipment in Canada and elsewhere.

After further successful trials, orders were placed the following summer by the British Ministry of Aircraft Production for

75 sets for Lancasters and 15 for Venturas, and 45 sets were ordered by the R.C.A.F. to be installed on Liberator, Mosquito, Canso, Lodestar, and Hudson types of aircraft. In order to fulfil all these requirements, it was necessary to produce seven different types of heater elements to suit the different propeller blades, and two different types of hub generators to suit both radial aircraft engines and in-line types such as Rolls-Royce or Merlin. A good deal of research still had to be done by the Chemistry Division on the incorporation of acetylene black into neoprene for production on a commercial scale. Installations on service craft began in 1944. Wide-scale service trials followed, and many favourable reports of the effectiveness of the equipment were received. In no case was failure to remove ice reported when the equipment was in a serviceable condition.

On at least one occasion in the earliest days the new equipment saved an aircraft and its crew. The following extract from the flight log of an R.C.A.F. Canso on Atlantic operations in 1944 tells its own story:

19 Dec.—On night patrol some 300 miles off Sydney, aircraft suddenly became sluggish and lost altitude. Found due severe icing conditions. Ice already formed on propellers. Heaters placed on high, ice thrown off in large chunks against hull. By this time aircraft had lost altitude to 500 ft. and airspeed to 80 knots I.A.S. [Indicated Air Speed]. Were just able to hold this altitude and speed to Sydney, landing with 2½ inches clear-ice still on wings, propellers free of ice. *Had propellers not cleared would not have reached base.*

Stall Warning Indicator

The great value to a pilot of an ice-free warning device which would indicate when icing of his aircraft was approaching a critical degree because of the deterioration of the aerodynamic properties of the wing (which, if carried on far enough would end in a stall or spin), was drawn to the attention of the National Research Council by airline operators, and an instrument of this kind was developed by the Electronics Section of the Instrument Laboratory. It operated "on the principle of reversal of airflow at a critical point on the upper wing surface, using a small heater element and a differential thermometer to indicate the direction of flow." The device was successfully tested in an R.C.A.F. Hudson aircraft, and a number of sets were later made up for installation for test flights on T.C.A. aircraft.

Carburettor De-icing

To test the heated propeller-edge mentioned earlier by actual flying through severe icing conditions, the experimental aircraft used had to be protected against engine failure due to ice fouling and choking the air intake to the carburettor. For this reason research on de-icing the induction system was also carried out during the tests of the propeller heating.

One method was to inject alcohol into the inflowing airstream. This kept down the icing, but it introduced new problems. Methanol was the most satisfactory alcohol in many respects, but it was poor in fuel value and did not mix well with gasoline. The Chemistry Division and the Mechanical Engineering Division investigated a number of materials for blending with the fuel and discovered that iso-propyl alcohol, with an octane rating of 138, was outstandingly good.

More satisfactory than relying wholly on the injection of alcohol, however, was the provision of a muff on the exhaust ring to heat the intake air, while an alcohol injection system was retained for emergency use in the event of complete failure. A careful study of the low temperatures sometimes encountered in the air induction system showed that it was necessary to provide for a rise in temperature of as much as 140°F.

Another attack on this problem was to jacket parts of the induction system and heat them with hot engine oil. Still another, developed by the Aerodynamics Laboratory, used a water-separating airscoop, in which centrifugal force whirled out the free water from the air, draining it off by a lip. This method removed a very large percentage of the free water, but it required a means of heating also, to prevent ice from forming on the intake walls.

Wing De-icing

The success achieved in the electro-thermal de-icing of propellers suggested an inquiry into the use of the same principle for aircraft wings. A number of experimental rubber heater elements

AIR

183

were installed on an RY3 aircraft in July 1945 for flight-testing,
and a survey was made of high-performance aircraft generators
suitable for providing current. Later flights and laboratory tests
proved highly promising.

Windscreen De-icing

The importance of maintaining a clear windscreen through all
sorts of weather needs no elaboration, yet it was not an easy
condition to ensure. Early in 1940, experiments were made with
an electrically heated spinning windscreen, in which centrifugal force would assist in the removal of ice already formed,
as with the electrically heated propeller. Mechanical difficulties,
however, discouraged further development. The experimental
aircraft used in testing the de-icing of propellers were fitted with
a hot-air sandwich-type of windscreen, the hot air being derived
from the cabin heating system. This equipment proved fairly
successful. Various types of alcohol sprays were also fitted and
tested, and both hydraulic and electric windshield wipers tried
out.

During 1942, the R.C.A.F. suffered a series of accidents to
aircraft taking off from water during the winter season. Water
from the bow wave, freezing on the windscreen, seemed to
be responsible for the accidents, and the National Research
Council was asked to provide a remedy. One immediate answer
was suggested in the form of a thin layer of transparent celluloid,
which was laid over the windscreen before take-off, and then
stripped from the window when the aircraft became airborne.
This method proved effective, but as it was only good for one
icing, further research was conducted. An inner plastic windscreen was designed and fitted to Canso aircraft, forming a
sandwich through which hot air from the combustion heaters
could be circulated.

Meteorology in Icing Conditions

As an aid to designing effective de-icing equipment, a means
for obtaining more precise information about the physical condition of the atmosphere was highly desirable, and new
meteorological instruments for the purpose were designed and

made. One of these used an electrically heated forward-facing intake, in which water in the air was evaporated on heated cascades and the humidity of the resultant heated air was measured by an automatic photo-electric dew-point hygrometer. To obtain a measure of cloud droplet size, the Electronics Section of the Instruments Laboratory designed and constructed a special high-speed camera fitted with a rotating prism, the required illumination being provided by a high-intensity spark-gap. A photo-electric cloud-density instrument was also made which measured the extinction of illumination through the presence of cloud droplets in the air.

Rain Repellents for Windscreens

An attack on the problem of obscuration due to water was made by the Chemistry Division, where Dr. D. F. Stedman produced some effective rain repellents to be applied to the windscreens. The theory was that while ripples of raindrops running together in a continuous film broke up the light and prevented the pilot from seeing clear outlines, a suitable repellent would shed the rain as separate drops, which the wind would keep rapidly moving, so that they could be largely disregarded by the pilot.

Some ingenious theoretical chemistry led to the synthesis of a silicon compound with a chain of two or more silicon atoms, with all side chains hydrocarbon: hexa-ethyl-disilicon was found to be very promising, and other organic silicon compounds which looked useful from a theoretical standpoint were made. The repellent had to work on both glass and plastics of various kinds, be capable of application at high temperatures as well as below freezing point, and on wet as well as dry surfaces. Provision had to be made for renewal during flight in the event that hail or long exposure to rain wore it away, and the effects of alcohol or heat used for de-icing, or of gasoline or oil splashed upon it, had to be considered and met. After prolonged experimentation, a final product of a very satisfactory nature was found, a suitable technique worked out, and extensive tests carried out both in Canada and the United States. Provision was then made for commercial production for use in the R.C.A.F. and by civilian airlines.

Frost on Parked Aircraft

The popular idea of the research scientist pictures him raptly examining a test tube, or peering into a microscope, with the exclamation "Eureka!" forming on his lips as he drags from reluctant Nature one more of her profound secrets. Scientists do, of course, have their thrilling moments, but a large part of their lives is spent in the methodical, painstaking elimination of unprofitable lines of attack, often by trial and error, and in this way gradually isolating the most promising approaches for more intensive investigation.[6]

Nor is the goal always as dramatic as atomic energy or the proximity fuse. It may be as prosaic as a new kind of paste to help keep aircraft flying in cold weather.

These observations are aptly illustrated, in fact, by the work of the Chemistry Division in doing exactly that. In seeking a material for coating grounded aircraft so that ice and frost would not adhere, or in any event so that it could be more readily removed, the following list of requirements for an ideal substance was compiled:

(a) It must be cheap.

(b) It must be easily applied.

(c) It must not collect dirt.

(d) It must not produce a slippery surface.

(e) It must be effective on all classes of base materials.

(f) It must be insoluble, and not chemically changed by rain.

(g) It must not lose its effectiveness because of the usual accumulation of dirt, oil, and gasoline residues.

(h) It must not deteriorate from exposure to sunlight.

(i) It must not damage wing paints (camouflage).

(j) It should preferably be invisible, or at least nearly so, on all base colours and finishes.

(k) It must remain effective for a reasonably long time.

(l) It must be effective over a great range in weather conditions, with the consequent variations in the type of frost produced.

[6] "Science is experiment; science is trying things. It is trying each possible alternative in turn, intelligently and systematically; and throwing away what won't work, and accepting what will." From "A Sense of the Future", a broadcast by J. Bronowski over the BBC in May 1948.

    (m) It must not interfere with other de-icing procedures, and
           should still remain effective after such procedures have
           been used.

"This", says the official report of the Chemistry Division, "is
a formidable list of requirements, and although over 200,000
tests have been made to date, no material has yet been found
which is entirely satisfactory." Typical of the obstacles encountered in this sort of research: all materials investigated
which were stable to ultra-violet light also damaged some wing
dopes, while all materials which did not cause paint damage
were destroyed by ultra-violet radiation. One mixture was
found which met very satisfactorily eleven of the above thirteen
requirements: unfortunately it failed to pass tests (d) and (m);
moreover, one hour's dry flight in mid-winter entirely destroyed
its usefulness just where it mattered most—on the upper wing
surfaces. It illustrates how even relatively simple investigations
have a way of touching on the still unmeasured phenomena of
nature that the failure of this material at high altitudes appeared to be due not to the greater intensity of ultra-violet light
there, but to the presence of shorter, very destructive wave-lengths
of electro-magnetic energy, which are not present at ground
level because they are absorbed in the atmosphere. Work with
this problem was still going on when the war ended.

Low-temperature Oils and Greases

Among the many interesting minor jobs done by the National
Research Council on lubricants for use in extremely low temperatures was a search on behalf of the Meteorological Services
for a grease which would give adequate lubrication in radiosonde
equipment at temperatures as low as −70°F. The pre-war
source had been a French oil prepared from porpoise fins, and
nothing available commercially in Canada proved suitable.
The Chemistry Division decided to test the use of fractions
refined from ordinary fuel oil. After treatment with sulphuric
acid and sodium metal, the oil was clarified with bentonite
and distilled. The product was an entirely stable yellow oil
which formed no gum and remained very fluid down to very
low temperatures. The radiosonde equipment remained properly
lubricated with the temperature down to −80°F.

CHAPTER IX

MATERIALS AND FOOD

THE war potential of any country is derived largely from the wealth and extent of its economic resources. Sustained offensives on a great scale are impossible without command over strategic materials (or adequate substitutes) and food. Canada's natural resources are world-famed, though in peace as in war we are far from being self-contained. We faced the material and economic demands of the Second World War as a partner in a strong team of nations. Nevertheless, enemy successes on a global scale created, early in the war, some acute and awkward material scarcities. Moreover, Canada, as the chief overseas supplier of food for Britain after the dark days in 1940, carried some heavy responsibilities connected with the maintenance of a flow of palatable and nutritious food, in the teeth of unprecedented attacks by Nazi "wolf pack" submarines and formidable surface craft. Many of these problems called for the aid of science. The writer's intention in this chapter is to offer some illustrations of the help provided by the National Research Council and its Associate Committees toward the solution of such problems.

Magnesium and Magnesia

Everyone knows that a modern war could not be fought without an adequate supply of metals. What is not so well known is that the supply of metals in turn is dependent upon a supply of suitable materials for refractories in which the metals for war munitions can be reduced from ores, or otherwise processed. Magnesia is one of these materials. Added to its importance in this respect is the fact that it is a source for the metal magnesium. During recent years magnesium has come into active demand for light aircraft alloys, parachute flares, night bombs, for certain shells, and for pyrotechnics.

As far back as 1925 an investigation into Canadian sources of basic refractory materials had begun at the request of the Dominion Government. From being an importing country where the only native source of such materials developed commercially was thought to be of an inferior quality, Canada had moved by the end of World War II to the status of an exporter of special refractory products to foreign consumers on all continents. During the twenty-year period in which the investigation had been carried on, over one hundred Canadian and foreign patents had been issued on more than thirty different processes and products.

When hostilities broke out in 1939, it was obvious that the magnesia requirements of the Commonwealth and Allied countries would be vastly increased, both for refractories to be used in the metallurgical industries, and for the production of metallic magnesium. New supplies were imperative. The Metals Controller asked the National Research Council to survey potential sources in Canada, and the following were recommended as being of nearly equal promise:

1. Magnesitic dolomite occurring at Kilmar, Quebec. (Operations at this property were greatly enlarged during the war. It was Canada's major source of basic refractories, and exports were made to many countries.)

2. Brucite rock near Wakefield, Quebec, from which magnesia was recovered by a method worked out by the Bureau of Mines. (This was developed and became an important source of refractories.)

3. Sea-water treated with calcined dolomite. (A suitable site for this operation was discovered in Nova Scotia. The method was never developed commercially in Canada, but very large plants using this process were built in the United Kingdom and the United States.)

Dolomite was recommended as the most promising source of the metal magnesium in Canada. A commercial plant was subsequently built at Haley, near Renfrew, Ontario, for this purpose. This was one of the more thrilling partnerships of science and business during the war, and will be told in somewhat more detail.

The industrial production of metallic magnesium on any significant scale had begun in 1896 at Bitterfeld, Germany, where a method of electrolysis of fused magnesium chloride was employed. The metal had been isolated by Sir Humphrey Davy for the first time in 1808, and small amounts of it were produced during the latter part of the nineteenth century for photographic purposes. As late as 1937, however, world production was still estimated to be only 27,000 tons annually, of which one-half was produced in Germany. In that year an Associate Committee on Metallic Magnesium was created in Canada, on which sat representatives of the Departments of National Defence and Mines and Resources, and of the National Research Council.

The task given this Committee was to study the literature, and to make laboratory tests for the recovery of metallic magnesium, so as to assess the technical difficulties of using Canadian raw materials for this purpose. Major-General A. G. L. McNaughton, then President of the National Research Council, assigned a young graduate of McGill, Dr. Lloyd M. Pidgeon, to direct this research.

This later turned out to be a far-sighted and profitable move. By November 1940, Pidgeon had worked out the laboratory details of a new process, more direct, more rapid, and safer than the method earlier employed; within the next twelve months the Pidgeon process had been proved commercially, and by the end of 1942 a new $3 million Canadian plant was operating at peak production. Secrets of the new process were shared with the United States, and five plants costing over $35 millions had been erected in that country by the end of the war, with a total daily production of over 135 tons of the metal. By the end of 1943, Canadian and American production was sufficient to meet all essential war requirements and far exceeded that of the Axis countries.

The early experimental work in Canada followed the traditional process. Since in it magnesium chloride was the source of the metal magnesium (using electrolysis), the first step was the production of magnesium chloride from Canadian raw materials. Magnesia was used as the primary ingredient, and the magnesium chloride thus produced in the early experiments was used in small-scale Canadian tests of the production of the metallic magnesium by electrolysis.

Pidgeon and his associates were fully aware of how complicated was the production of magnesium chloride suitable for the electrolytic process, and Pidgeon's attention turned, as had that of many earlier investigators, toward the *direct* reduction of the metal from magnesia (MgO). Though in other parts of the world such a process had been frequently contemplated, and a number of patents for such a process had even been issued, the numerous technical difficulties to be overcome had hitherto stood in the way of successful commercial operation. Indeed, one authority, after an extensive investigation, had published a report stating that the direct reduction of magnesia, using ferrosilicon—the process which especially attracted the Canadian group—was quite impossible. This reminds one of Nansen's saying: "The difficult is that which can be done immediately; the impossible that which takes a little longer"—a motto which could be used with propriety in many chapters of the science story.

The ferrosilicon process started with dolomite;[1] it used a temperature of not more than 1200°C., and it formed compact magnesium metal at one operation. Cheaply mined dolomite is readily available in Canada, and this country is a large producer of ferrosilicon in its electric furnaces. These considerations led to work on the development of a commercial process based on the ferrosilicon reaction even before the earlier experiments with electrolysis and magnesium chloride were completed.

Dr. Pidgeon and his associates soon discovered that by employing calcined dolomite and 75 per cent. ferrosilicon, the production of magnesium metal from MgO could be made to proceed at a satisfactory rate, provided the following method was employed:

1. The materials used to charge the retort were finely pulverized, mixed, and briquetted, in order to bring them into the most intimate contact possible.

2. The temperature used was about 1100°C.

[1] Dolomite is a combination of magnesium carbonate and calcium carbonate with a formula $MgCO_3 . CaCO_3$.

3. The process was carried out under a sufficiently high vacuum to remove, as vapour, all magnesium metal as rapidly as it was formed.

The metallic magnesium, under these conditions, distilled out of the reaction mixture and condensed in the cool end of the retort.

One difficulty encountered by previous experimenters using a similar method was that a small amount of sodium, always to be found in dolomite, was also reduced from the ore and condensed in the end of the retort in association with the pure magnesium. When the retort was opened the sodium caused the metal to ignite, so that all the product was lost.

One possible solution, that of cooling the retort before opening it, was both uneconomical and inconvenient. The problem was solved by the fractional condensation of the sodium, in the outermost part of the retort. A method was devised for opening the retort, removing the product and the spent charge, and reloading it, without having to remove the retort from the furnace. The success of this in laboratory operations suggested a workable commercial operation similar to that already used in a "horizontal retort" zinc process.

By the autumn of 1940, a small furnace with a four-inch retort was in regular operation, and the time had arrived to consider commercial production on a large scale for war purposes. A group of Toronto industrialists, after examining the process, agreed to form a company under the name of Dominion Magnesium Limited. While it was organized as a private company, it was financed by the Dominion Government under the supervision of Wartime Metals Corporation, and it operated without profit or fee. By July 1941 a pilot plant using larger retorts had been erected and put into continuous production. In November 1941 plans were drawn up for a commercial plant. The site at Haley, in the midst of a wilderness of pine and birch, rock and sand, was located close to an adequate body of dolomite ore, and convenient to sources of hydro-electric power and to two transcontinental railway lines.

The first sod for the plant was broken in February 1942: fifteen days later the first concrete was poured; six months later operations began. The first "crown" of magnesium, processed from brucitic limestone from Quebec, was taken out of the reduction furnace on August 15, while on November 9 plants for the utilization of the dolomite right "in its own backyard" (as *The Industrial Front* phrases it) were sufficiently advanced to permit the first use of adjacent ores. By December 15, 1942, construction work was complete, and the plant was approaching its capacity output of 15½ tons of metallic magnesium per day.

While all this was going on, the United States had been plunged into World War II, and the American needs for vastly increased quantities of magnesium metal had driven them to take a keen interest in the new Canadian process.

In November 1941 the Canadian pilot plant was visited by officials of the United States War Production Board. A special committee of the Board, of which each member was an authority on magnesium, followed this up with a further examination on the spot in January 1942. Their recommendations led to a decision on the part of the United States to adopt the Canadian process for a total daily production of 135 tons. Information was freely given to American engineers, and the following five plants were rapidly erected:

New England Lime Company ....15 tons per day
Magnesium Reduction Company 15   "   "   "
American Metals Company 15   "   "   "
Permanente Metals (H. Kaiser) 30   "   "   "
Ford Motor Company 60   "   "   "

Throughout 1942 the Canadian pilot plant operated day and night, testing dolomite ores from a number of American locations, and training men for plant operation. Since the process was new and had never been commercially operated, problems were numerous. Development work, directed toward improving the process, continued until the spring of 1944. The production of metallic magnesium in North America, insignificant in 1939, had by that time become amply sufficient to fulfil all requirements.

Aluminum

Canadian success in producing aluminum for the war needs of the Allies in 1939-45 has been described as "possibly the most spectacular story of wartime expansion in any industry in any country."[2] Since this book is an account of scientific research, even so sensational an account of industrial expansion and engineering triumphs lies outside its scope. In connection with the aluminum industry, however, there was at least one item of war research in Canada which should not be omitted. That was an investigation of the feasibility of producing aluminum from clay.

As is very generally known, the chief source of Canadian-made aluminum is bauxite from British Guiana. During the Battle of the Atlantic, especially after the U.S. entered the war, when Nazi submarines invaded the coastal waters of North America with deadly effect, it began to appear problematical whether the flow of bauxite ore from South America up the Saguenay could be maintained, and anxious thought was given to all other possible sources.

The most obvious was clay, which, though it contains only about half as much alumina as bauxite, is literally "dirt cheap" to mine, and occurs nearly everywhere.

For some years The Consolidated Mining and Smelting Company of Canada, at Trail, B.C., had been making sulphuric acid from the sulphur dioxide in their waste gases, combining it with ammonia made by synthesis, and thus producing ammonium sulphate for use as a fertilizer. It was suggested that this procedure could be combined to advantage with the treatment of clay, the ultimate products being ammonium sulphate, as formerly, and in addition, alumina. This in turn, if it could be sufficiently purified, would serve as a raw product for the production of aluminum.

A means was found of dissolving with sulphuric acid more than 90 per cent. of the alumina from a kaolin (clay) containing 40.6 per cent. of that substance. The clay, however, contained some iron, and when ammonia was added to precipitate the alumina, the dissolved iron also came down, thereby contaminating the alumina. Three possible methods of purification were tested and proved feasible. They were worked out only on a small laboratory scale, but appeared to give considerable promise of the cheap production of alumina of high

---

[2] *The Industrial Front*, prepared by the Department of Munitions and Supply (The King's Printer, Ottawa, 1943), p. 212.

quality. The process did not advance to the pilot-plant stage, presumably because the tables had by this time been turned in the Nazi Atlantic offensive, and an adequate supply of bauxite was once more assured. Under other circumstances this inquiry might have grown into a matter of great importance.

Rubber

The coming of war in 1939 rapidly increased Canada's consumption of rubber, more than three-quarters of which was eventually required for automotive tires and tubes used on military vehicles. At the same time shipping difficulties slowed down the accumulation of an adequate stock-pile, while the rapid advance of Japan into south-eastern Asia after Pearl Harbor cut off the main supply sources of the Allies. An incident in the acute shortage of natural rubber which followed was the aggressive examination of substitute and alternative sources in Canada. The answer was finally found in the massive North American production of synthetic rubber, in which the Polymer Corporation plant at Sarnia played a valuable role; but by that time some interesting by-paths had been explored.

The Canadian public took a keen interest in the search for rubber substitutes, and a flood of letters and packages descended on the National Research Council at Ottawa, asking for information, forwarding samples for analysis, and recommending plants ranging from cucumbers to bananas. Considerable research had already been done in the United States on such plants as guayule and goldenrod, and it was known that Russian scientific literature contained a large volume of information on sources of natural rubber production in the temperate zone. Early in the spring of 1942 a cooperative research programme was organized involving the University of Toronto, the Department of Agriculture at Ottawa, and the National Research Council, to explore all phases of the problem.

The common milkweed was the only native Canadian plant with a rubber content sufficiently high to warrant further studies on extraction. A preliminary investigation showed that the rubber is concentrated in the leaves. Since there were good milkweed stands in the Ottawa district, a substantial supply of dried plants was obtained during the late summer and early fall of 1942 for extraction studies during the winter. The gum extracted from the leaves was found to contain about 40 per cent. resin and 35 per cent. rubber. Up to 1943 the rubber-like substance in milkweed had never been exactly identified. A cooperative study by the Divisions of Physics and Applied Biology showed that it was a true rubber (polymerized isoprene, chemically the same as that obtained from the Malayan rubber tree). Early tests indicated that it might be a valuable blending agent in compounding the early synthetic rubbers which were beginning to be available from industrial plants in the United States. The mixing of 15 per cent. milkweed rubber-gum with 85 per cent. GR-S improved the compounding in several respects, though the resiliency was meantime somewhat reduced. At any rate the results were such as to justify experiments on a larger scale, and recommendations went forward to the Department of Agriculture to plant as large an acreage as the supply of seed permitted. Five tons of milkweed gum were requested for large-scale testing, either from plantings or wild stands. If the usefulness of the milkweed gum should be proved, plantations covering 15,000 acres were proposed for 1944. Thousands of school children, patriotic citizens, and Indians on some of the reserves cooperated to collect about 71,000 pounds of dried milkweed leaves during the season of 1943. A pilot plant for the mechanical extraction of the rubber-gum was developed capable of producing about 25 pounds daily. Canadian rubber companies initiated blending tests, comparing milkweed rubber-gum with other available agents. The milkweed programme slackened off once it was established that milkweed rubber had no special advantages over other blending agents, which could be more readily and more cheaply obtained. Tests on milkweed rubber containing some resin showed that it gave at best a tensile strength of only 1500 pounds per square inch in a tread-type compound. A milkweed rubber entirely free from resin would be a satisfactory rubber substitute, but the cost of purification appeared to be prohibitive.

Several pounds of seed of the Russian dandelion, Koksaghyz, were obtained from Russia in 1942 and distributed by the Department of Agriculture to universities and experimental stations across Canada. The first shipment of roots reached Ottawa in December of that year, and the first samples of rubber extracted from the plant were displayed at a National Research Council meeting on December 23. The results of preliminary work were such as to warrant the planting of expanded acreage in 1943. The first pilot-plant scale of extraction of rubber from Koksaghyz was possible when half a ton of fresh roots became available from the Ontario Agricultural College at Guelph. The rubber obtained was made into oxygen masks by the Gutta Percha and Rubber Company of Toronto, and it had particularly desirable qualities for this purpose. Altogether, about 200 pounds of rubber were obtained from the experimental plantings of 1943. The Division of Chemistry found that Koksaghyz rubber was almost equal in quality to rubber from Malaya, although its cost was too high to make it a competitor under normal circumstances. Its molecular weight appeared to be somewhat lower than that of natural rubber.

Rubber from milkweed and dandelions was at best an interesting side-show to the main effort being made concurrently in North America to produce enough synthetic rubber to measure up to the colossal demands of the war machine. Butadiene, a starting-point for the mass production of synthetic rubber, could be made from either petroleum or alcohol. Alcohol in turn could be made from grain. Owing to the acute shipping shortages of war, intensified by the Battle of the Atlantic, hundreds of millions of bushels of wheat were piling up in Canada. The possibility of using wheat as the raw material not only of synthetic rubber but of many other war materials had to be very seriously considered. For a country like Canada, capable of producing in a normal year several hundred million bushels of wheat beyond domestic requirements, the story of this investigation is of live interest in peacetime as in war.

The fact that grains can be fermented, and that they produce alcohol in the process, has been well known to man for many generations. Yeasts and bacteria, present almost everywhere in nature, attack the starches and sugars of grains, and produce ethyl alcohol. Such fermentations can be carried out in open vats. But there are almost countless other bacteria and moulds, many of which also thrive on the starches and sugars of grains, and in doing so produce a variety of products other than ethyl alcohol. There are strains of bacteria, for example, which cause fermentations that produce a substance called butylene glycol. This is a chemical discovery which would have been of little interest to the general public except for the fact that butylene glycol is what a chemist calls a "4-carbon compound". These "4-carbon compounds" came into great prominence early in the war because the manufacture of both synthetic rubber and aviation gasoline requires them. Fermentations producing butylene glycol would thus provide possible raw materials for either. This indicates the line of research aggressively suggested by the needs of North American war industry in the years 1939-45.

While it was already known, as a laboratory discovery, that certain bacteria produced butylene glycol through the fermentation of carbohydrates, a great deal remained to be learned about the bacteria themselves, and there was no knowledge of such processes carried beyond the laboratory stage into industrial scale of production. Intensive work in Canada started in March 1942, shortly after Japan had begun its lightning drive into the rich rubber and oil areas of south-east Asia. Canadian scientists began the isolation of suitable strains of bacteria for the production of butylene glycol. The Northern Regional Laboratory of the U.S. Department of Agriculture at Peoria, Illinois, had done pioneer research in this field a few months earlier, and their findings were freely shared with the Canadians. The Peoria Laboratory was actively studying the fermentations produced by species of *Aerobacter aerogenes,* and the Canadian scientists at first pursued this line of inquiry, isolating many new strains of the bacterium.

So as to enlist all possible help in a pressing problem, the Associate Committee on Grain Research was approached and asked to undertake some aspects of the inquiry. So was a group at the University of Alberta formed under the direction of Dr. A. G. McCalla. The Division of Bacteriology at the Central Experimental Farm, Ottawa, began a study of the nutrition of *Aerobacter aerogenes.* In April a conference was held at Peoria for progress reports on this particular fermentation process.

Meantime scientists at Peoria had isolated an active strain of another organism, called *Aerobacillus,* which seemed to offer certain advantages over fermentation by *Aerobacter.* The former fermented wheat mashes directly without requiring saccharification of the starch, aeration was not essential, and the product showed promise for use as an anti-freeze (a product then in short supply and in increasing demand both for war and civilian use). It was decided to concentrate at Ottawa on *Aerobacillus,* while the group working at the University of Alberta continued to study the *Aerobacter* fermentation.

Where does a scientist look for bacteria? They exist almost everywhere, but the soil in particular is full of them. A spoonful of fertile soil contains many millions of living micro-organisms of a bewildering variety. Since the search for *Aerobacilli* began in winter, the investigation opened, oddly enough, with a scientist digging soil from an Ottawa garden. The air temperature at that moment was about thirty degrees below zero, and a layer of snow had to be removed before any excavation was possible. The variety of bacteria wanted had to be first found among all the others, isolated, and then grown. Since bacteria often reproduce themselves in a matter of minutes, evolutionary changes can be very swift. From a single bacterial strain, as many as six variations showing different characteristics have developed. In the work with *Aerobacillus,* 100 strains of *Aerobacillus polymyxa* were obtained for comparative studies, of which about 80 were isolated in the laboratories at Ottawa and the remainder obtained elsewhere. Two years later, several hundred different variants had been selected from these original cultures. A large number of these strains were tested and extensive studies made of those which gave high yields of butylene glycol, and were otherwise preferable. In the course of the work, promising results were obtained from several other varieties of bacteria, but fermentation by strains of *Aerobacillus polymyxa* received the most attention.

Butylene glycol had remained a laboratory curiosity for forty years. It was now necessary to produce it in quantity if the commercial-scale production of synthetic rubber and

SYNTHETIC RUBBER PLANT BY DAY

Polymer Corporation at Sarnia, Ontario

SYNTHETIC RUBBER PLANT BY NIGHT

The plant produces both buna-S and butyl

other war commodities from it was to be explored. The first step-up at Ottawa was from the test-tube stage to a special laboratory unit, with a capacity of twenty-five gallons of wheat mash and a production rate of a gallon of butylene glycol a week. Contracts for a small-scale industrial unit (pilot plant) were also let in 1942, but slow wartime deliveries retarded construction and the main work of installation was done between December 1943 and March 1944. It cost $100,000 and constituted by far the largest chemurgic experiment ever undertaken in Canada. Operations began in April 1944, and thereafter the plant ran continuously.

It is difficult for the non-technical reader to guess how many tests, experiments, comparisons, and calculations are involved in the evolution of an industrial process from the test-tube stage to the factory. This may seem to be a simple process of fermenting grain so as to produce a glycol or diol. But such matters as these had to be investigated: Should the wheat be ground or the kernels left whole? How much sterilization or cooking of the mash in advance is permissible? Exactly how acid should the mash be permitted to become? Aside from the starch, what other constituents of wheat should be left in the mash? What is the effect of removing the carbon dioxide which fermentation produces in large quantities? Under what conditions is the largest proportion of butylene glycol to alcohol produced? What is the most satisfactory fermentation temperature? How can the several products be most cheaply and most efficiently recovered at the end of the fermentation process? These are only typical of the many questions to be answered. Since this was a new process, the answers had for the most part to be worked out for the first time by trial and error, illuminated by theory, hunch, and the laws of probability.

Glossing over two years of intensive research on many angles of the process, what came of the experiments? First, it was shown that a bushel of Canadian wheat could be broken down by a carefully controlled fermentation, using *Aerobacillus polymyxa* as the agent, with end products of about 10 pounds of butylene glycol, 6 pounds of alcohol, and recoverable stock feed of 17 pounds.[3] Secondly, methods were worked out for

[3] The remainder of the 60 pounds was lost, chiefly in the form of carbon dioxide and water.

converting butylene glycol into synthetic rubber, although the economic feasibility of the process still had to be established. Thirdly, butylene glycol was shown to be a new industrial chemical with promise in several fields. It can be obtained by fermentation from many crop products. It can be combined with water and other ingredients to make an excellent anti-freeze. It is a source of chemicals useful in the plastics industry. Its long-term possibilities include conversion to materials needed for making synthetic rubber or pure octane motor fuels. Though this particular research did not directly relieve the war problem of strategic shortages in 1939-45, it added a great deal to our knowledge of the industrial utilization of wheat and other cereals.

Charcoal for Fuse Powders

A minor but interesting service in providing a war material in short supply was rendered by the National Research Council when an urgent request was received in August 1940 from Britain for six tons of charcoal for the manufacture of slow-burning fuse powders. British supplies had been obtained in the past from the wood of the shrub known as dogwood or alder-buckthorn (*Rhamnus frangula*). The traditional source was France and this had been cut off by the Nazi advance. Alder-buckthorn is not native to Canada, but an exhaustive search by members of the Department of Applied Biology disclosed two stands of it in Eastern Canada, one near Ottawa. These stands were at once harvested to prevent loss or sabotage, and extensive timber-cruising in swampy land and miles of tramping in wet woods were undertaken in the search for further stands or other alders which might prove to be a suitable substitute. Slightly over six tons of fuse powder were produced at Ottawa and sent to a Canadian explosives plant. Research on charcoals showed further that the product of certain native alders met the British requirements. By a microscopic examination of these charcoals in polarized light, some progress was made in finding out the relation between the optical properties of the various isotropic and other forms of charcoal found within the same sample of charcoal, and their performance as an ingredient of fuse powder.

Bacon for Britain

Bacon and eggs may not win wars; but for a beleaguered island they may be safely ranked as morale-builders both for the military and civilian members of the population. A considerable part of the war work of the Division of Applied Biology was connected with the problem of maintaining a flow of food to Britain that was edible, nutritious, and as far as possible, appetizing and palatable too. As the German navy was doing its utmost all the while to bring about the starvation of the British people, the work of this branch of the National Research Council can be regarded as a sidelight on the Battle of the Atlantic, in which the scientists were backstage participants.

It is unnecessary here to dilate upon the prominent part bacon plays in normal times on the British food table. Bacon is a tasty commodity which must however be classed among the perishable foods. It has always been a problem for the Canadian producer, even in peacetime, to get his product to the British breakfast table before some deterioration of quality can develop. On the average, Danish bacon in pre-war years reached the English retailer only eighteen days after killing. This was one reason, though by no means the only one, why Denmark regularly captured more than one-half of the British market, while Canada has averaged over the past forty years about 17 per cent., and fell in 1931 to an all-time low of one-half of 1 per cent.

War disrupts shipping; submarine campaigns necessitate slow convoys; every loss of a refrigerator ship aggravates the problem; bombing of ports slows down the handling of cargo. Pre-war export curing practices had been designed for a ten-day voyage from Canada; the use of convoys extended the period to twenty days or more. In order to be sure of receiving Canadian bacon in fit condition to eat, the British Ministry of Food early in the war had to sacrifice some palatability and request the Canadian government to return to a harder cure. When Denmark was overrun in May 1940, Canada became overnight the chief remaining source of British bacon; and, as it later proved, three-quarters of the British wartime

bacon ration came from Canada. Early in 1941, British shipping losses reached the point where consideration had to be
given to the shipping of Canadian bacon under completely
unrefrigerated transport. These facts are cited as the background against which the work of the National Research Council was conducted.

When war broke out it was anticipated that better methods
of preserving Canadian bacon would be needed, and on its
own initiative the group associated with food research (within
the Division of Applied Biology) began a series of investigations.
More than 100 chemicals were tested extensively for their
effectiveness in maintaining quality in bacon. While some of
the better treatments offered distinct possibilities for extending
the storage life, about doubling the possible holding or shipping
period at a given temperature, none was entirely satisfactory.
Smoking and drying produced the best results, and except for
a heavy mould growth, bacon so treated was in a satisfactory
condition after two months' storage at 60°F.

When convoys came into use, and the British asked for a
somewhat harder cure, standard curing practices were recommended to all Canadian packing plants which would increase
the salt content while decreasing the average time required for
curing. These recommendations were substantially accepted by
the Canadian packing industry. While this wartime cure was
somewhat too salty for the British palate, the reports received
from the other side indicated that as a war measure it resulted
in a satisfactory product. The conclusion of these early studies
was that refrigeration was the best preservative of all. When
a shortage of refrigerator ships in 1941 led to the prospect that
Canadian bacon would have to go forward in unrefrigerated
vessels, the food section of the National Research Council attempted to find an answer in the rapid installation of emergency
refrigeration units in ordinary cargo holds.

Cables from London in April 1941 broke the bad news. The
shortage of refrigerated shipping space had reached a difficult
if not a critical stage. Bacon would probably have to be shipped
as ordinary cargo. The salt cure adopted when the convoy
system went into effect had been based on the assumption that
bacon would still be shipped at temperatures near the freezing

point. But if bacon was to be forwarded in unrefrigerated vessels there would probably have to be a return to still harder cures, using borax and boric acid, as in the First World War. "Such an embalmed product may have been nutritious, but it was almost inedible," wrote a member of the food group. "The resulting British prejudice against Canadian bacon did our post-war trade [i.e., after 1918] untold harm." For the sake of the British consumer and the reputation of the Canadian producer too, it was highly desirable to explore every other possibility before returning to the borax cure. Conferences were called at Ottawa. In the United States, shippers suggested that bacon might be hard-frozen before stowage and then shipped either in heavily insulated space without refrigeration, or surrounded with one or several layers of some cargo with good insulating properties, such as lard. But limited Canadian facilities did not offer much hope of adopting the practice here. The Canadian group then suggested that ordinary cargo holds could be converted into refrigerated space by the installation of emergency refrigerating equipment.

Authority was given to the National Research Council group to explore this possibility with the shipping companies, the supply firms, and the Ministries of Food and Transport. Scepticism concerning its success was wide-spread, but, provided the scheme met certain necessities of the shipping situation, cooperation was freely promised for an experiment with the plan. It was stipulated that the emergency installations must not delay the sailing date of the vessels, and that the cargo holds selected must not be obstructed by air trunks or other permanent gear.

Before the refrigeration specialists at Ottawa had proceeded very far with their designs for emergency equipment, a long distance call from Montreal on May 20, 1941, brought a message from the Transport Controller announcing that the *Vancouver Island*[4] had been assigned for the first trial shipment of bacon to Britain, and that it would be loading at Montreal between June 10-20.

This was short notice, but every effort had to be made to

[4] Formerly the German *Weser,* captured off the coast of Mexico by the *Prince Robert* some months earlier.

get the equipment assembled and installed in such a way as
not to delay the sailing date. The National Research Council
picked up the challenge. Even in wartime, one of the first
questions to be answered when new projects were proposed
was: Where is the money coming from? Fortunately there
was in existence the "Santa Claus" fund, mentioned earlier
in this volume (see pp. 19-22). The Bacon Board reimbursed
the Council in the long run, but in the meantime there was
no delay because of finances.

That same afternoon, special motors required for the refrigerating units had been located by long distance telephone.
A Toledo firm, which had been previously advised that Canada
might require such motors for a special war job, had held
them, and now started them on their way to Canada only
an hour after the definite order was received.

Three complete refrigeration units had to be assembled, each
into a compact box 5½ feet wide, 11 feet long, and 6 feet
high. In normal peacetime operations, many weeks or even
months would have been demanded for such a complicated
assembly with its fabrication of fine tubing. Toronto workmen stayed on the job thirty-six hours at a time without a
break, and the job was completed in the ten days allowed.
The units were finished on a Saturday night. Ontario laws
forbade truck transport on the Sabbath, but special dispensation was obtained from the Minister of Highways, and the
refrigeration plants were rushed to Montreal. Elaborate tests
were applied with facilities available at McGill University,
and when the vessel arrived in port the units were ready for
installation.

Again the race against time. Without stopping for sleep,
or at best catching a few minutes' rest stretched out on cheese
boxes stacked in an adjoining hold, or by luck in one of the
ship's cabins, Montreal workmen stayed 36, 48, even 72 hours
continuously on the job, and in three days the units had been
installed, the air ducts erected, and the refrigeration system
was working exactly as planned. The Bacon Board had arranged
to have a cargo of bacon on the dockside ready for shipment.
It was there, and was loaded into the cooled space in record

time. The departure time of the *Vancouver Island* was not delayed by a single minute.

It was not the ideal job the refrigeration experts would have liked to see, of course. There was no insulation in the vessel: nothing between the sea-water of the Atlantic and the cargo, except the steel plates of the hull and the cargo battens. But a cable came back from Britain a few days later reading: "Bacon with temporary refrigeration discharged generally satisfactory condition." On the next voyage of the *Vancouver Island* improvements were made, including the insulation of the hold with blankets of Nova Scotia eel grass, and the condition of this cargo on arrival was highly satisfactory. Automatic defrosting controls were installed on the third trial, but on this voyage the former German vessel *Weser*, which the Nazis had sworn to destroy on her maiden voyage as a British ship, became a victim of enemy action. However, the method had been proved. Rt. Hon. A. V. Alexander, First Lord of the Admiralty, in an address at London, England, in February 1945, praised the Canadian contribution to the emergency refrigeration programme. All in all, nineteen vessels had been converted by September 1944, five of them in Canada. The converted vessels had a capacity representing ten weeks' ration, or one-fifth of the nation's bacon ration requirement. Lord Alexander added that while imports of other foodstuffs fell in 1944, those of meats and bacon remained steady and finally increased.

Dried Eggs by the Billion

The Nazi invasion of the Low Countries in 1940 cut off the principal British supply of shell eggs. Later, the Japanese occupation of the Chinese ports ended the export of dried eggs from that country. The egg ration in Britain fell to one egg per person per month. Britain turned to the Western Hemisphere for ways of making up the deficiencies. The problem of finding sufficient shipping space for shell eggs—which had to be refrigerated—became increasingly difficult throughout 1941. Liquid egg is seventy-five per cent. water: the oval shell is highly wasteful of cargo space. In March 1942 the critical shipping situation drove the British Ministry of Food to cease importations of shell eggs. The substitution of dried eggs subsequently saved, it is said, one million tons of shipping annually, since a case of eggs (thirty dozen) could be put into a ten-pound package of powder occupying one-sixth of the space.

The Food Ministry's dictum caught Canada unprepared. There were only three egg-drying plants in the country, producing a total of less than 600,000 pounds of powder per annum of a quality more suitable for trade baking purposes than for table use as scrambled egg or omelette. Two years later, production of powder in eleven Canadian plants had been multiplied about thirty-five times, equivalent to about a billion eggs a year; and largely through the studies of the National Research Council, the quality and keeping virtues of the product had been materially improved.

Requests for help came from the Department of Agriculture. Expectation that the problem would arise had led the National Research Council to begin investigations more than a year before, in February 1941. A group of able scientists were assigned to examine various aspects of the problem.

The first need was for a yardstick of quality. Many foods are assessed by jury panels of human tasters, but something more objective was desired. An answer was found in fluorescence tests. This phenomenon has been known for many years. In a darkened room with ultra-violet light, many objects take on strange appearances: rock specimens glow with many colours; chlorophyll in growing plants appears as a vivid red; eggs fluoresce with a rich blue glow. The significant thing is that as the egg deteriorates in quality, the deeper the blue of the fluorescent glow becomes.

A new method of measuring quality based on fluorescence was thus evolved. A beam of ultra-violet light was thrown upon defatted egg powder in a protein solvent, causing the solution to fluoresce. The intensity of fluorescence was measured by an Electric Eye placed at right angles to the incident ultra-violet beam. Tests showed that, in general, the worse the powder tasted, the more it fluoresced, and vice versa. Supplemented by other methods, it proved a more precise and objective means of investigating quality.

These tests, applied to manufacturing and processing operations in Canada, soon produced fruitful new information. Egg powder proved to be considerably more perishable than had been suspected. It was particularly vulnerable to slightly raised temperatures. The practice had hitherto been to barrel hot egg powder just as it came from the drier. Since the powder was a good insulator, it remained hot for days, and even before it was shipped, serious deterioration in quality had thus occurred. The practice was now changed. Facilities for cooling the powder within a few minutes of drying were installed in all Canadian plants.

Lower drying temperatures were recommended. This in turn, however, permitted a higher number of bacteria to survive the drying process, and additional care had to be given to reduce initial contamination. Bacteriological studies showed that the liquid egg prepared for the driers should never be held at temperatures higher than 45°F. Plant operators had to install additional cooling equipment to meet this requirement. Recommendations were made that shipments of powder should always be cooled below 60°F. before storing them on board ship. Further inquiry showed that powder with a low moisture content kept better: so highly resistant packages were devised. Packing in carbon dioxide was proved to have a definitely preservative action.

Before the end of the war, Canada had acquired the reputation of producing dried egg of the highest quality in the world. J. A. Peacock, Director of Egg Supplies, British Ministry of Food, on a visit to Canada in 1943, asserted that dried eggs were proving to be one of the greatest single food contributions of the war, and that the Canadian product was astonishingly good. Tributes came from unexpected sources. E. W. Harrold, Associate Editor of the Ottawa *Citizen,* in his weekly diary "Our Own Pepys", recorded the following under date of London, England, Thursday, May 4, 1944:

" . . . and so had lunch on an omelette and salad at the Royal Societies Club in Dover Street, and the omelette so tasty I thought it real fresh egg, but it was made of the powdered kind which amazed me."

Dehydrated Pork

When the Battle of the Atlantic was at its peak, British authorities advised Canada that it might be necessary to begin importing meat from Canada in a dehydrated form. An investigation was started in the Division of Applied Biology. Pork was cooked in an open steam-jacketed kettle, followed by mincing and tunnel-tray drying in four hours or less. The product retained a high percentage of thiamin and was as palatable as the initial cooked material. A trial shipment to Britain brought the response that if shipping problems made it necessary, the British people would be only too glad to accept dried pork of similar quality. It proved to be much more stable than other dehydrated products. Storage for a year in tin plate containers at normal and somewhat elevated temperatures caused little decrease in palatability. The shipping situation gradually improved and it did not become necessary to embark on the dehydration of Canadian meats on a large scale.

Wartime Food Packaging

As a major source of food for Britain and our other Allies, and for our overseas forces, Canada had to solve the problem of getting perishable commodities to their destination in a fit and usable condition. Protection had to be provided against water, water-vapour, greases, moulds, insects, and rough handling, and in special circumstances against oxygen in the atmosphere and other agencies of deterioration. The problem exists in time of peace, but the conditions of 1939-45 seriously complicated it. There was a great increase in shipments of dehydrated products, which are especially susceptible to water-vapour. The supply of tin was restricted; the use of other strategic materials was of course denied; shortages of caps and closures, lack of suitable packaging machinery, transport difficulties, availability and cost, for the most part, ruled out non-strategic metals and glass. The choice of packaging materials was, therefore, narrowed down to wood products, their derivatives, and plastics.

It is relatively easy to devise a package to shed water, but water-vapour is another matter. Packaged foods had to be distributed from the tropics to the polar regions, carried at lofty altitudes by aircraft, and into the depth of the ocean by submarines. For certain commodities packages must retain their resistance to water-vapour over a wide range of temperatures and stand up to the bending or flexing caused by variations in atmospheric pressure. Impregnation with wax may make paper—the cheapest packing material—completely water-proof, but cellulose fibres protruding through the coating offer easy wicking channels which will transmit water-vapour readily, especially if the pressures differ on the two sides of the paper. Vapour-resistant coatings that seal off the fibres at the surface of the stock provide more effective barriers. Denser paper stocks and regenerated cellulose products were not only better moisture barriers in themselves, but because of smoother surfaces, permitted more effective coatings to be applied.

Treated materials must be relatively thin if they are to be fabricated into containers, for thick layers will not fold easily without weakening the stock or impairing the coating. A barrier which is excellent in sheet form may produce a mediocre package if ineffectively sealed and closed. Even under the best conditions the final package proved to be from two to ten times as permeable to moisture as was the original stock tested in flat form. These were some of the observations made by the food packaging group working within the Division of Applied Biology during the war years, which subjected hundreds of materials to severe tests.

Films could be made flexible by plasticizing: in some packaging materials this was done by adding an agent which retained some water, thus keeping the film moist and flexible. But such wrappers were better not placed directly in contact with a hygroscopic dried food, since the latter was likely to extract moisture from the film-coating, thus making it brittle to the point where it would crack easily and allow water-vapour or other moisture to pass through.

These findings were applied to specific packaging jobs. For the shipment of dried egg powder, for example, the group developed a bag-in-carton type of package, with several obvious advantages: it used wax-coated cellophane, which was a good moisture barrier and reduced flexing difficulties to a minimum; the outer carton provided mechanical protection; facilities for manufacture were available; and the British could use all the untreated kraft that came to hand for subsequent pulping and paper-making of their own. Dried milk powder presented a special problem, since it had to be protected from the oxygen in the air, which caused deterioration of the butterfat fraction. A solution was found in a wax-coated laminated cellophane package packed with carbon dioxide. From such a package the carbon dioxide slowly escapes and the package collapses, since the oxygen and nitrogen of the atmosphere penetrate very slowly. The escaping gas causes the bag to be drawn tightly about the contents, giving a vacuum-type pack with a hard, brick-like feel. Failures and leaks are readily detected because the package becomes soft again. In factory-scale tests with such packages, failures of not more than two per cent. were recorded.

CHAPTER X

THE MEDICAL FRONT

IN DEVISING new engines of war, the comfort and physiological well-being of the prospective human operator of the machine are seldom in the forefront of the inventor's mind. Yet there is little or no gain in devising sensational new military weapons for offence or defence if, in order to operate them, man must expose himself to environmental hazards which he will not in all probability survive, or which will rapidly reduce his efficiency to the point where the new apparatus fails to work. The military scientist thrusts fighting man into new frontiers of physical environment, often highly inimical; war exposes man to hostile bacteria and pests unknown in his native habitat, and against which his own body has never evolved defences. For these and other reasons, the science of war calls for aid upon the biologist, the physiologist, the bacteriologist, the psychologist, the surgeon, and others, to devise protective and compensatory equipment, so as to make the maximum use out of new discoveries in military fields, to provide a maximum of well-being for the soldier, to modify an unfriendly environment wherever possible; and finally, if in spite of all these measures the fighting man becomes a casualty, to offer whatever may be possible by way of restoration, salvage, and repair. Moreover, in pushing back the frontiers of feasible operation, ever testing new limits of practicability, it is found that some individuals are equipped by nature to withstand the strains better than others; and so the physiologist and psychologist, by devising suitable screens for non-susceptibility, superior acuteness of senses, endurance, and other qualities, can select the best men for certain tasks and thus help the fighting forces do a better job.

In all these fields Canadian scientists and medical personnel played an important and valuable role in the Second World War: indeed, in some of them, advances were made here earlier than in any other country. It is the writer's aim and purpose in this chapter to relate a few of the highlights.

The limits of human endurance which are tested by modern war machines can be seen in a clear and varied way in the field of aviation; and it was in aviation medicine that Canadian scientists and medical men achieved perhaps their most spectacular successes. The operation of fast modern aircraft at increasing speeds and loftier altitudes exposes airmen to a number of serious new threats and strains. Above ten thousand feet, the oxygen supply in the air is inadequate and must be supplemented in some way. Rapid changes of direction or the buffeting of winds and air currents may bring on motion sickness. Rapid and material changes in atmospheric pressure such as are experienced in ascents to 30,000, 35,000, and 40,-000 feet may expose the airman to "decompression sickness", an ailment which the diver—who suffers the same symptoms—calls "the bends". The centrifugal forces brought to bear on the body of an airman who brings his aircraft quickly out of a power-dive tend to whirl all the body fluids outward (i.e., downward) as though they were in a centrifuge, and as a result the eyes, the brain, and the upper part of the flier's body may lose their accustomed blood supply long enough to cause a dim-out, black-out, or complete unconsciousness. The temperature at 35,000 feet above the ground—even if the ground in this case is a sweltering desert—may be as low as −40°F., and military aircraft are usually stripped down heroically for speed and range with small provision for the heating of cabins or other amenities. Before full advantage could be taken of the gains made by aeronautical engineers and physicists through the devising of modern aircraft, it was necessary to cope with these and other physiological conditions. As scientists and engineers go on extending the range of speed and altitude and manoeuvrability of aircraft, the challenge to the physiologist will, of course, continue, and to an increasing extent.

Aviation medical research had received a powerful stimulus during World War I, but it then fell into a period of neglect which ended only when Hitler had made manifest to the world that another global war was on the way. Late in 1938, Major A. A. James, representing the Royal Canadian Army Medical

Corps, approached Sir Frederick Banting, Professor of Medical Research, University of Toronto, to suggest that some problems of aviation medicine be investigated in Sir Frederick's research department. A beginning was soon made in this direction. But Sir Frederick Banting immediately saw the advantages of organizing aviation medical research on a *national* basis, and he went to Ottawa to interview the head of the National Research Council (Major-General A. G. L. McNaughton) and Air Vice-Marshal Croil, then Chief of Air Staff, R.C.A.F. After considerable discussion and exchange of correspondence, an inter-departmental committee was set up at Ottawa, the first meeting being held on June 27, 1939. In the following March, as a result of strong recommendations from Dean C. J. Mackenzie, Acting President of the National Research Council, supported by Sir Frederick Banting, the status of the committee was changed to that of an Associate Committee of the National Research Council. Among the many advantages to be derived from the change were these: trained non-medical personnel, such as biochemists, could be more readily engaged; the research equipment of the Council would be fully available; the liaison service of the Council with Britain's scientists could be utilized; appointments, purchasing, and accounting would be greatly simplified and facilitated.

The problems singled out in June 1939 as having the highest priority in aviation medicine were decompression sickness, oxygen supply, and psychological tests for the selection of aircrew.

Decompression Sickness

In order to investigate the causes of decompression sickness, believed to be due to the gradual liberation of gases within the body and the formation of tiny bubbles which lodge in small blood vessels and cut off the normal flow of blood to certain areas, the Committee, as early as June 1939, strongly recommended the building by the National Research Council of a decompression chamber. This was done in the following year, the unit being installed at No. 1 Clinical Investigation Unit, R.C.A.F., Toronto. So as to test the effects of low temperatures as well as of changes in pressures, the equipment took the form of a large cold room in which the temperature could be lowered to —65°F., and at the same time the pressure could be reduced until it was equivalent to an altitude of 50,000 feet above sea level. It was the first equipment of its kind on the continent. The value of this early beginning in aviation research was not confined to Canada or even to the Commonwealth. Dr. C. B. Stewart, of the National Research Council, who was present at the first meeting of the Committee on Aviation Medical Research in June 1939, and was later appointed Secretary, notes[1] that "To this low-temperature, low-pressure chamber at Toronto, American investigators brought equipment and models for testing while similar installations of their own were being built. The scientists of the neighbouring countries worked in close harmony on all such problems." Concerning the early start in the general attack on aviation medicine, Dr. Stewart said: "When war came in September 1939, the nucleus of an aviation medical research team was already in existence and equipment available or in process of construction. Some of this equipment was of totally new design and permitted investigation of problems hitherto almost untouched. As a result, Canadian research workers were more than a year ahead of American groups in some fields."

Low-pressure chambers were also constructed at London, Ontario, at Regina, and at Halifax: the first extensive studies undertaken anywhere on decompression sickness due to ascent to lofty altitudes were conducted at these points, beginning in December 1940. Volunteer medical students acted as subjects in repeated and exacting tests. It was demonstrated that decompression sickness could be acutely incapacitating, and that at altitudes between 30,000 and 40,000 feet its incidence was frequent enough to constitute a serious military hazard. The severity of symptoms ranged from unpleasant pain in a limb to a general muscular stiffening and signs of impending collapse. The lowest altitude at which severe symptoms occurred in any student was 25,000 feet, with over a third of the volunteers showing symptoms at a simulated altitude of 35,000 feet.

Though some progress was made in understanding the exact

[1] In "Canadian Research in Aviation Medicine", *Public Affairs* (March 1947).

FOOD

A vitamin assay laboratory

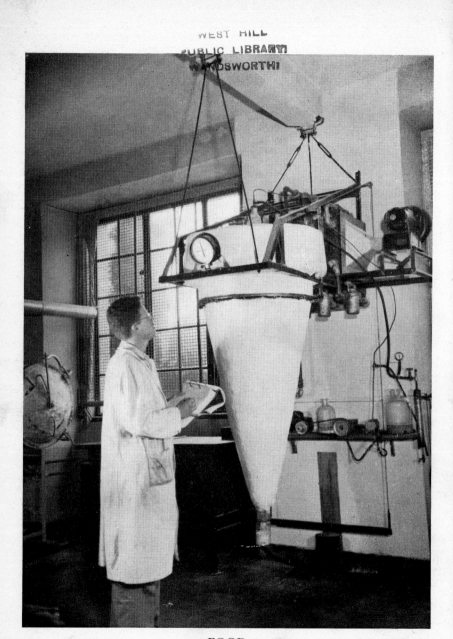

FOOD

Laboratory model spray drier for drying milk and eggs

cause of decompression sickness, much still remained obscure at
the end of the war. It was fairly generally assumed that the
sickness arose from the liberation of gas from solution, mainly
nitrogen, but it was not clear whether this gas was freed in
the blood stream or in other tissues, or whether the symptoms
were produced by local gas formation or to some extent by
the formation of gas in the central nervous system.

A fairly satisfactory preventive for decompression sickness
was found in the inhalation of pure oxygen for some time
before ascending. This reduced the nitrogen in the blood
stream. A system of overnight breathing of oxygen permitted
an interval of several hours before take-off without the beneficial
effect being lost.

Some individuals were found to be more susceptible to decompression sickness than others, and tests were devised so that
crews could be chosen with a lower probability of their becoming victims to the distress in flight.

As the war progressed, the likelihood emerged that most
aerial battles would be fought at altitudes below the point
where serious trouble was to be anticipated, and thereafter
attention was focused mainly on the needs of high-altitude
photographic reconnaissance operations and other flights into
the stratosphere. The early prospect of pressurized cabins in
aircraft operating at the loftiest altitudes was also a factor
affecting research in the later stages of the war.

Effects of an Inadequate Supply of Oxygen

Owing to reduced atmospheric pressure, it becomes increasingly difficult and finally impossible for the human system to
obtain sufficient oxygen for its needs as aircraft ascend above
10,000 feet. The effects of insufficient oxygen are insidious,
because there is often no sense of discomfort and an airman
may continue blissfully ignorant of his increasing need of oxygen until his sudden collapse. The oxygen supply system provided for Canadian, British, and American fliers as late as
1939 was wasteful and inadequate in other ways. The low
temperatures at lofty altitudes frequently stopped its operation
owing to the freezing of condensed moisture from the breath or
from the moisture then always present in commercially avail-

able supplies of oxygen. The weight of equipment necessary to supply the quantity needed to service the wasteful masks and the large tanks required for carrying oxygen in gaseous form compelled aircraft designers and equippers—concerned as they were about speed and range—to cut down the oxygen supply to inadequate levels, and it was not unusual for it to be exhausted long before a mission was over. All of these matters required urgent and thorough attention if fliers were to be protected from anoxia (the technical term for the condition arising in the human body from insufficient oxygen) and if the efficiency of the flying force was to be maintained.

This problem was faced by the Committee on Aviation Medical Research at its second meeting on October 16, 1939. Funds were allocated to the University of Toronto to investigate the problem, to develop an emergency oxygen apparatus, and to design a portable apparatus for producing gaseous oxygen. This work was continued when the Associate Committee on Aviation Medical Research was formed in 1940, and on December 19, 1941, a sub-committee working exclusively on oxygen equipment was formed. In conjunction with R.C.A.F. personnel, this team designed the first oxygen mask used by the Allies which did not freeze up at low temperatures. This was used throughout the war on transatlantic flights by R.A.F. Ferry Command and by R.C.A.F. aircrew in Canada. Essential features of this design were incorporated into late British and American models.

This project began late in 1940 when a sample of the latest R.A.F. oxygen mask was made available to Sir Frederick Banting and tested in the new low-pressure low-temperature unit at Toronto. It was found not to be resistant to freezing, and improvements were suggested. A standard American type of oxygen mouthpiece was tried out by Banting in a wind tunnel: it was unsatisfactory for service use, and it, too, froze up in low temperatures. Americans were known to be working on a frost-proof model, but supply difficulties made it unlikely that the R.C.A.F. would be able to draw upon either improved British or American models, and so work continued actively in Canada. Sir Frederick Banting was able to procure from the British in 1941 samples of currently used German oxygen masks, and these were found to be resistant to freezing. A Canadian version of this mask gave sufficiently good results to warrant the development of an all-Canadian type, and such a project was launched on April 28, 1941.

Among the specifications which had to be met was that such a mask must be usable with the different types of oxygen supply currently in use in the R.A.F. and in the R.C.A.F., and it had to work well with the intercommunication equipment being developed for the R.C.A.F. A commercial mould was ready by December 1941. Another problem was to fit masks to faces of different proportions and face-shapes: this first mould proved suitable for small faces, and a mould suitable for average faces was ready by April 1942.

The earlier oxygen systems were wasteful of the gas, and a number of different approaches were explored to provide a system which would conserve the supply of oxygen and yet deliver whatever quantity was needed at higher altitudes. The Department of Physics of the University of Toronto was asked, in the spring of 1941, to work on this project. A valve was to be developed which would deliver either pure oxygen or a mixture of half oxygen and half air, as determined by a manual control light enough to be worn attached to the airman's clothing. This was accomplished before the end of the year. Meanwhile the R.C.A.F. began the development of a "demand" valve, intended to operate on the principle that the instinctively deeper breathing of the flier as altitude increased would automatically increase the supply of oxygen as needed. To make the richness of the mixture supplied increase exactly with the altitude, an aneroid diluter valve was developed, providing a barometric control of the percentage of oxygen in the mixture supplied. This was a joint project of the University of Toronto and the R.C.A.F., financed by a special grant. A number of such valves were made and thoroughly tested. By the end of 1943 complete manufacturing drawings were delivered and the valve went into commercial production. It became standard equipment for operational aircraft in the R.C.A.F., and application was made for Canadian and United States patents. Further improvements and modifications included a type with automatic safety pressures above 28,000 feet (increasing the flow to the lungs), another type which incorporated a manually controlled pressure breathing attachment for use above 35,000 feet, and a new "demand" valve with an auxiliary reservoir flow for safety at high altitudes. Ultimately a mask was developed which allowed our fighters to exceed 40,000 feet and bring down German reconnaissance aircraft fitted with pressure cabins, hitherto out of reach of Allied airmen.[2]

The gain to be expected in the reduced weight of the containers carrying liquid oxygen rather than gaseous oxygen (which required relatively large containers) was realized from the beginning, but in the early stages of the war the method of controlling flow from a liquid oxygen supply was unsatisfactory, while the introduction of elaborate and heavy control equipment to overcome this would defeat the aim of reducing weight. However, as the size and carrying capacity of aircraft increased, and as the need for larger and larger supplies of oxygen grew, the problem had to be re-examined. In July 1943 the Department of Physics of the University of Toronto was asked to devise liquid oxygen equipment suitable for large passenger transports. Prototype models were built and flight trials carried out in the spring of 1944. In November 1944, such a liquid oxygen system suitable for a crew of seven and twenty passengers was fitted into an aircraft for a transatlantic flight, and was flown to Britain, at 20,000 feet for most of the journey. The system was further examined and tested in Britain and subsequently authorized for use in R.C.A.F. transports flying between fixed bases. The first two of a group of passenger transports built for the R.C.A.F. were equipped with liquid oxygen units built at the Department of Physics. The liquid oxygen evaporator, which formed a part of the unit, used some novel features, provided definite advantages in flow control over other models, and promised to be of definite post-war value in civilian transport.

Centrifugal Force

As early as the Munich Conference, when war began to appear inevitable, discussions arranged by Sir Frederick Banting turned upon the problem of protecting fliers from the effects

[2] Dr. C. B. Stewart, *op. cit.*

of centrifugal force such as they experienced when making tight turns (i.e., of short radius) at high speed, or when pulling suddenly out of a power dive. Under these circumstances of high acceleration, the human body is subjected to unaccustomed forces, and if the acceleration is sharp enough the flier will lose consciousness. In effect, the airman is pushed down against his seat with a force several times greater than gravity, or normal weight. The airman's normal weight is usually symbolized as "G" and the degree of increase measured in multiples of this normal weight. Thus, at an acceleration of 5G, a man whose normal weight is 150 pounds temporarily weighs 750 pounds. One effect of this is to make it difficult for the airman to move his arms and legs, which have temporarily become so much heavier than normal. But there are even more serious results. Between 3G and 5G the first symptoms of loss of vision appear. Between 4G and 6G (individuals differ somewhat in their resistance to the force) the threshold of complete "black-out" or loss of vision is reached. At about 1G higher than the acceleration bringing about loss of vision, the airman loses consciousness entirely. Consciousness and vision return when the aircraft levels out and the centrifugal force is no longer operative.

The adverse effect on the flier during high acceleration was believed to be due to the inability of the heart to pump blood to the head against the centrifugal force created by the sharp turn of the aircraft, and the problem set in 1938 was to discover some means of offsetting or obviating the effect upon the circulatory system.

First experiments under the Committee on Aviation Medical Research began immediately after the outbreak of war in September 1939. Using a small centrifuge and experimenting with mice, it was learned that accelerations which would kill the animals when unprotected failed to prove fatal when they were suspended in thin rubber envelopes in water. This gave rise to the decision to attempt to build a flier's suit which would utilize this principle.

Dr. W. R. Franks, who directed the research in this project, was one of the two senior members on the staff of Sir Frederick Banting's Department of Medical Research. As Wing Commander Franks he was director of Aviation Medical Research for the R.C.A.F. overseas from 1941 to 1943, and in 1944 became director of the Canadian programme.

Franks and his colleagues decided in 1939 to build a tight rubber suit containing fluid, with the idea that the tendency of the blood and other movable structures of the body to be displaced downward during acceleration would thus be counteracted. The same centrifugal force acting on the liquid in the suit would drive it downward and increase the external pressure upon the lower part of the flier's body. This would in turn increase the internal pressure within the lower part of the body, prevent or reduce the downward displacement of blood, and thus assure to the upper part of the body the supply of blood needed to maintain sense efficiency and consciousness.

It was early recognized by Sir Frederick Banting that an investigation of this kind could not be successfully pursued without a human centrifuge, in which the tight turns at high speed of the modern aircraft could be readily simulated. On his recommendation the National Research Council financed the design and construction of such a centrifuge at No. 1 Clinical Investigation Unit, Toronto. A car or gondola resembling an airplane cockpit was suspended from a horizontal arm in such a way that when the arm revolved the car was swung in a circle 32 feet in diameter. The airman seated in the cockpit underwent the same sensations and physiological changes as in actual aerial manoeuvres in a modern aircraft. This was the first such installation in any Allied country. It was later copied by the United States, two such devices being built in civilian laboratories there, one at the Mayo Foundation and the other at the University of Southern California.[3] Meanwhile, Americans used the Canadian centrifuge to test their own air-filled "anti-G" suits, thus completing them a year earlier than would have been possible.

When the experiments began, little was known as to how extensively the body should be protected and how the pressure should be distributed. The earliest designs were more elaborate than later proved necessary. A technical problem of some

[3] See James Phinney Baxter 3rd, *Scientists Against Time* (Little, Brown and Co., Boston, 1948), p. 391.

difficulty was that of making the fabric and seams strong enough to withstand the water pressures created by great centrifugal force, and several rubber companies in Toronto made valuable contributions in this respect. As later perfected, the Franks suit fitted the wearer closely, and the water was contained in a number of overlapping bags so that the pressure was transmitted from one to the next. The bags covered only a small part of the body, but the pressure developed in them was distributed over the remainder of the body by tension on the fabric.

First flight tests were conducted in a Spitfire in the early days of June 1940. These vindicated the general principle of the suit, but pointed to the need of drastic improvements. These were accomplished in the course of additional research and testing. Improved models were prepared for the R.A.F. and the U.S. Air Force. It is a sad sidelight that Sir Frederick Banting was killed in Newfoundland in an airplane crash while *en route* to Britain to communicate the details of his anti-blackout suit to the R.A.F. Wing Commander Franks was on his way to Britain by surface vessel at the time in connection with the same project.

Preliminary flight tests were carried out at Farnborough, England, in the summer of 1941, which showed that the suit provided increased resistance to the effects of acceleration, and protected the flier against fatigue. Trials were considered sufficiently successful to justify the production in the United Kingdom of a considerable number of suits for large-scale trials. Some objections were voiced against the use of the suit. Pilots complained of discomfort while waiting "at the ready", and of difficulty, while wearing the suit in simulated combat operations, in turning to search for enemy aircraft coming from behind. Moreover, as the improving fortunes of war had enabled the R.C.A.F. to switch from defensive to offensive operations, their operational need for an anti-G suit fell off somewhat.

However, the Fleet Air Arm of the Royal Navy responded with more enthusiasm to trials being held at the same time. The Franks suit was used operationally for the first time by the Fleet Air Arm at Oran in November 1942, where it was found to give valuable tactical advantages enabling the pilots to out-manoeuvre the enemy. This was the beginning of its considerable use by the Fleet Air Arm on actual operations.

The human centrifuge at Toronto permitted a scientific investigation of the physiological and medical results of acceleration of human beings, and records were obtained on a total of over 5500 runs on over 540 subjects. Medically fit aircrew between the ages of eighteen and thirty-five were used. A more detailed study of the physiological effects of acceleration was possible with the use of cats and monkeys on a small centrifuge constructed in the Montreal Neurological Institute. Coloured motion pictures of the cerebral vessels were made through windows in the skull. Acceleration in a direction tending to drive blood from the head to the feet did not empty the cerebral vessels, but they became darker as though the blood had become stagnant. A blanching of the cortical tissue indicated some loss of blood from the capillaries.

Motion Sickness

Motion sickness, of which the variety best known to the civilian in the past has been seasickness, was of concern to all three branches of the armed forces; and all services conducted research in this field. In both the Navy and the Air Force, personnel were frequently exposed to motion likely to cause sickness, and particularly susceptible individuals were likely to be grounded if repeatedly disabled, or in any event, on prolonged missions were likely to become only gradually adjusted to the motion. As the war progressed it seemed likely that the most serious consequence of motion sickness might apply to Army invasion troops, launched in landing craft, assault boats, or in aircraft and gliders, exposed to violent motion for a relatively short time, but needing to arrive on hostile territory in the best physical and psychological condition, not disabled or reduced in efficiency because of motion sickness. Accordingly, as the date drew near for the invasion of Europe, efforts were redoubled to find the best possible preventive, especially by the sub-committee set up under the Associate Committee on Naval Medical Research. The keen interest of the Army in the problem led to supplementary work in an Army committee under the direction of Dr. R. L. Noble, at the Institute of

Endocrinology, McGill University. In the Associate Committee on Aviation Medical Research, work began in February 1942 at Regina, and was supplemented by experiments conducted at Toronto in 1942 and 1943.

One handicap to effective work in this field was that many important details of the cause and mechanism of the production of motion sickness were not known at the outbreak of war; and although in the following six years a tremendous amount of work was done in Canada, the United States, and the United Kingdom, advancing man's knowledge of the subject, no radically new drugs or methods of treatment were uncovered, nor was the nature of the sickness fully disclosed. But new combinations of already known remedies were evolved which acted as preventives in a high percentage of cases.

In order to make scientific studies of motion sickness, it was necessary to establish objective criteria or standards as to what signs and symptoms indicated an onset of the sickness. Psychological factors had to be eliminated by the use of dummy pills, or placeboes, given to a proportion of the tested subjects. Also, an apparatus had to be devised which would bring about the condition. Tests with these laboratory equipments were frequently followed by actual trials at sea.

A study of motion sickness was one of the first investigations undertaken by the Associate Committee on Naval Medical Research when it was created in 1941. Experimental methods of producing sickness were explored by machines constructed at Montreal and Toronto. At first it was supposed that complicated combinations of horizontal and vertical motions were necessary, but later on, simple swings were shown to be effective. Six swings were installed at H.M.C.S. *York* and two at the Montreal Neurological Institute. Studies were made of the physiological causes of motion sickness. The theory earlier held, namely, that the chief cause of motion sickness was oscillatory stimulation of the labyrinths of the ear, the organs of balance, tended to be confirmed by these tests. Neither the position nor the movement of the body appeared to be of much importance, but the exact position of the head was found to be a determining factor. Visual and psychological elements, although sometimes very significant, were usually of secondary importance. Any idea that seasickness is all a matter of imagination was thoroughly disposed of. Sights and smells and unpleasant associations of memories might contribute to the onset of the sickness but were not found to be fundamental.

A study of the most effective drug or combination of drugs was undertaken by the Associate Committee on Naval Medical Research. Early Canadian work suggested that a combination of hyoscine, hyoscyamine, niacin, and a thiobarbiturate (V-9) was more effective than any one of these drugs used alone. Since the barbiturate tended to induce sleep, a small amount of benzedrine sulphate was at one time added to offset the hypnotic effect. Unfavourable effects attributed to the thiobarbiturate were detected and this was then removed from the compound. A combination of the other three drugs was widely tested in actual sea trials in the United Kingdom and on coastal and transatlantic convoy routes, more than 25,000 individuals being tested with various remedies. In a joint trial with the U.S. Navy and the National Research Council of the United States, the Canadian formula was tested against a U.S. remedy and against hyoscine alone. All were effective, and no significant difference could be shown among them. The U.S. official history reports that the improved combinations tested during the war were found to be effective in about 70 per cent. of the individuals who would otherwise have suffered from motion sickness. Another of the thiobarbiturate series, called V-12, was found to be a preventive, though it did not appear to be as effective as the earlier combination evolved in Canada. However, no deleterious effects of V-12, as contrasted with the earlier thiobarbiturate tested, were apparent. Sea trials were subsequently conducted on a combination of hyoscine, hyoscyamine, and V-12, and this was the final recommendation for a seasickness preventive by the Medical Research Committee of the R.C.N.

The Army picked up the problem at the stage where the R.C.N. "Pink Pill" had received a wide reputation as a more effective remedy. In 1942 the thesis was presented that it might be possible to find a new drug, such as one of the barbiturates, which would specifically affect those brain centres involved in motion sickness. Two commercial laboratories prepared and contributed some 175 compounds and derivatives for experimentation. Tests on dogs, conducted in swings and on the open reaches of the Ottawa River, showed that many barbiturates had the power to prevent motion sickness in 100 per cent. of the dogs, and without giving rise to undesirable side reactions. Extensive tests of these new drugs, none of which had hitherto been administered by mouth to living creatures, were conducted to measure their toxicity and their anaesthetic qualities. Obviously any drug which induced sleepiness, foggy vision, or other impairments of the efficiency of the soldier, was useless for actual invasion use. Experiments on humans were conducted at Camp Borden. Some of these barbiturates were found to possess little or no hypnotic action or other objectionable side effects, and arrangements were made to test human volunteers, from Reserve Army units in Montreal and from McGill students, on a special machine developed at the Montreal Neurological Institute.

The barbiturate V-12, already mentioned in the account of Navy tests, proved to be the most effective remedy against motion sickness in humans as produced on swings. Sea tests confirmed the real value of V-12, but, as already noted, it was no better than two of the other best remedies developed in Canada and the United States. To sum up, some progress was made during the war on a preventive for motion sickness, but there is every likelihood that more can be learned about the physiological mechanism of its production, as a result of which even more effective remedies will be discovered.

Protective Clothing

A tremendous amount of work was done on the design and manufacture of service clothing for protection against cold, heat, moisture, insects, chemical warfare agents, and other conditions, in the three Canadian services and in committees and sub-committees set up under the National Research Council. Only a few of the major investigations will be reported here.

A sub-committee on protective clothing was set up by the Associate Committee on Aviation Medical Research, with Group Captain G. E. Hall, A.F.C., as Chairman. Between February 20, 1942 and June 18, 1945, it held thirty meetings at Ottawa and Toronto. At first, protection against extremes of low temperature was given primary emphasis, but after the successful invasion of Europe the prospect of campaigns against the Japanese in tropical climates altered the pattern of the research. In July 1944, at No. 1 Clinical Investigation Unit, R.C.A.F., Toronto, construction began of a room for the simulation of tropical climates. The temperature range provided was from 50° to 160°F. (dry bulb), and the humidity control covered a range exceeding that found under normal tropical conditions.

The relationship between thickness of fabric and its effectiveness in providing thermal insulation was established in a series of tests. A double-pile wool fabric, made as light and pliable as possible by reduction of the number of threads per inch to the minimum necessary to hold the pile, proved to be the best of all the many fabrics tested. A test method was developed in which, for the first time, it was possible to measure scientifically the degree to which a material allowed water vapour to permeate it. This proved valuable for designing flying suits and also for tropical clothing, and the same method could be applied to leather for tests on Army boots.

In order to measure with some precision the protective qualities of clothing against cold and wind, devices were developed which could take into account the heat production, skin temperature, and loss of body heat of a test subject sitting in the clothing being tested, under various conditions of exposure to cold. The results so obtained were corroborated by the development of an "artificial man". This contained an electric heater controlled by a thermostat and a fan to circulate the air within it. The amount of electricity needed to maintain the internal temperature, under different conditions of exposure, gave the measure of the effectiveness of the clothing draped over the "artificial man". The analysis of heat exchange in clothing was extended to tropical conditions and under the direct rays of the sun.

Aircrew suits of battle-dress style were devised with some novel features. A two-piece winter flying suit used the double-pile fabric and was constructed with knees and elbows bent to suit a sitting man. Flying gloves, with fingers curved in the natural position of the hand at rest, were also produced.

Much work was done on electrically heated suits for the R.C.A.F. A master thermostat in the second of two models gave the wearer sensitive control with a single regulator: this model was accepted by the Air Force and produced for use by reconnaissance crews. Of this suit, Dr. Stewart, in the article already cited, wrote: "An excellent electrically heated aircrew suit was developed, which was used in patrol craft off the Canadian coasts. Many of the features of its design and the physiological data on which they were based were also used by the air services of our Allies." Electrically heated undergloves and underboots were also specially developed.

Against the opposite condition, that of excessive heat, a tropical uniform, cap, and boots were designed in 1945. Tests were made on a new style of air-conditioning belt, fitted with a small blower. The idea was to circulate air within the clothing, and provided the shirt was first wetted to provide water for evaporation, this feature proved helpful even under intense heat such as would be experienced in an aircraft parked in the sun.

A section of the Associate Committee on Naval Medical Research made studies which resulted in many radical changes in the clothing used in the naval service which added comfort to the men ashore and afloat while at the same time showing an advantage in operational and functional requirements over earlier types. Large-scale inter-service trials were conducted during the winter of 1943-44. Tests were held on all classes of ships operating in the Royal Canadian Navy, on some ships of the United States Navy, and on submarines. Of the many hundreds of items assembled for testing, about 150 were found suitable for sea trials. These were said to be the most comprehensive and most satisfactory tests ever carried out on cold-weather clothing for use at sea. These trials, supported by work done earlier and in other services, resulted in a modification of the R.C.N.'s Weather-Proof Protective Suit, in a new type of rain-proof garment to replace oil skins, a new type of cold-weather working garment to replace duffle coats, a modification of the winter cap, new types of two-piece mitts, heavier types of socks to replace stockings, and new types of cold-weather footgear.

During the winter of 1943-44 extensive winter test trials were held also by the Army. These were conducted in different areas to cover dry cold and wet cold, on the land, at sea, in the mountains, using vehicles, on foot, on ships, and in submarines. Originally planned to test protective clothing, they were broadened out to tackle the larger problem of maintaining the fighting efficiency of the soldier in all respects when facing extreme cold weather conditions. Over four hundred items of clothing and equipment, including sleeping bags, tents, winter gas-masks, goggles, breathing devices, skis, stoves, toboggans, and first-aid kits, were tested. Combat rations were given extensive trials. Tents were tested for their retention of carbon monoxide. Plasma was given at sub-zero temperatures. Oxygen was used for the treatment of frostbite.

These were the forerunners of even more comprehensive trials conducted after the termination of hostilities, which do not come within the purview of this book, but which are continuing to add greatly to man's knowledge of how to live and thrive within the hostile environment of the sub-arctic and arctic regions of Canada.

New life jackets were devised for the R.C.A.F. by the Associate Committee on Aviation Medical Research, some with permanent flotation using a filling material like kapok, others which could be readily inflated by gas or air. A light which flashed automatically and with long-life batteries was developed by combined work with the R.C.N. In 1943, on short notice, a waterproof "ditching" suit was evolved, the first satisfactory protective device in any service for the airman forced down at sea in a frigid climate, such as was met with in the North Atlantic. It consisted of a waterproof nylon rubber-coated suit, weighing only a few ounces, which could be donned over all gear in a few seconds and drawn tight at the neck with a zipper or drawstring. In sea tests off Halifax in the winter of 1943 its value was emphatically demonstrated, and its use was recommended for the R.C.N. also.

A new life-saving jacket designed for the Navy was credited with saving many lives. What was wanted was a jacket with adequate flotation power, protection from underwater blast, warmth for cold latitudes and icy waters, lightness to facilitate rescuing a man from the water, and a self-righting quality which would keep the wearer head up in the water if he should be unconscious. All of these requirements except the last were met. The difficulty there was that in providing adequate protection against blast, the padding of kapok around the lower trunk caused the upper portion of the trunk and the head to be held down to the surface of the water. To pad the upper trunk proportionately (and thus restore the balance to keep the head up) would have greatly exceeded the bulk that could be permitted by operational requirements. Experiments were then begun to provide additional air-inflated compartments across the upper chest and back, so as to provide a self-righting quality. Tests to measure protection from underwater blast were of course conducted with animals, but valuable testimony was soon forthcoming from survivors of a ship loss, in which an underwater explosion had taken place while survivors were in the water. One survivor without a jacket required operative treatment for underwater blast, while others who were closer to the centre of the explosion were protected by the jackets.

An inflatable life-saving vest which could be carried without discomfort by personnel serving in the tropics, and by engine-room crew in all climates, was developed. This could be inflated by a small cylinder carrying CO_2, or by the mouth, and provided thirty pounds of flotation.

Carbon monoxide poisoning and destructive levels of noise were two hazards to which service personnel were occasionally exposed, and at times without any clear appreciation of their seriousness. For example, tests made in Camp Borden workshops and repair hangars showed that personnel were inhaling air containing 65 to 400 parts per million of carbon monoxide, although the maximum permissible concentration recommended by medical men was 100 parts per million. A single tank engine idling at 1000 revolutions per minute in a previously aired hangar for 30 minutes produced a carbon monoxide concentration of 250 per million; three tanks idling for 15 minutes produced concentrations in excess of 600 per million. Casualties were inevitable if a large number of tanks warmed up simultaneously. Steps were taken at Camp Borden and elsewhere to remedy these conditions.

As for noise at unbearable or injurious levels, the investigations of Surgeon Commander D. Y. Solandt and Lieutenant C. R. Cowan for the Navy may be cited. Boiler-room personnel were found to be exposed to noise over 110 decibels, a level which, on prolonged exposure, would cause deafness, while in the engine-room of Fairmiles, Lieutenant M. L. Bunker found intensities greater than 140 decibels, the limit of the measuring instrument. Even on the upper deck of Fairmiles, in the vicinity of the engine-room, noise levels from 114 to 122 decibels were measured. Aside from the incipient damage to the ears of personnel, the noise made oral communication impossible. Some improvement was introduced by the use of ear plugs of an advanced design. In the Army, considerable scientific work was done on noise levels and hearing, Professor E. G. Burr of McGill outlining some of the fundamental characteristics for the apparatus devised and employed. It was necessary to educate soldiers and sailors to protect their ears. The Army Research Medical History cites the experience of a crew of a small escort vessel which was engaged briefly with a German submarine. No fewer than seven men in the Canadian crew were afterwards found to have ruptured eardrums from their own gunfire.

The Battle Against Micro-organisms

The environment and circumstances of World War II, as in all previous conflicts, exposed the fighting man to numerous infectious diseases caused by micro-organisms, some of them carried by insects or rodents. The war on the medical front included new attacks on some of these old evils. Valuable progress was made by Canadians in the fight against typhus, in the mass production of the wonder substance, penicillin, and in the control of disease-bearing insects.

This work in Canada was coordinated by the Associate Committee on Medical Research. A Sub-committee on Infections studied gas gangrene and conducted some pioneer experiments on the local application of sulphonamides. It supervised the production of typhus vaccine and Shiga toxoid. It broke new ground in the production of penicillin and from its pilot plant supplied large quantities of penicillin for use among the armed forces and lesser amounts for civilians, helping to bridge over the period when commercial production was being stepped up to meet all demands. Work was done on preparation of a vaccine against influenza.

Pioneer work of the greatest importance was done in the laboratory of Dr. G. B. Reed at Queen's University on gas gangrene and the local application of sulphonamides to war wounds. It began when a Sub-committee on Gas Gangrene[4] was authorized in March 1940, under which a grant was made to Drs. G. B. Reed and J. H. Orr for a study of gas-gangrene anaerobes. The Sub-committee's work was broadened out in December 1940 to cover all types of wound infections. In this field, Dr. Reed devised a rapid method of identifying anaerobes and a method of collecting a high yield of toxin from toxigenic strains, for use in preparing anti-toxins. Drs. A. Frappier and V. Fredette investigated the relative values of anti-toxic and anti-bacterial serums. Drs. Reed and Orr studied the topical (local) application of sulphonamides to infection from anaerobes in experimental work on animals. Sulphathiazole proved to be the most effective of the sulphonamides tested. It was shown that the concentration of the drug in the wound area could be maintained at a high level without toxic systemic effects. Local treatment was superior to oral treatment. Properly controlled, there was no retarding effect on the processes of healing (i.e., phagocytosis or fibroblastic growth).

Penicillin

The story of the discovery and development of penicillin— the greatest medical advance to come out of the war—is one of the most thrilling in medical history. For the purposes of this narrative, it is necessary here to recall only the barest outlines of the earlier phase. When Sir Alexander Fleming was Professor of Bacteriology, working in the laboratories of St. Mary's Hospital, London, England, he found an enzyme capable of destroying harmless bacteria. In the autumn of 1928 he accidently noticed a curious effect around a spot of greenish mould which had begun to grow on a culture dish containing

[4] Of the Associate Committee on Medical Research of the National Research Committee.

a colony of the bacteria called staphylococci, the cause of several serious infectious diseases. To Fleming's astonishment, over an area around the green mould the bacteria were being destroyed. He followed up the discovery, identified the mould as *Penicillium notatum,* and proved that the substance produced by the mould was effective against cultures of streptococci, gonococci, and meningococci, as well as against staphylococci; and that it was non-toxic to mice and rabbits. No attempt was made immediately to produce the substance in quantity, nor to try it on human beings.

The next advance was begun in 1939 by a group under the direction of a native of Australia, Sir Howard Florey, then Professor of Pathology at Oxford, and his colleague, Ernest Chain. By 1941 Florey and his group were satisfied that penicillin was a new medical substance of the greatest importance in the war against bacterial disease, but the problem of mass-production was proving to be almost insuperable, entirely so for such resources as Britain could allocate at the time. The incalculable value of such a drug at this stage of the war stimulated the search, however, and Sir Howard Florey was sent to North America to solicit the aid of the production resources of the United States and Canada.

In Canada, culture studies on penicillin were begun in the fall of 1941 in the Department of Pathology and Bacteriology, University of Toronto, by Dr. Philip Greey, assisted by Dr. Alice Gray. As these studies progressed and it was found possible to obtain a promising yield of penicillin when the mould was grown on 100 cc. of culture fluid, the chemical aspects of penicillin production were investigated by Dr. C. C. Lucas and Dr. S. F. MacDonald of the Banting and Best Department of Medical Research. They succeeded in extracting and purifying small quantities of penicillin in a form suitable for clinical use.

As Dr. Robert D. Coghill and the staff of the Northern Regional Research Laboratories of the U.S. Department of Agriculture at Peoria, Illinois, had had extensive experience in mould fermentations, and as Dr. Florey had interested them in the problem of large-scale production of penicillin, the Associate Committee on Medical Research arranged for Dr. Greey to visit these workers. He was informed of their discovery that corn-steeping water added to the culture media upon which the mould grew increased greatly the yield of penicillin, and was supplied with strains of the mould found to give the best yields of penicillin.

By January 1943, the labours of Dr. Greey and his colleague in Toronto had been so successful that the Sub-committee on Infections of the National Research Council recommended the erection of a pilot plant in the Banting Institute to explore methods applicable to large-scale production and to provide quantities of the new substance for clinical trial in Canada. Progress was rapid. In July of the same year the Sub-committee on Infections recommended to the Director-General of Medical Services (Army) that large-scale production of penicillin be undertaken in Canada as a project under government auspices This recommendation was promptly acted upon and arrangements were made with the Connaught Laboratories, University of Toronto, and Ayerst, McKenna and Harrison Co. Ltd., Montreal, to establish penicillin plants, each designed to produce a billion units of penicillin per month. The former Knox College property in Toronto was purchased and the building remodelled to provide facilities for the mass-production of penicillin as well as for the processing of human blood serum, in which the Connaught Laboratories were also engaged.

A report prepared for distribution at the 77th Annual Meeting of the Canadian Medical Association thus described the method employed on this Toronto project in the new quarters:

"The first medium of preparation for penicillin was the growing of the mould in a suitable medium using ordinary milk bottles as containers. Cultures of the mould of *Penicillium notatum* were cultured with the strictest care to maintain the purity of the strain. Each bottle contained approximately 300 cc. of sterile medium. Since the amount of penicillin obtained was very small, enormous numbers of bottle cultures were required, and at one time the Laboratories accommodated approximately 300,000 culture bottles. After growing for seven days in air-conditioned incubator rooms, the mould was separated from the medium and the penicillin was obtained by a complex chemical process involving the use of solvents and precipitants. . . . Penicillin in liquid form is not a stable product, and it was early found necessary to distribute penicillin as a dried powder in sterile vials. It was further found essential that the drying be accomplished in a frozen state. The equipment for drying of penicillin is of a very special character."

Reference is made above to the pioneer work in the production of penicillin in the U.S. The magnitude of the American achievement is reflected in part in the long time taken to achieve substantial production. After listing the impressive group of laboratories and commercial firms mobilized there to tackle the problem, Dr. Baxter, official U.S. historian, says: "It was six months from the time of Florey's visit to Peoria before there was sufficient penicillin to treat one case, eighteen months before there was sufficient to treat 200 cases, thirty months before any could be allocated to nonresearch civilian use."[5] Making due allowance for the aid received from Peoria, the Canadian achievement is highly creditable. "Within a few months the pilot plant [at Toronto] was producing up to two million units[6] of penicillin *per diem*."[7] The penicillin so produced was at once turned over for use in the armed services for combatting staphylococcal infections, and for clinical investigations by research scientists of the Medical Committee. Commercial production of penicillin, using a new method of growing the mould in large tanks, was rapidly introduced in the United States and Canada, but the pilot-plant production of the Medical Committee in Canada meanwhile continued to supply the substance for the armed services and to meet urgent civilian demand.

Investigations were made under the direction of the National Research Council on such things as the effectiveness of penicillin in local application in gas-gangrene infections, the effect of penicillin on the growth and respiratory metabolism of cells, and the effect of pituitrin on the excretion of penicillin in rats. Agar pastilles of penicillin, which gave excellent results in "trench mouth", were produced, and creams were developed in which penicillin was stable at ice-box temperatures for upwards of two months.

[5] Baxter, *op. cit.*, p. 347.

[6] Enough to treat twenty patients with 100,000 units per day each.

[7] Dr. G. H. Ettinger, *History of the Associate Committee on Medical Research* (National Research Council, Ottawa), p. 16.

Typhus and Other Diseases

Typhus fever, carried by the human body louse, and caused by a micro-organism called *rickettsia*, is one of the diseases against which penicillin is without effect. But in recent years a vaccine has been developed which later proved highly effective in the European theatre of war. In 1940 Dr. James Craigie, of the Connaught Laboratories, Toronto, applied to the National Research Council for a grant to investigate the preparation and antigenic qualities of European typhus vaccine. This was given, and the grant was renewed and enlarged repeatedly during the war period. The United Kingdom requested large quantities of the vaccine, and in response Dr. Craigie and his associates devised methods applicable to large-scale production. Improvements in technique greatly enhanced the yield of *rickettsia* required for the production of the vaccine. Of this development in Canada *The Industrial Front*, produced by the Department of Munitions and Supply in 1943, said:

"Quantity production and new methods lowered the cost per litre to less than one-third of the original price. An interesting fact is that the vaccine is obtained by a process employing 1,000 hens' eggs a day. Because of the shortage of eggs, the Germans make some of their vaccine from lice, and it would take about 36 million vermin to produce an amount equal to that obtained from 25,000 eggs."[8]

Scrub typhus is carried by a mite, and reports that it was being encountered in the south-western Pacific and in Burma led to increasing attention on the development of a vaccine effective against that variety. Dr. Craigie commenced work on scrub typhus in 1945. In 1946, the Typhus Commission of the United States, created by Executive Order of President Roosevelt in 1943, recognized Dr. Craigie's achievement in the field of typhus vaccine by awarding him the United States of America Typhus Commission medal. His citation read that he had "rendered exceptionally meritorious service in improving typhus vaccine during the period January 1942 to December 1945. The ether-extraction method developed by Doctor Craigie in 1942 greatly increased the immunizing potency of typhus vaccine used for the protection of troops. Distinguished among

[8] p. 110.

investigators of typhus, Doctor Craigie made his discoveries available to the military and civilian organizations of the United States as well as to those of his own country. Through contributions to science and by his cooperation on an international scale, he benefited the public health of the world."

Shiga dysentery was another infectious disease on which some advance was made during the war. Dr. Leone Farrell was given a grant by the National Research Council in 1941 to investigate means of creating immunity against it; and she produced a toxoid which gave such satisfactory results both in man and animals that the Sub-committee on Infections of the National Research Council in 1944 recommended that Canadian troops in theatres of war where Shiga infection might be expected should be given the toxoid. However, the incidence of Shiga infection among Canadian troops in the theatres of war where they were operating apparently did not warrant a field trial of the toxoid.

Beginning in December 1940 and continuing for five years, a study was conducted by the Connaught Laboratories, at the request of the National Research Council, on the virus responsible for influenza in Canadian Military Camps. A vaccine was developed and 80,000 doses were supplied to the Department of National Defence. This study was still in progress when hostilities came to an end in 1945.

Food for the Fighting Services

Extensive and systematic studies of nutrition were made during the war by the armed services directly, and also through projects directed by the Associate Committees of the National Research Council, supported by the Council's grants. It was recognized how large a part proper food played in maintaining the health, efficiency, and morale of the fighting man. Revised rations were prescribed in the light of modern knowledge of the subject, and their adequacy was repeatedly checked by subsequent surveys. For example, there were periodical tests in the large Shore Establishments of the Royal Canadian Navy at Halifax and in Newfoundland, the nutrients being weighed against the recommended allowances of the National Research Council, U.S.A., 1941, with respect to the proportions of protein, fat, and carbohydrate. The mineral contents of the diets were determined by analysis. The intake of vitamins was investigated closely. The supply of ascorbic acid was at first unsatisfactory, but improvement was brought about by adding a daily issue of citrus fruits or their juices, tomatoes or tomato juice or fresh fruits in season, and by improved methods of preparing vegetables and other foods. Three hundred and seventy-four men who had served approximately one year in the Newfoundland Command (Naval) were examined thoroughly for nutritional deficiency. Multiple deficiencies were found in only five men, though 12.3 per cent. were found to have some deficiency, ascorbic acid and riboflavin being the most marked inadequacies. On the whole the survey indicated that nutrition in the Newfoundland Command was adequate. To improve riboflavin and calcium intakes, special efforts were made to improve the fresh milk supply in the Navy, and a small amount of edible bone meal was added to the bread supplied by the naval bakeries. New emergency rations for ship-wrecked personnel were developed.

The Army carried out wide-spread research on compact military rations, on methods for maintaining nutrition in isolated units, on the relationship between food and the operational efficiency, physical fitness, and general health of the soldier, and finally on the problem of adequate nutrition for hospital patients. Work was done at the National Research Council, at McGill University Medical School, the Fatigue Laboratory of Harvard University, Macdonald College, Queen's University Medical School, the Central Experimental Farm, Ottawa, and the Department of Public Health of the City of Montreal, as well as in the field. Over forty reports on food were presented to the National Research Council, and others to the Subcommittee on Nutrition, Department of National Defence.

Some interesting discoveries were made during a comparative trial of nine Canadian, U.S. Army, and British compact rations north of Prince Albert, Saskatchewan, during the winter of 1943-44, as part of a large-scale, inter-service, sub-Arctic trial of the *materiel* of war.

One of these concerned pemmican. This had always been favoured by Arctic and Antarctic explorers because it kept so

well and was high in caloric value. Dr. Vilhjalmur Stefansson
had nominated it as a possible "single complete military ration"
for those regions. Pemmican was accordingly manufactured to
Dr. Stefansson's specification by Canadian meat packers, and
a plan for testing it was evolved, using a "tough" and well-led
platoon of test troops.

Sad to relate, the traditional and romantic commodity was
thoroughly "found out" in this scientific test. The official
account says that the third day of the trial "brought the platoon
to the point of disintegration as a military unit. On the morning of the fourth day they were operationally useless. Examination revealed a group of listless, dehydrated men, with drawn
faces and sunken eyeballs. Their breath smelled strongly of
acetone. Each man had lost about 7 lbs. in weight during the
three days, and neurological changes were present. Biochemical
studies showed ketosis, dehydration, and salt and ascorbic
acid depletion." What made the findings even more decisive
was that the physique and morale of each man had been excellent when the test began; the week before they had marched
47 miles in 36 hours across broken snow-covered country.

In the same tests the unsatisfactory nature of U.S. Army
biscuits was also exposed, owing, it seemed, to the effects of
overbaking (420°F. for 20 minutes) on the skim-milk powder
used in the biscuits. "As a result of these findings, the specifications for U.S. Army biscuits were changed, and a superior
non-toxic biscuit was produced."

A study of metabolism in hospital patients brought to light
the fact that the human body's stores of protein could be rapidly
depleted by various types of injury and infection; and that
unless special attention was given to the diets of such hospital
patients, the intake of protein was not enough to offset the
breakdown. A study of food in two military hospitals (Chorley
Park and Camp Borden) showed that patients were actually
getting only about half of the calories and proteins laid down
on the scale of issue. Wastage during cooking, the unpalatable
food left untouched on the plates, the patient's tendency to
feel that since he was in bed he should not be eating very
much, and doctors' ignorance and neglect of proper feeding
methods, were found to be factors in the unsatisfactory situation.

To remedy matters, a "nutritional team" was sent to all military hospitals in Canada to give lectures and demonstrations. A later survey showed a considerable improvement in the food intake by patients. A method of supplementing patients' diets, using special milk shakes much higher in protein and food value than the ordinary variety, was introduced both in Canada and in the Canadian hospitals overseas. It was impossible to ship fresh milk and raw eggs across the Atlantic, but with the assistance of Dr. W. H. Cook, Director of the Division of Applied Biology, National Research Council, Captain D. R. Gibson of N.D.H.Q., and the Borden Milk Company, a powdered milk supplement, high in protein, was developed, and beginning early in 1945 a programme was worked out for making it available in quantity to the Canadian hospitals in the United Kingdom and later to hospitals in Canada.

Repair of Battle Damage

Medical science is invoked in war to prevent the impairment of fighting efficiency and to build up protective devices which will reduce casualties. But casualties are inevitable in spite of all such preventive measures; and a major part of medical effort must be directed towards the saving of life among the injured, and the restoration of combatants' bodies and minds to normal health, vigour, and usefulness as far as that is humanly possible. A very substantial amount of the scientific effort on the medical front between 1939 and 1945 was devoted to this end. The fields explored were so numerous and the findings so important that they gave rise to scores of medical reports and could readily form the basis of a whole book of this size. In order to keep this chapter in proportion with the others, it will be necessary to select and illustrate, rather than aim at an exhaustive treatment.

Loss of blood, extensive skin burns, destruction and dislocation of bone and tissues, and the general condition known to army doctors as "shock", were from the very beginning matters which preoccupied this section of Canada's war effort. When war broke out, the Associate Committee on Medical Research (of the National Research Council) cabled the Medical Research Council of the United Kingdom offering help. Sir Edward Mellanby, in grateful reply, cited storage of blood and aviation medicine as matters of the most pressing importance, and invited Sir Frederick Banting and others to come over and learn of their needs at first hand. In October 1939, a sub-committee on Blood Storage was set up, later styled the Sub-committee on Shock and Blood Substitutes.

When war began in September 1939, Dr. C. H. Best, Professor of Physiology at Toronto, already had under way a series of studies on the treatment of surgical shock using blood serum and blood substitutes. When the college session began in the fall, Dr. Best collected blood from three hundred student volunteers, separated and concentrated the serum, and used the product to treat patients suffering from shock without hemorrhage. This was the first Canadian experiment in the use of blood derivatives. The Associate Committee awarded a grant to Dr. Best in December 1939 for experiments in concentrating serum; and with his colleagues he rapidly devised a successful method for drying it. By March 1940 the experiments had proceeded to the point where Dr. Best was asked to prepare a quantity for shipping to Britain, and a recommendation went forward to the Department of National Defence advising that this dried blood serum be prepared for the Canadian Active Service Forces. Funds were made available by the Department of Pensions and National Health, and two processing plants established, one at the Connaught Laboratories, Toronto, and the other at the University of Montreal.

The Canadian Red Cross Society undertook to organize the collection of human blood from voluntary donors across Canada, assisted by most of the provincial universities. By 1945 a peak of over 75,000 donations a month had been reached.

The process of drying blood serum is graphically described in the account of the war work of the Connaught Laboratories, prepared for the 77th Annual Meeting of the Canadian Medical Association, referred to above in connection with penicillin (p. 233).

"Blood was collected in special sterilized bottles, equipped with the necessary rubber tubing, sterile needle, etc. The serum was separated from the clot, clarified by centrifugation, pooled in large quantities representing donations from several hundred donors, and filtered through bacteriological filters.

"The filtered serum was then tested for sterility. It was filled in 400 cc. quantities into sterile bottles and dried in special vacuum cabinets. Drying was an important part in the process in making serum available in a suitable form. If dried with heat, the protein in the serum would be altered so that the serum could not be reconstituted by the addition of distilled water. The method involved the drying of the serum from the frozen state.

"This procedure required expensive equipment, and to accommodate this equipment, additional laboratories had to be constructed. Accommodation was provided in various parts of the Laboratories and finally extended to almost half of the Spadina Division—the former Knox College property [see p. 233]. The work was directed by Dr. Albert Fisher and ably assisted by members of the Laboratories and other departments of the University.

"The supplying of approximately 500,000 bottles of dried human serum and comparable quantities of sterile pyrogen-free distilled water for reconstituting the serum, the assembling of thousands of serum administration sets, and the preparation of thousands of vials of typing serum present an achievement which is a notable example of what can be accomplished by co-operative effort."

In the United States (beginning somewhat later since that country was not at war until December 1941), a parallel programme was undertaken. A transfusion unit for use on the battle-field consisted of a bottle containing powdered serum or plasma, another with sterile distilled water, needles, and tubing. The preparations for a transfusion took only five minutes, the powder dissolving readily in the distilled water. Exact data on the number of lives saved by these programmes are not obtainable, but as an emergency treatment transfusion of blood serum proved invaluable. It was not as satisfactory as whole blood transfusion, but had the great advantage that it could be given in the field and even in the front lines.

Studies were made of possible substitutes for human-blood plasma. Among these was isinglass. In 1941 Professor N. B.

Taylor, University of Toronto, was given a grant for the investigation of this substance. He reported that satisfactory results were obtained in treating animals suffering from traumatic shock or shock with hemorrhage. Clinical trials gave good results and undesirable side-reactions were rare. From both Britain and Canada requests came for substantial quantities of the product. The fact that adequate amounts of dried serum from human blood were available reduced the importance of this inquiry in 1944.

Though the term "shock" had been freely employed during World War I and since, and though there was general agreement among medical men about the nature of the collapse which frequently followed war injuries, a great deal was still obscure about the exact mechanism of the condition and in consequence the most effective treatment. As early as October 1939 the Executive of the Associate Committee on Medical Research examined the need for additional information on this topic, and Sir Frederick Banting and Professor J. B. Collip were asked to draw up a research programme. Grants were provided for a number of important investigations.

Material contributions to our knowledge of shock were made in these inquiries. Studies were made of shock in rats and it was found that in such animals some resistance to it could be built up, either by inflicting a series of non-lethal injuries or by an increase in the protein in the diet—a kind of commando training, as the official history puts it. Resistance to shock in rats was first shown one week after the initial treatment; it reached a maximum after two weeks and persisted for an undetermined time, longer than one month. Tissue extracts were studied for their ability to produce and to protect against traumatic shock, with some results. It was demonstrated that the serum potassium was increased in shock, but that administration of equivalent potassium could not reproduce the shock. Ability to store liver glycogen is reduced in shock; some material is released from the damaged limb which is noxious to the sound tissues: local fluid loss alone is not the fundamental factor in shock. These studies were made by Drs. R. L. Noble, J. B. Collip, C. G. Toby, R. E. Haist, R. A. Cleghorn, Surgeon Lieutenant Commander William Locke, Nursing Sister (Tech-

nician) Margaret Stock, and associates. Dr. H. Selye presented
evidence for his hypothesis that shock follows the draining
from the uninjured areas of essential compounds, requisitioned,
as it were, by the needs of the injured areas; and that it was
not due to the release of toxic materials owing to tissue changes.
Several investigators who explored the relation of shock to the
adrenal cortex came to the conclusion that cortical extracts
could neither prevent shock nor alleviate it after it became
evident. Dr. J. S. L. Browne and collaborators recovered and
identified a cortin-like compound, with gluconeogenic qualities,[9]
from human urine, which was increased up to twenty-fold in
shock. Drs. B. Rose and P. G. Weil found that blood histamine
falls in shock owing to wounds or burns. Dr. W. Bourne reported
that blood-pressure, after hemorrhage, could be raised and
maintained by a combination of pitressin and ephedrine more
successfully than by other drugs. An extensive investigation of
shock made in the clinic of Professor J. C. Meakins in Montreal was the basis of a thorough report by Dr. P. G. Weil
which appeared in the Canadian Medical Association Journal
in 1942; and the following year a *Memorandum on the Early
Recognition and Treatment of Shock* was prepared for and
issued by the National Research Council. This had a wide
circulation in the Armed Services, in Medical Schools, among
Medical Officers, and through the agency of the Department
of Pensions and National Health.

When Dr. Wilder Penfield of Montreal returned from a
visit to Britain in 1941 and reported his findings to the Associate Committee on Medical Research, it was decided that
the most urgent surgical problem in the war was the treatment
of *thermal burns,* and conferences were held to draw up a
memorandum for the guidance of medical officers and students.
At that time the treatment most favoured was tannic acid.
The theory was that a spray of tannic acid would precipitate
tissue protein and thus form a sort of second skin to relieve
pain and prevent further loss of fluid from the body surface.[10]
But experience with tannic acid treatments, and such studies

[9] Capable of forming glycogen, or animal starch; the release of glycogen
is believed to be an important source of physical energy.
[10] Baxter, *op. cit.,* p. 326.

as those conducted in Canada by Dr. A. W. Ham, led to the disrepute of tannic acid dressings, which, when absorbed, apparently did some damage to the liver; and in a revision of the *Memorandum on Treatment of Thermal Burns* of October 1943, the treatment of first choice was occlusive pressure dressings, while tannic acid was accepted as one of the "other methods" which included a polyvinyl alcohol film, and a sulphathiazole emulsion. In a second revision of 1945 treatment with tannic acid was omitted altogether, as possibly dangerous and inferior to other recommended treatments.

Dr. Penfield was the Chairman of the Sub-committee on Surgery. This began as a small committee in 1942, but as the war grew in intensity and range and as battle casualties increased it had to be expanded so as to take in representatives of the university centres, of all the services, and a number of the outstanding surgical specialists of Canada. Six sections were set up to cover plastic surgery, traumatic injuries of the nervous system, surgical radiology, thoracic surgery and orthopaedics, as well as burns. In due course these sections dealt with a great many of the surgical problems connected with war wounds, amputations, damage to the limbs and to the nervous system, skin grafting, artificial limbs, and related matters. A series of conferences led to recommendations of great value to the Services with respect to the treatment of the amputee, the paraplegic, and of low back pain, and nerve injuries.

Extension of Sense Facilities

Some operations in wartime called for personnel with especially acute hearing or night vision, or made other demands upon sense qualities, and new devices for precise measurement were badly needed. Scientists were able to come to the aid of the armed services in a number of these respects, and in more than one field Canadian research performed pioneer work, the fruits of which were passed along for adoption by the Allied nations. In some situations, the efficiency of the sense organs could be aided by new apparatuses, and other gains made by a more reliable means of selecting personnel with superior sense powers for special tasks.

An interesting example of this was the work done for the Naval Service in selecting operators for the anti-submarine detection device known as Asdic. As will be remembered, the principle of this was the projection of a short blast of sound, under water, at a pitch or frequency somewhat above that audible to the average ear, and the receiving of an echo from the hull of a submerged enemy submarine. The presence of such an enemy warship submerged in the vicinity of the patrol craft was made known, of course, by the echo thus received, and the time which elapsed between the brief blast and the hearing of the echo was a measure of the distance of the Nazi submarine. The echo, when received, was stepped down in frequency to a pitch audible to the human ear. The more acute the hearing of the Asdic operator, of course, the greater the likelihood of detecting at an extreme range the presence of a submarine which might be approached by the patrol craft. Also, the movement of the submarine relative to that of the patrol craft could be roughly gauged by the exact pitch of the echo received, since by the "Doppler Effect", the note would be somewhat lower than normal when the two were separating, and somewhat higher when the distance between them was being reduced. These considerations made it important to employ Asdic operators with acute hearing and also with a sharp sense of discrimination between notes of nearly the same pitch or frequency.

The work on Asdic operation began in 1941 under the Medical Research Division of the R.C.N., which was the research unit for the Associate Committee on Naval Medical Research of the National Research Council. A test to measure the capacity of naval personnel to discriminate between notes of a similar frequency was worked out by Dr. D. Y. Solandt. Testing equipment was installed at five naval stations. Dr. C. H. Best directed the establishment of standards for both auditory acuity and frequency discrimination (ability to distinguish pitch). All prospective Asdic operators were given these tests, and experienced operators were tested from time to time. Feeling the need of more knowledge of this essential function of frequency discrimination, Dr. Solandt initiated studies on the effects of fatigue on one's ability to discriminate the pitch of signals. These were carried out by Dr. Ruth C. Partridge and associates. Equipment able to simulate Asdic signals was set up at Toronto. Tests showed that while all listeners could hear a weak sound as well at the end of a two-hour listening period as at the beginning, the ability of many individuals to discriminate pitch gradually deteriorated until it was markedly inferior to their ability at the beginning. To examine this phenomenon of fatigue more closely, studies were made of the effects of rest periods, of benzedrine sulphate, of motion sickness, of the use of alcohol, of alternation between Asdic and hydrophone listening, of the relative loudness of the tones used as signals, the relative pitch, and other factors. In approximately two-thirds of the subjects tested, ability to discriminate between two closely related tones deteriorated during the listening period. These subjects were classed as fatiguable; the remainder showed no significant change and were classed as non-fatiguable. Rest periods were found to reduce fatigue markedly; administration of a 10 mgm. dose of benzedrine sulphate reduced or prevented fatigue. Its effect was apparent one hour after administration and was maintained for at least eight hours. After the administration of this drug, thirty-six subjects who usually showed fatigue were able to discriminate pitch differences as well through a ninety-minute period as they could at the beginning. This and other experiments suggested that the fatigue occurred in the cerebral cortex rather than in the auditory sense organ. The effect of *practice* on their ability to discriminate pitch differences was tested. While one-half of the group tested showed improvement, two-thirds of these were later found to be fatiguable, and after thirty minutes of continuous listening, their powers of discrimination were inferior to what they had been before the beginning of training. The selection of non-fatiguable subjects with a high acuity of hearing thus appeared to be a more fruitful procedure than attempts at training Asdic operators in frequency discrimination.

Night vision was of concern to all the armed services. The Air Force was the first to become keenly interested. When Professor A. V. Hill was British Air Attaché in Washington, early in 1940, he drew attention to the importance of the best

STUDYING THE EFFECTS OF GRAVITY

The accelerator centrifuge. The subject to be tested sits in the gondola
while the medical officer below checks his reactions

ANTI-GRAVITY SUIT

The inventor (W/C W. R. Franks, *centre*) discusses principles of the
suit with a pilot

possible night vision for fliers, who were beginning (thanks to new radar and other navigational devices) to be able to operate in the dark. Efforts to improve night vision through the use of vitamins proved unsuccessful, but more precise methods of measuring individual sensitivity to low intensities of illumination offered the hope that those pilots with the best natural gifts could be selected for night-flying and dangerously night-blind individuals inducted into other operations. Some gains through the night-vision training of those with good natural eyesight seemed certain, and there were other improvements possible through a precise knowledge of the physiology of the eye.

Elementary text-books on the eye refer to rods and cones in the retina. The cones are used in day vision, while the rods come into play in extremely dim lighting conditions. It was known that the average human eye requires something like forty-five minutes in an environment of virtual darkness before the rods become sufficiently sensitive to give the maximum ability to see in the dark. Re-exposure to a bright light very rapidly destroys this acquired sensitivity of the rods, and the pilot or other fighting man again becomes unable to see readily in the dark, until prolonged darkness has again conditioned the eye. Thus, even a glance at a brightly lighted instrument panel in an aircraft or on the bridge of a naval vessel might temporarily blind the operator. Early in 1940, Dr. D. Y. Solandt and associates, aided by Dr. C. H. Best, began some investigations on the lighting of instrument boards on aircraft. It was learned that deep red illumination of a rigidly pre-scribed wave-length and intensity was free from most of the blinding effect of the lighting earlier employed; a pilot could read the panel so illuminated and then peer out into the night sky with very little or no loss of sensitivity. Actual night trials were carried out in R.C.A.F. aircraft in November and December 1940, under the direction of Wing Commander T. R. Loudon and the late Squadron Leader Evan Briggs. These were the first adequate service trials of red lighting on record. In January 1941, the results were presented to the United States Naval Air Service authorities in Washington: this type of illumination was later put into extensive use aboard fighting vessels of the United States Navy and on certain selected types of naval aircraft.

In March and May 1941, similar lighting was tested on the bridges of ships of the Royal Canadian Navy: again, this was the first such installation on record anywhere, so far as is known. Following further tests later on in the year, the Canadians who had undertaken this experimental work spent some time overseas with the Home Fleet of the Royal Navy, and as a result the question was reopened in Britain and red lighting adopted there. Professor Walter Miles of Yale University attended a meeting at Toronto in which the early findings on red lighting were reported, and he subsequently developed red goggles which were widely employed in many services. A number of senior officers of the Royal Canadian Navy testified later that red illumination had been responsible for saving vital moments under emergency conditions.

Since persons employed on lookout duty at night frequently had to work under conditions of extremely low illumination, it was of distinct value to measure the native night-vision of personnel who might in future be engaged in such activity, while they were still in training. The most satisfactory test would be a precise measure of retinal sensitivity, and an apparatus for this purpose was built in Professor Selig Hecht's laboratory at Columbia University, incorporating a number of features suggested by Canadian scientists. Instruments of this type were widely used during the war. For example, over 40,000 individuals were so tested for the Canadian Navy. Highly dangerous night-blind individuals were thus weeded out, and personnel with normal or exceptionally good night vision were picked out for special training in night duties.

A visual problem faced by anti-aircraft lookout personnel attempting to observe tracer bullets, while looking towards or actually into the sun, was solved in the Naval Research Division. Dr. D. Y. Solandt suggested that by using suitable filter material in the glass, goggles could be produced which would protect the eye against the ultra-violet and infra-red components of sunlight, and yet allow enough of the light emanating from the tracer bullet to pass through so that it could be readily followed. This experiment was carried out by M. L.

Bunker, and under ideal conditions an observer with such goggles could see tracer bullets actually crossing the ball of the unoccluded sun. Somewhat lighter goggles were more useful where the lookout task required only brief and discontinuous observations of the sun and the sky in its immediate vicinity. The Army, which also tested the new equipment, found this lighter goggle to measure up to their requirements more closely than any previously tested.

Night-vision training and testing in the Army was stressed by Major-General G. Brock Chisholm, when he became Director General of Medical Services in the fall of 1942. His interest in the matter went back to the First World War, when he was a scout for his infantry battalion, in which capacity he had observed how differently individuals were gifted in their ability to see in the dark. Under his stimulus, the Army proceeded to work out a combined testing and training method, aided by the Associate Committee on Aviation Medical Research. Lieut.-Col. D. S. McEachern and associates were largely responsible for the achievement, and Professor E. G. Burr of McGill provided some facilities and valuable advice. Wing Commander K. Evelyn of the R.C.A.F., whose aid in this field has been fully recognized by U.S. Medical Research, joined McEachern in the development. The method evolved was adopted by the Canadian Army Overseas, and by D-Day of the Normandy invasion, a large proportion of key personnel in the Canadian Army had received instruction and had been graded as to their night vision. The test divided men into four groups in respect of night vision: excellent (10%); good (40%); fair (40%); poor (10%). The grades did not alter a man's Medical Category, but were there, inscribed in his paybook and other documents, for the guidance of the platoon or section leader, who could use them in allocating men to jobs on night patrol and similar duties.

The Lighter Side

Medical research in war was, in the main, a sober business. There were a few lighter moments, however. The Army Medical History cites the try-out of mud shoes which were designed by Dr. R. L. Noble. Several truck loads of mud were carted into the field-house on the McGill University campus, where the experimenters wallowed in mud to their heart's content. When the trials were over, it cost forty dollars to get the mud moved away. "Later, Army officers were to be seen navigating merrily on the mud flats near New London, Conn."

All kinds of suggestions came to Army authorities. A Winnipeg engineer, who had lived in the Orient, reported that grapefruit seeds were a rich source of quinine. This was news to chemists and horticulturists, but in the absence of any conclusive evidence, arrangements were made with the Chateau Laurier Hotel at Ottawa to collect all grapefruit seeds over a period of two weeks. Several buckets of them were thus accumulated and taken to the Dominion Analyst. Unfortunately, the seeds were found to contain no quinine.

One invention, says the Army History, "which it was not thought necessary to submit to field trial, was claimed to enable a man to march at a rate of 18 miles per hour. The device consisted of a series of springs in the soles of army boots. These acted like a pogo stick and were supposed to bounce the man through the air in great leaps. The invention was entitled 'The Human Jack-Rabbit'."

Some Notable Contributions

In a condensed sketch of this kind, it is difficult to avoid grave errors of omission or misplaced emphasis. Without adding long lists of names, many men who played a key role in medical war research cannot be mentioned at all. The invaluable administrative work of such men as Dr. G. H. Ettinger, Honorary Secretary of the Associate Committee on Medical Research, and S. J. Cook, of the National Research Council, who acted as Executive Secretary, is likely to be overlooked. The work of the various committees owed much to the enthusiasm and unremitting labour of the five chairmen: Sir Frederick Banting, Dr. J. B. Collip, Dr. C. H. Best, Dr. Hurst Brown, and Dr. Duncan Graham. In concluding his official story of the Associate Committee on Medical Research, Dr. Ettinger praised the contribution especially of Sir Frederick Banting, General

McNaughton, Dr. C. J. Mackenzie, and Dr. J. B. Collip, and added:

"Praise is also due the Chairmen of the Sub-committees. The work they directed was arduous and continuous; the brilliant achievements were in proportion to the vision with which the work was planned. The members of the various Sub-committees and Sections, too, served the country well. For the most part they were men in busy specialist practice, or attached to the Services, or burdened with heavy teaching duties in the Medical Schools. They undertook committee-work with great enthusiasm and at much personal cost; they demonstrated that competent members of a great profession will give unselfishly of their talents and experience in time of national need."

CHAPTER XI

SCIENCE AND THE FUTURE

V-J DAY brought final victory and a suspension of hostilities on the last of the major battle-fronts, but not yet a state of world peace. Demobilization in Canada did not mean a return to pre-Munich indecision, spiritual paralysis, or virtual defencelessness. Irreversible changes had occurred throughout the whole of Canadian society as well as in international relations, and neither the extent nor the character of Canadian scientific research would or could revert to a pre-war status. Canada emerged from the war as a leader among the "Middle Powers", and not without influence even among the "Big Five". The coming of the global bomber and the imminence of long-range guided missiles, coincident with new ideological tensions and new political orientations, added enormously to the significance of Canada's location at one of the aerial crossroads of the world, in peace or war. Canada stood out among the nations as a prime source of uranium, raw material for atomic power. Dunkirk had warned Canada of the need of greater self-reliance, the fall of France had led to closer cooperation with the United States, while the Battle of Britain had heightened Canada's awareness of her intimate emotional ties with Britain. The magnitude of Canada's war achievement and her colossal economic contributions through loans to Britain and the Mutual Aid programme had enhanced both her national reputation and her national self-consciousness. These and other factors tended to transform many Canadian institutions and attitudes.

It is not within the scope of this book to trace in any detail the story of Canadian scientific research from 1945 up to the date of publication. It does, however, seem appropriate to bring it to a close by a few observations on the changes in

Canadian research brought about by World War II as they
appear to a layman and journalist who has had the opportunity
of tracing some of the more outstanding achievements of
the war years.

Challenged by the grim exigencies of 1940-45, Canadians
had found it in themselves to do many things they would
have earlier voted impossible; and this was as true in the
field of applied science as anywhere else. Under the spur of
events, we found the answers to many formidable problems, and
we produced intricate war gear and complex chemical substances in impressive quantity. While the pattern and nature
of the conflict made close cooperation with Britain and the
United States desirable and, indeed, unavoidable, the relationship was that of a fully qualified member of a strong team
rather than of a subordinate or inferior. Canada became a full
contributing partner to the Allied pool of knowledge. To
their satisfaction, Canadian scientists and technicians found that
the fruits of their best work compared favourably with anything done anywhere in the world. A conviction grew up that
in almost any field of scientific or technical research, Canada
could, at a pinch, match quality, if not quantity, with any
other nation. This sense of self-reliance and quiet conviction
of capability was one of the most valuable products of the
war. In her earlier colonial days, Canada had relied almost
exclusively on technological "blood transfusions" from more
mature countries, but during the Second World War, she grew
to nationhood in the scientific field and began to reduce to
some extent the earlier top-heavy debit balance in her exchange
of scientists and scientific discoveries with the rest of the world.

The growth of the scientific community and of the facilities
and equipment for scientific research in Canada in the decade
following 1939 is impressive. The staff of less than 300 scientists and technicians of the National Research Council in 1939
had now grown to more than 2600, the single Laboratory
Building on Sussex Street, Ottawa, had been augmented by a
cluster of fine buildings on the Montreal Road, by the twenty
million dollar atomic energy plant at Chalk River (served by
the dormitory village of Deep River a few miles away), new
acoustical laboratories by the Ottawa River, a radar research

station on the Metcalfe Road and at Scarboro, and a Flight Research Station at Arnprior. The Prairie Regional Laboratory was rapidly taking shape at Saskatoon, and plans were being pushed for a new Maritime Regional Laboratory at Halifax. The Defence Research Board had taken over from wartime authorities the great experimental station and proving ground at Suffield, Alberta, and was developing new laboratories and stations elsewhere.

In quality as well as quantity the gains and advances were gratifying. At Chalk River, Canadians had built an atomic (or nuclear reactor) pile not surpassed in efficiency anywhere; the laboratory at Ottawa for research in physical chemistry was winning a world-wide reputation, and at Toronto the Institute of Aviation Medicine had "a research plant which is unsurpassed on this continent or elsewhere."[1] Reversing to some extent the previous consistently one-sided pilgrimage of young Canadians seeking post-graduate education in American and European universities, Canada was beginning to attract young scientists from other lands, and with its scheme of post-doctorate fellowships, was encouraging the use of the facilities of Ottawa and Chalk River laboratories by scholars from far and wide. In an address to the Business Paper Editors Association at Ottawa on February 28, 1949, the President of the National Research Council, Dr. C. J. Mackenzie, said: "I believe that our government laboratories are rapidly becoming the equal of any in the world—if not in size, certainly in the quality of the work being done. I am sure that these laboratories are contributing as much (perhaps in a less spectacular way) to the peacetime demands of Canadian industry as the same units did in the military field from 1939 to 1945."

Post-war expenditures on research reflected the new expansions and achievements. In 1920 it was estimated that the sum of $100,000 would have covered the cost of *all* governmental research in Canada. By 1939, the National Research Council alone required a budget of $900,000. The big increases were, however, still to come. In 1949-50 the federal estimates included $10.6 millions for the National Research Council, $6.3 millions for the Atomic Energy Control Board, and $21.2

[1] Dr. C. B. Stewart, "Canadian Research in Aviation Medicine", *Public Affairs*, 1947.

millions for Defence Research and Development. To these must be added large provincial and university expenditures. The research undertaken by private enterprise had in the meantime increased markedly, though not to such an extent as governmental research. The scale of scientific research activity as a whole in the post-war years was of an altogether different order of magnitude than in 1939.

The sudden cessation of pressing war problems in 1945 by no means brought immediate ease to those concerned with Canada's scientific research policy. There were urgent problems in the transition period which demanded bold and imaginative action. For one thing, it was necessary (in the words of Dr. C. J. Mackenzie) "to make sure that the substantial corps of scientific and technical workers, brought together by government agencies for important war research, was not disbanded at the end of hostilities, but retained by the Dominion Government."[2] Dr. Mackenzie was speaking at the time chiefly of industrial research, but as it turned out in the early post-war period, the matter of national defence also continued to be urgent, and as a result a Defence Research Board was set up under the Department of National Defence, whose first task was "to take over those parts of the wartime groups that should be continued in peace; to put them on a permanent basis; and to remould them to meet the needs of the future."[3]

Another matter which demanded early attention was the restoration of fundamental or pure research to a position more in keeping with its importance. There is a notion widely held by non-scientists that war is a great stimulator of research. This is not true of research in its purest form. However, it *is* true that it greatly accelerates the application of existing knowledge. Technology flourishes tremendously; developmental and applied research receive a great impetus. "War in its technical aspects," as Dr. Mackenzie phrased it, "is simply industry functioning at a feverish tempo." But much of this gain is at the expense of fundamental research. Universities are ruthlessly

[2] From a paper entitled "Industrial Research in Post-war Canada", presented to the Engineering Institute of Canada at Quebec City, February 11, 1944.

[3] Dr. O. M. Solandt, Director-General of Defence Research, in a CBC radio broadcast on January 18, 1947.

raided in wartime: their wisest teachers and most ingenious investigators are conscripted for applied research. Young scientists are shifted from the laboratory to the fighting fronts. "War," writes Sir David Rivett, "is a sterilizing influence in science: the amount of new fundamental knowledge uncovered anywhere between 1939 and 1945 was almost negligible compared with that of any other six years of this century."[4] War "ground up the seed corn of scientific progress in the next generation to make a day's feed for the war machine," in the language of Dr. Raymond B. Fosdick, President of the Rockefeller Foundation. Pure research, explained Dr. Mackenzie, in the address referred to above, is the capital, and application the return, and no country or person can progress or live long on its capital alone or, even worse, on borrowed capital. One of the most pressing problems then, at the end of actual warfare, was to see to it that scientific research in Canadian universities, the birthplace of most Canadian scientific discovery, was strengthened and extended. The enlarged enrolment in universities, the great increase in applications for the National Research Council's scholarships, fellowships, and other grants, and the equipment being installed in university laboratories, all serve to indicate that this post-war development is not being neglected. In 1949, the demand for research personnel was from five to ten times greater than in 1938.

Much modern research work in physics requires very costly and elaborate equipment beyond the reach of private institutions, and thus calling for state contributions. Mention may be made here of a few outstanding recent university installations, partly financed by government grants. In 1949, what scientists call *accelerators,* used to produce particles with tremendous velocities and energies for nuclear research, were in operation or being assembled in several universities: the McGill *Cyclotron,* rated at 100 million electron volts; the Queen's *Synchrotron,* rated at 70 million electron volts; the University of Saskatchewan's *Betatron,* rated at 20 million electron volts; and the University of British Columbia's *Van de Graaff* generator, rated at five million electron volts. At the University of Toronto, a

---

[4] "Soviet Science", *Meanjin: A Literary Magazine,* (Second quarter, 1948), p. 128.

super-sonic wind tunnel was under construction with assistance from the Defence Research Board. At McMaster, aided to some extent by the National Research Council, research was being conducted with the mass spectroscope; and at the University of Montreal, a number of nuclear projects were under way, including the photographic detection of cosmic rays. A great deal of work on radio-active particles in the study of the human body, of plant processes, and in other fields, was in progress in various institutions.

So much has already been published about the applications of war discoveries to peacetime problems and activities that only a few illustrations will be listed here.

One development of the greatest promise came about as a by-product of the atomic energy programme. When elements are placed in an atomic pile, such as the heavy-water reactor at Chalk River, and thus are subjected to its intense radiations, they become radio-active. The atoms of these elements continue to behave chemically as before, but the exposure to the atomic pile gives some of them the additional property that they can be detected by suitable instruments or by their action on photographic plates. "Atoms with tail-lights," as Dr. MacKenzie once called them. These radio-active isotopes of common elements can be used as "tracers" to follow the most intricate and complex biological and chemical reactions. "The use of radio-active tracers," Dr. O. M. Solandt told the Royal Canadian Institute at Toronto on January 29, 1949, "is regarded by many as the most important new scientific tool since the discovery of the microscope."

Examples of the way this new research tool is being employed in Canada were given in a radio address on August 30, 1949, by S. J. Cook, Officer in Charge, Public Relations Branch, National Research Council:

"Out in Saskatchewan, Dr. Spinks,[5] at the University there, was interested in knowing what happened to phosphate fertilizer when it was put in the soil along with wheat seed. So he made up some fertilizer in which he mixed a little radio-active phosphorus with ordinary phosphorus and sowed it, with

[5] Dr. J. W. T. Spinks, Professor of Chemistry and Head of the Department, University of Saskatchewan, Saskatoon.

the wheat seed, in special plots. The radio-active phosphorus did not change the effect of the fertilizer in any way except that it made it possible for Dr. Spinks to watch it being used while the plant was growing. From time to time he put a photographic plate against the plant stem, and sure enough, the rays from the radio-active phosphorus made black marks on the plates. In this way he was able to see where the fertilizer was in the plant and to measure how much was being used. From these experiments Dr. Spinks has been able to give western farmers very helpful advice regarding the kind and quantity of fertilizer to use in wheat growing, to get the best results.

"A great many uses for radio-isotopes are being found in medicine and surgery. For example, iodine is known to concentrate in the thyroid, and in certain cases, doctors need to know how much or how little iodine is being accumulated there. When radio-active iodine, instead of ordinary iodine, is given a patient, the doctor can trace the iodine through the patient's system, and, by the use of Geiger-Mueller counters outside the body, he can actually measure the amount of iodine taken up by the thyroid.

"Many Canadian industries are finding radio-isotopes of great value in their processes. The thickness of paper can be automatically controlled as it comes from a paper machine. Radio-active material is placed under the band of paper; an electronic measuring device above the paper records the amount of rays passing through the paper. When the paper is too thin, more radiations get through and the instrument immediately changes the control mechanism so as to produce a thicker layer. The same method can be used in rubber mills to control the thickness of rubber sheet. Paint manufacturers can study and measure the thickness of paint films with radio-isotopes.

"A large Canadian implement manufacturer is now using radio-active cobalt to detect possible flaws in the metal of a certain gear that could not be conveniently examined by X-rays. If these flaws were not found, they would cause early failure of the gear when it was put into service.

"One can think of a host of uses of radio-isotopes in the

chemical industry. The strength of dye used in the colouring industries can be followed by using a radio-isotope in one of the materials. Continuous sampling in rayon production can be eliminated by using radio-active sulphur in the sulphide solution."

"Almost unbelievable things can be done by isotopes," Dr. Mackenzie told the Business Editors in the address cited above. "There are many," he added, "who feel that as a research tool only, isotopes will some day repay all the rather large expenditures that have been made on atomic energy."

The airborne magnetometer (or Magnetic Airborne Detector) was developed during the war, chiefly by the United States, as a means of detecting submerged Nazi submarines. It worked on the principle that the presence of a mass of steel or iron slightly distorted the earth's magnetic field, and that with sufficiently delicate measuring instruments the presence of a submerged Nazi craft could thus be detected by aircraft flying a few feet above the ocean. The same principle may serve to reveal the presence of magnetic ores under the surface of the earth. It is also of the greatest use in making magnetic surveys, which are of particular interest in northern Canada, where the behaviour of the magnetic compass is highly irregular or erratic, and where it is important for navigators to know as much as possible about the direction of magnetic lines of force. Beginning in 1947, the Department of Mines and Resources, with help from the National Research Council, undertook extensive surveys in northern Canada with this new instrument.

Wartime developments in radar have made possible new standards of safety in navigation by sea and air, under the most adverse conditions of visibility. Radar installations at Halifax as early as 1947 made it possible to view incoming vessels in any conditions of fog, storm, and darkness, to a distance of 25 miles. Since every buoy was constantly visible on the radar display, no matter what the weather, or the hour of day or night, the exact location of every inbound vessel could be followed and plotted (to an accuracy of 50 yards) as it proceeded on different courses from buoy to buoy. Surplus 10 centimetre war radar sets were installed on many ships of the Canadian merchant marine. For the airman, an adaptation and development of wartime radar discoveries promised to provide him with a "radar distance indicator" which would enable an aircraft pilot to ascertain his distance and direction from one or more pre-selected ground stations, thereby determining his exact position. The distance could be read directly in miles on a simple meter and no interpretation or computation was necessary. An extension of wartime studies in ultra-sonic sound-ranging offered some possibilities in determining the depth of shallow overburdens on ore bodies or mineralized strata. High-frequency sound proved to have other uses, including the destruction of certain bacteria, the effect being literally that of shaking them to pieces.

Penicillin was not a wartime discovery, but without the impetus of war its production in useful quantities might have lagged indefinitely. Other antibiotics, such as streptomycin, were found. War discoveries profoundly affected medical practice. There was a rapid advance in the science of preserving and processing human blood and in the art of blood transfusion. Of the discovery and production in Canada of an effective vaccine against Rinderpest, a deadly disease of cattle, Dr. O. M. Solandt told a Canadian radio audience in January 1947: "This discovery alone may well contribute enough to the food supply of a starving world to justify the whole of Canada's wartime expenditure on research."

In the course of writing this book, it was necessary to refer at considerable length to the war research of the leading Allied nations and the Axis partners. In addition to the weapons and devices actually employed between 1939 and 1945, there were dreadful hints and forebodings of new and more terrible weapons to come. It was impossible not to be deeply moved, if not indeed appalled, at the diabolical new engines of destruction which man's ingenuity is capable of invoking if war is to prevail. Some thinkers have become so convinced that man is concocting his own complete annihilation that they would call an immediate halt to all scientific research: a few would even brand the scientists as arch-criminals who somehow have betrayed their fellow men. Fortunately for the present writer, there is no call here for a disquisition on the ethical and moral responsibilities of the scientist, or for any prophetic glimpse into the future course of mankind. It would not be difficult, of course, to summon up testimony on behalf of the scientist. The great gifts of science to the welfare, comfort, and longevity of man need no recital. The same brilliance, devotion, and ingenuity which made the atomic bomb possible can, when directed to man's welfare, overcome many of the most pressing economic and social problems now facing the world. These, however, are large themes calling for more than cursory comment. A few more modest observations on the present status of Canadian scientific research and those policies which appear to deserve wide-spread public support will be attempted in conclusion.

Canada's post-war expenditures on scientific research have been of a new order of magnitude compared to those before 1939, as has been said, but they are still running far short of parallel per capita outlay in the United States, the United Kingdom, and, so far as can be deduced, in the U.S.S.R. It is not easy to calculate the optimum expenditure of a modern industrial nation on research. There is general acceptance of the assertion that "the inherent material strength of any modern country is directly correlated with the strength of its resources and activities in science, technology, and research."[6] The British Parliamentary and Scientific Committee, in discussing the future of research in Britain (in 1943), asserted that "we should certainly look forward to spending at least ten times as much annually after the war if we are to provide the basis without which neither our agriculture nor industry can effectively meet the needs of the future." The Federation of British Industry in the same year expressed the opinion that "the investment of one per cent. of the total value of the country's industrial production would yield an annual return of many times such expenditure." Measured by such a yardstick, Canada's research expenditures in 1949, though so much larger than in the 1930's, fall short of the most profitable magnitude of expenditure. One per cent. would represent nearly $100 millions a year. There are, of course, limits on useful expendi-

[6] Dr. C. J. Mackenzie, in an address entitled "Research: A National Necessity," presented to the Canadian Club of Toronto, December 11, 1944.

ture in this field, quite apart from the possible resistance of the taxpayer. Until the corps of top-level scientists has been built up to an adequate level for Canada's needs, so much additional money could not be profitably spent, even if it were voted. It is possible to waste public money in research, just as in all other departments, as, for example, through the failure of industry to use the new information made available, or in second-rate research, which, as has been aptly said, is not worth doing at all, since its results will always be replaced by those of better work done elsewhere.[7] But in two branches of Canadian research, pure or fundamental research at the universities and industrial research undertaken by Canadian companies, there is still room for great expansion; and as scientifically trained personnel become available, the opportunities for profitable expenditure by government agencies and departments will also grow.

The value of research of a first-rate quality needs no labouring. Even tested by the most mercenary and realistic book-keeping, it can be shown to add to the national income much more than it costs. The British Committee referred to above came to the conclusion that from the expenditure of £440,000 in direct support of British industrial research projects in the pre-war years, an estimated *annual* saving (direct and indirect) to industry of £3,250,000 had been obtained. An even more striking illustration can be found closer to home. The value of the annual prairie wheat crop is of the order of $500 millions a year (in 1949 it was closer to $700 millions), and it is the considered judgment of authorities that if a few hundred thousand dollars had not been spent on rust research in the 1920's, very little wheat would be grown to-day in that area.

As the "main reservoir of scientific knowledge and the source of our trained scientists", the universities of Canada must be adequately supported if fundamental or pure research is to flourish. If Canadian industry is to do more than "keep up with the Joneses", largely by the use of imported technological discoveries or "blood transfusions", it must give increasing attention to applied research. In the words of Dr. Mackenzie, "a nation's strength both in peace and war is measured by the

[7] Dr. O. M. Solandt, in a CBC radio broadcast on January 18, 1947.

SCIENCE

The ionization chamber of a 600,000-volt X-ray apparatus

AND THE FUTURE . . . ?

scientific development of its industry." The large corporations will naturally support large laboratories, but even small industries can benefit greatly by having at least one man with scientific training on the payroll, and by electing scientists to the Boards of Directors. They can, of course, draw increasingly on the new discoveries of governmental laboratories. The great value of having one or two people who keep in touch with the latest scientific developments was illustrated by Dr. Mackenzie in another connection:[8] "It is absolutely impossible to find out or appreciate what is going on in the early research and development stages of any project unless we have a few scientists at least actively working in the same field. Again and again, by setting up a small research team, *we have had opened up to us a vast reservoir of experience and knowledge that otherwise would have been denied us.*"

The creation of the Defence Research Board in 1947 and the status given to the Director-General of Defence Research as equal to that of the Chiefs of the Armed Forces, was a recognition of the fact that a country with Canada's responsibilities and geographical location cannot neglect war research or continue to rely on its neighbours and allies for most of its scientific knowledge. The philosophy behind its creation was stated by the Director-General of Defence Research (Dr. O. M. Solandt) in an address to the Canadian Club at Montreal, on January 24, 1949: "Canada has embarked upon the largest peacetime defence programme in its history because of the firm conviction of the majority of Canadians that we must be strong if we would be free. We do not think that the might of the Canadian Forces will deter any large aggressor from starting a war, but we are sure that we, and others who share our love of freedom, can only remain free if we show that we are both able and willing to fight for our freedom if necessary. If all the free nations make this attitude clear, they may be able to maintain stability in the world until it is possible to evolve some kind of an organization that will prevent war."

The Defence Research Board has undertaken the task of making available to the Armed Forces in peacetime all the scientific resources of Canada and of other friendly nations.

[8] In the Canadian Club (Toronto) address cited above.

If war comes, it will be expected to be the chief agency of mobilization in Canada of such resources. In addition, it is operating research establishments. It cannot do first-class research in all fields of interest to the Armed Forces. Nor is there need of trying to occupy every possible field, since in the event of war, Canada would almost certainly be fighting as the member of a team of nations. The logic of the situation calls for research in fields in which Canada has peculiar or unique needs or resources, having in mind the research personnel available in Canada, our special industrial capabilities, our climate and geography, and our assets, strength, and vital needs. Scientific research in the Canadian Arctic is an outstanding illustration. In Dr. Solandt's words, "A thorough knowledge of the Arctic and its problems is essential, both to the regional defence of North America, and to the normal peaceful development of the Canadian North." Such a programme, as has been pointed out, includes further mapping and charting, a study of snow and ice, the flora, fauna, geology, mineralogy, and archaeology of that region. Geophysics is especially important in the Canadian Arctic, since Canada includes the North Magnetic Pole, and a larger part of the maximum auroral belt crosses Canada than any other country. Ionospheric studies for further knowledge of radio-wave propagation are especially important in an area where the auroral belt produces such peculiar effects. The study of meteorology in the Canadian Arctic is a vital preparation for defence, but it is also likely to add greatly to our knowledge of weather further south and to the accuracy of long-term predictions.

In both the United Kingdom and the United States the organization of research in the post-war world was changed to reflect more accurately some of the findings of the war period. The United Kingdom set up an Advisory Council on Scientific Policy. In an official publication reporting its creation, it was stated that this recognized "that science represents a body of knowledge and a method which must be taken into account in the direction of national affairs. The Council, together with the new Defence Research Policy Committee, which deals with those branches of science more particularly related to war, may be regarded as the most recent stage in

the evolution of government machinery for the promotion
and use of scientific knowledge. They carry the implication
that the advice of scientists, like that of economists, is now
considered to be of immediate importance in the formulation
of general national policies, in peace no less than in war. The
extent of government support of science for peaceful purposes
is often unappreciated."[9] In the United States, legislation to
create a new independent executive agency called the National
Science Foundation is before Congress. It will supersede the
Office of Scientific Research and Development, which was
called into being in May 1941 by the exigencies of a threatened
war. The duties of the new Foundation include the establishment of a national policy for the promotion of basic research
and education in the sciences, the initiation and support of
scientific research in the fields of national defence as well as
of basic research in all the sciences, the granting of scholarships and fellowships, the fostering of exchange of scientific
information among U.S. and foreign scientists, and the correlation of its own research with that of other public and
private institutions. The Foundation's authority in the field
of basic research will be almost complete; and there is no
ceiling set in the act on expenditures, though Congress must,
of course, vote an annual appropriation.

In Canada the separation of defence from peacetime research
has freed the National Research Council from the difficult
manoeuvre of "looking both ways at once", while the presence
of the President of the National Research Council on the
Defence Research Board is a safeguard against duplication of
effort. As matters stand, the National Research Council will,
in addition to its own peacetime research, continue to carry
out work for the Department of National Defence and the
Defence Research Board in the fields of radar and aeronautics.

Though the National Research Council has in the past two
decades become the operator on a massive scale of great
research laboratories, such was not the primary purpose en-
visaged when it was created. It was designed essentially to
serve as the government's agency for the stimulation and
coordination of scientific and industrial research in Canada.

[9] *Economic Record*, No. 4 (April, 1947), p. 3.

It is possible that as the magnitude of its operations grows there will be a separation of these functions, with the laboratories operated under a separate board, leaving the National Research Council more free to concentrate on the formulation and co-ordination of overall scientific policy and the encouragement of university research. The extraordinary value throughout the years of its scholarships and fellowships becomes apparent when the academic biographies of Canada's leading research scientists of to-day are perused. Another Council device, first developed in this country, that of the "Associate Committees", has also proved to be of the highest value. It is a mechanism which has enabled the National Research Council to "pull together" quickly into a working unit the "ten best men in Canada" in almost any field of proposed research.

For a final sentiment I am disposed to quote a few sentences written by a great American scientist, Vannevar Bush, Director of the Office of Scientific Research and Development, in his Report to President Roosevelt in July 1945. Dr. Bush was writing about the United States, but his words apply with almost equal relevancy to this country:

"The pioneer force is still vigorous within this nation. Science offers a largely unexplored hinterland for the pioneer who has the tools for his task. The rewards of such exploration for both the nation and the individual are great. Scientific progress is one essential key to our security as a nation, to our better health, to more jobs, to a higher standard of living, and to our cultural progress. . . .

"Science, by itself, provides no panacea for individual, social and economic ills. It can be effective in the national welfare only as a member of a team, whether the conditions be peace or war. But without scientific progress no amount of achievement in other directions can ensure our health, prosperity, and security in the modern world."

APPENDIX A

Radar Research

It seems fitting that a few of the more outstanding pioneers in Canadian radar should be singled out and that some of the contributions made in this field by Canadian universities should be cited.

By May of 1941 there were 116 scientists and technicians on the staff of the National Research Council at Ottawa, 27 members of the staff of Research Enterprises Limited working at Ottawa, and 33 additional members on the staff assigned there from the Canadian Navy, Army, and Air Force, a staff total of 176. It would clearly be impossible to do justice to the contributions of all these men and women, and so the names included here are those chosen by Dr. John T. Henderson, Chief of the Section, in his Secret Progress Report of May 1942:

"J. W. Bell has been responsible for many of the ideas and methods developed in the Radio Section, and his activity has covered practically the whole field. He was responsible for the over-all design of the APF set for the G.L. and for many of the associated circuit details in the motor control units and the ZPI unit. He is at present in charge of the Special Research and Development Section.

"Dr. D. W. R. McKinley, having returned from England where he had done a very capable job as liaison officer for the Radio Section, was put in charge of the E.W. [Early-Warning] project, and has since been given charge of the Air Force Section.

"Mr. H. R. Smyth, having been in charge of CSC [Canadian Submarine Control] development, and installed some of the early experimental equipment in a number of ships, was then given the SS-2C [a microwave naval set] project to supervise, and has now been placed in charge of the Navy Section.

"Mr. C. W. McLeish, working under Mr. Smyth, has done valuable work on the CRDF [Cathode Ray Direction Finder] programme.

"The above four men," recalled Dr. Henderson, writing in May 1942, "together with myself, constituted the entire pre-war engineering staff of the Radio Section. Since the war, many able men have been added to the staff, and it would be impossible to detail all their accomplishments, but one or two outstanding cases deserve particular mention:

"Dr. F. H. Sanders joined the staff of the Radio Section shortly after the outbreak of the war, from the Ultra-sonic Section of the Division of Physics and Electrical Engineering. Having first accomplished considerable work on horn radiators and corresponding antenna patterns, he was placed in charge of the 10-centimetre development work. He was the leader of the group of men who took the G.L. set to Great Britain, is now in charge of the Microwave Section.

"Mr. H. E. Parsons has been responsible for all the mechanical design of the various equipments produced, and his combined radio and mechanical knowledge has been most ably applied. His work on the CD [Coast Defence] aerial and on the multitudinous mechanical details of the G.L. equipment has been most valuable. He is now in charge of the Mechanical Section of the Radio Branch.

"Mr. K. A. MacKinnon came to us from the Canadian Broadcasting Corporation, where his long experience in antenna work and radiation theory made him a most valuable asset to us in all matters pertaining to aerials and antenna design. He has been in charge of the antenna work, and in particular is responsible for the development of the high-quality CD aerial, which has given such excellent performance. He has been very ably assisted in the antenna problems by Dr. G. A. Miller and others.

"Mr. W. Happe, who assisted Dr. Sanders in the early days of G.L. development, was given the problem of engineering the laboratory design of the G.L. to a more suitable model for production, after the laboratory model had become a working experimental set. He produced the set which was sent to Great Britain, and which forms a very close facsimile to the factory model. He is now in charge of the Army Section.

"Mr. G. R. Mounce, who has been a most able experimenter and assistant, is responsible for the development of the range system which made the Canadian G.L. possible, and in fact was one of the first additional engineers we obtained from outside, on our augmented programme, having been with us since February of 1940.

"Mr. D. L. West, who is now in charge of the Model Shops, deserves special mention for the excellent job he has accomplished in setting up the Model Shop, and in a short space of time, organizing it in a very efficient manner."

Valuable assistance was given the Radio Section (later Branch) by a number of Canadian universities, not only to the gun-laying project, but to radar research generally. A group working at the University of Western Ontario under Professor Dearle and Mr. Woonton made many measurements of field-strength patterns at three and ten centimetres. Research was conducted at the same centre on problems connected with the use of crystal detectors in microwave radar receivers.

Queen's University "specialized in the development of microwave impedance measurements, matching, measurements of dielectric properties, and design of resonant cavities.

"The main contributions by McGill were in the field of microwave antenna design.

"In addition to this experimental work, a body known as the Special Committee on Applied Mathematics, composed of members of the Departments of Physics, Mathematics, and Electrical Engineering of the University of Toronto, undertook mathematical analysis of some of the problems involved in radar work."[1]

Special mention deserves to be made of the contribution of Colonel F. C. Wallace, who had originally come over from Britain with the Tizard Mission, and who remained in Canada, at first in the Radio Branch of the National Research Council, and later as the Vice President in charge of production at

[1] J. T. Henderson, *Progress Report for Period June 1939 to 1 January 1942* (National Research Council of Canada: Radio Section, Ottawa, 1942), pp. 4-5.

Research Enterprises Limited. Colonel Wallace gave most valuable help in the G.L. development at Ottawa, his services including advice on operational requirements for the equipment in the field. During his numerous trips to the United States he was able to keep American interest in the set active. Indeed, by his almost single-handed efforts, he may be said to have "sold" to the United States the value of getting wholeheartedly behind the G.L. programme.

APPENDIX B

NATIONAL RESEARCH COUNCIL
DURING THE WAR YEARS

President

C. J. MACKENZIE, M.C., B.E., M.C.E., M.E.I.C., Ottawa, Ontario.

(MAJOR-GENERAL A. G. L. McNAUGHTON was recalled to active military duty in 1939.)

Directors

Division of Biology and Agriculture: ROBERT NEWTON, M.C., B.S.A., M.Sc., Ph.D., D.Sc., F.R.S.C.

Division of Chemistry: E. W. R. STEACIE, O.B.E., B.Sc., M.Sc., Ph.D., D.Sc., F.R.S.C., F.R.S.

Division of Mechanical Engineering: J. H. PARKIN, C.B.E., B.A.Sc., M.E., F.R.Ae.Sc., F.R.S.C., F.I.Ae.S.

Division of Physics and Electrical Engineering: R. W. BOYLE, B.Sc., M.Sc., M.A., Ph.D., LL.D., F.R.S.C.

(In 1941 the name of the Division of Biology and Agriculture was changed to the Division of Applied Biology, of which the new Director was W. H. COOK, O.B.E., B.Sc., M.Sc., Ph.D., F.R.S.C.)

Secretary-Treasurer

S. P. EAGLESON, ESQ., Ottawa, Ontario

Members

SIR FREDERICK BANTING, K.B.E., M.C., M.D., LL.D., D.Sc., F.A.C.P., F.R.C.P., F.R.C.S., F.R.S.C., F.R.S., Professor of Medical Research, University of Toronto, Toronto, Ontario.

PERCY BENGOUGH, ESQ., President, Trades and Labour Congress of Canada, 172 MacLaren Street, Ottawa, Ontario.

H. E. BIGELOW, A.M., Ph.D., F.R.S.C., F.C.I.C., Carnegie Professor of Chemistry, Mount Allison University, Sackville, New Brunswick.

E. F. BURTON, B.A., Ph.D., F.R.S.C., Professor and Head of the Department of Physics and Director of the McLennan Laboratory, University of Toronto, Toronto, Ontario.

W. R. CAMPBELL, ESQ., President and Treasurer, Ford Motor Company of Canada, Limited, Windsor, Ontario.

ARMAND CIRCE, B.Sc., C.E., D.I.C., Dean, Ecole Polytechnique, University of Montreal, 1430 St. Denis Street, Montreal, Quebec.

R. H. CLARK, M.A., Ph.D., F.R.S.C., F.C.I.C., Professor and Head of the Department of Chemistry, University of British Columbia, Vancouver, British Columbia.

J. B. COLLIP, M.A., Ph.D., M.D., D.Sc., LL.D., F.R.S.C., F.R.C.P., F.R.S., Gilman Cheney Professor of Biochemistry and Head of the Department, McGill University, Montreal, Quebec.

L. P. DUGAL, B.A., M.A., Ph.D., Assistant Director of the Institute of Human Biology and Hygiene, Laval University, Quebec, Quebec.

J. S. DUNCAN, ESQ., President, Massey-Harris Company, Toronto, Ontario.

E. P. FETHERSTONHAUGH, M.C., B.Sc., F.R.S.A., M.E.I.C., Dean, Faculty of Engineering and Architecture, University of Manitoba, Winnipeg, Manitoba.

PAUL E. GAGNON, B.A., B.Ap.Sc., D.I.C., Ph.D., D.Sc., F.R.S.C., Director of the Department of Chemistry and Chemical Engineering, and Director of the Graduate School, Laval University, Quebec, Quebec.

DUNCAN GRAHAM, C.B.E., M.B., F.R.C.P.(C), F.R.C.P., F.R.S.C., Sir John and Lady Eaton Professor of Medicine and Head of the Department of Medicine, University of Toronto, Toronto, Ontario.

J. A. GRAY, O.B.E., B.Sc., D.Sc., F.R.S., F.R.S.C., Chown Science Research Professor, Queen's University, Kingston, Ontario.

DAVID A. KEYS, M.A., Ph.D., F.R.S.C., Macdonald Professor of Physics and Chairman of the Physical Science Group of the Faculty of Arts and Science, McGill University, Montreal, Quebec.

BEAUDRY LEMAN, B.Sc., C.E., D.C.Sc., President and Managing Director, Banque Canadienne Nationale, Place d'Armes, Montreal, Quebec.

O. MAASS, B.A., M.Sc., Ph.D., Macdonald Professor of Physical Chemistry and Head of the Department of Chemistry, McGill University, Montreal, Quebec.

ROBERT NEWTON, M.C., B.S.A., M.Sc., Ph.D., D.Sc., F.R.S.C., President, University of Alberta, Edmonton, Alberta.

H. J. ROWLEY, M.A., B.Sc.(Chem. Eng.), Ph.D., F.C.I.C., Chairman, New Brunswick Resources Development Board, Fredericton, New Brunswick.

G. M. SHRUM, M.M., M.A., Ph.D., F.R.S.C., Professor and Head of the Department of Physics, University of British Columbia, Vancouver, British Columbia.

ARTHUR SURVEYER, B.A., B.Ap.Sc., C.E., D.Eng., Consulting Engineer, 1010 St. Catherine Street West, Montreal, Quebec.

R. J. TALLON, ESQ., Secretary-Treasurer, Trades and Labour Congress of Canada, 172 MacLaren St., Ottawa, Ont.

HIS EXCELLENCY MGR. ALEXANDRE VACHON, M.A., Ph.M., S.T.D., D.Sc., LL.D., F.R.S.C., F.C.I.C., Archbishop of Ottawa, St. Patrick Street, Ottawa, Ontario

R. C. WALLACE, Ph.D., D.Sc., LL.D., F.G.S., F.R.S.C., Principal, Queen's University, Kingston, Ontario.

(FRED MOLINEUX, ESQ., Trades and Labour Congress of Canada, 70 Connaught Avenue South, Hamilton, Ontario, was a member of the Council from April 1942 until March 1945. With the addition of his name the above list shows every member of the Council who served during any period of the war.)

INDEX

INDEX

Magnesium, 187-92
  chloride, 189
  metallic:
    Associate Committee on Metallic
      Magnesium, 189
    produced in Germany, 189
Magnesium Reduction Company, 192
Magnetic Airborne Detector, 149,
  259
Magnetic surveys, 259
Magnetism of ships, 124
  magnetic signature of ships, 126
Magnetometer, 148, 150
  airborne, 149
Malaya, 196
Malaya, 52
Malta, 7, 58, 110
Mann, Dr. K. C., 54
Maritime Regional Laboratory, Hali-
  fax, N.S., 254
Mark, Dr. J. C., 93
Marshall, Gen. George C., 98
Massachusetts Institute of Tech-
  nology, 19, 42, 43, 60, 62
Mass spectroscope, 257
Matapan, battle of, 7
Mayo Foundation, 220
Meakins, Prof. J. C., 243
Meanjin: A Literary Magazine, 256n.
Mechanical Engineering shop,
  Ottawa, 96
Medical Research Council (U.K.),
  239
Medicine, 211-51
  aviation, 212-25
  decompression sickness, 212, 213-
    15
  influenza, 236
  injuries, repair of battle, 239-44
  metabolism, study of, 238
  micro-organisms, 230-6
  motion sickness, 212, 222-5
  oxygen supply, 212, 213, 215-18
  penicillin, 230, 231-4
  protection from centrifugal force
    in flying, 218-22
  psychological aircrew selection
    tests, 213

Meitner, Dr. Lise, 6, 87
Mellanby, Sir Edward, 240
*Memorandum on the Early Recogni-
  tion and Treatment of Shock,*
  243
*Memorandum on the Treatment of
  Thermal Burns,* 244
Metallurgical Laboratory, Stagg
  Field, Chicago, 90
Metals:
  controller, 188
  supply of, 187
Metcalfe Road Field Station, 42, 43,
  59
Meteorology, 62, 111, 177
  automatic photo-electric dew-point
    hygrometer, 184
  in Canadian Arctic, 264
  in icing conditions, 183
  Meteorological Services, 186
  photo-electric cloud-density instru-
    ment, 184
MEW (Microwave Early Warning),
  60-2
  MEW/AS, 61
  See also Radar
Micro-organisms, 230-6
  rickettsia, 235
  typhus, 230, 235
"Micropup" pulsed triode, 19
Microwave: *see also* Radar
  gun-layer, 37, 38
  Height Finder, 62
  Microwave Early Warning
    (MEW), 60-62
  radar fire-control instruments, 22
  research and development, 19
Miles, Prof. Walter, 248
Military aircraft industry, 160
Milk:
  dried powder, 210, 239
Milkweed, 194-6
Miller, G. A., 268
Mineola, Long Island, 150